P9-CRO-600

P9-CRO-600

The Illustrated
Reference Book of
Modern Technology

Picture Credits

Credits are listed in this manner: [1] page numbers appear first, in bold type; [2] illustration numbers appear next, in brackets; [3] photographers' names appear next, followed where applicable by the names of the agencies representing them.

The Illustrated Reference Book of Modern Technology
This edition published in 1982 by
WINDWARD
an imprint owned by W. H. Smith & Son Limited
Registered No. 237811 England, Trading as WHS Distributors St John's House East Street Leicester LE1 6NE

© Mitchell Beazley Encyclopaedias Limited 1980, 1982

Pages 2-111 © Mitchell Beazley Encyclopaedias Limited 1976 and 1977
Artwork © Mitchell Beazley Publishers Limited 1970, 1971, 1972, 1973, 1974, 1975 and 1976
© International Visual Resource 1972
© Mitchell Beazley Encyclopaedias Limited 1974

ISBN 0 7112 0243 5

Phototypeset in Great Britain by Filmtype Services Limited, Scarborough
Printed in Yugoslavia by Mladinska Knjiga

The Joy of Knowledge
GENERAL EDITOR: JAMES MITCHELL

The Illustrated
Reference Book of
Modern Technology

WINDWARD

Preface

How to use this book

Modern Technology forms one complete section of *The Joy of Knowledge*. It includes all the general knowledge my editors and I think most interesting about the history and development of the world's transport systems and various media of communication. It has been our intention to present the mass of available information on this important subject in such a way that it will make sense to you, and tell a logical, relevant and coherent story.

The spread system
Every topic in *The Joy of Knowledge* takes the form of an article that occupies two facing pages of text and pictures; what we call a "spread". Each two-page spread in the book is organized in the same way. It is the heart of our approach to explaining things.

The spread system is a strict discipline but once you get used to it we hope you'll find the structure to be systematic and reassuring. You should start to feel at home in all sorts of unlikely areas of knowledge with the spread system to guide you. It works like this.

Each two-page spread in *Modern Technology*, as throughout *The Joy of Knowledge*, tells a self-contained story. It explains all the essential facts you need to know about its subject in as efficient a manner as possible. We believe that the discipline of having to get in all the essential and relevant facts in this comparatively small space actually makes for better results than a rambling essay could achieve — text that has to get straight to the point, pictures and diagrams that illustrate the salient points in a clear and comprehensible fashion, and captions that really work and explain the relevance of the pictures.

The spreads are, in a sense, the building blocks of knowledge. Like the various circuits and components that go to make up a computer, they are also systematically "programmed" to help the reader find out things more easily and remember them better. Each spread, for example, has a main article of about 850 words summarising the subject. This article is illustrated by an average of ten pictures and diagrams, the captions of which both complement and supplement the basic information in the main article. Each spread, too, has a "key" picture or diagram in the top right-hand corner. The purpose of this picture is twofold: it summarises the story of the spread visually and it is intended to act as a memory stimulator to help you recall all the integrated facts and pictures on a given subject.

Where to start
A good way to begin acquiring knowledge from this particular part of *The Joy of Knowledge* is initially to read the Introduction. The Introduction provides a useful framework for the information contained in the following pages. If, however, you prefer to plunge straight into the book (but don't have much basic general knowledge on the subject) I suggest you look first at the spreads "History of transport", beginning on page 2, "Traffic engineering" on page 58, "History of printing" on page 78 and "Communications: telegraph" on page 98. Once you have absorbed the information in these spreads you can build up a more comprehensive general knowledge by exploring the rest of the book.

Modern Technology is a book about the great technological advances which have enabled man to expand his horizons and establish contact with his fellows throughout the world. I hope you will find reading about the subject both stimulating and helpful.

Contents

Introduction
2 History of transport
4 Sailing ships
6 Modern ships
8 Hydrofoils and air-cushion vehicles
10 Submarines and submersibles
12 Carts, coaches and carriages
14 History of bicycles
16 History of motor cycles
18 History of automobiles
20 Classic cars
22 How an automobile works
24 Cars and society
26 Trams and buses
28 Special purpose vehicles
30 Small technology and transport
32 Locomotives
34 Railway transport
36 Railways of the future
38 Balloons, blimps and dirigibles
40 History of aircraft
42 Modern aircraft
44 How an aeroplane works
46 Helicopters and autogyros
48 Space vehicles
50 Man in space
52 Earth-moving machines
54 Moving heavy loads
56 Road building
58 Traffic engineering
60 Airports and air traffic
62 Tunnel engineering
64 History of bridges
66 Modern bridges
68 Harbours and docks
70 Canal construction
72 Building dams
74 Water supply
76 Sewage treatment
78 History of printing
80 Modern printing
82 Copying and duplicating
84 Newspapers and magazines
86 Books and publishing
88 Reference books and encyclopaedias
90 Information retrieval
92 Photography
94 Taking pictures
96 Cine photography
98 Communications: telegraph
100 Communications: telephone
102 Communications: radio
104 Communications: television
106 Sound recording and reproducing
108 Video recording and reproduction
110 Radar and sonar
112 Index
116 Bibliography

Editor's introduction

The term "to communicate" is increasingly being adopted purely to describe the presentation of information by any of the recently devised media, such as television, Teletext, Viewdata and video, all important products of modern technology. Yet it remains the only term that properly describes the *exchange* of information, ideas or impressions by all sorts of methods and for all kinds of purposes.

Communication is a two-way process.

The ability to communicate is not restricted to human beings; it is a natural faculty of many animals, too. Using coded sounds and displays, many animals communicate their intentions in matters of territorial rights and partnerships, for example, and even for co-operation in hunting. Some animal communications are highly developed – for instance bats and dolphins use supersonic sounds for echo-location (the principle of sonar).

It is the human brain, and not the means of making sounds or gestures, that makes man a superior communicator. Given a developed brain, man was able to establish complex social structures and to spread throughout most of the world. With such changes in life style, communication took on a new significance and a new urgency. With the advent of primitive writing techniques and means of transport, food, materials and people could be accounted for and moved both within and between communities. Territorial claims could be established by means other than fighting. Empires could be established over great distances as both transport and communications grew more sophisticated.

The written word

Much of what we know about the recent past is through the written word. Even so, the skills of reading and writing were once solely the domain of a privileged few. Today, thanks to the invention of printing using movable type in the fifteenth century, a wealth of knowledge stored in the form of the printed word is available to all.

More or less instantaneous communication at a distance – in the form of coded signals standing for letters or words – came with the invention of the electric telegraph in the early nineteenth century. By the 1870s, Alexander Graham Bell's telephone allowed speech messages to be sent along wires, and by the turn of the twentieth century the invention of radio freed both telegraphy and telephony from the constraint of wires linking the transmitter and receiver. A world-wide radio network followed, made even more reliable and efficient by the advent of satellite communications in the 1960s.

Modern technology was thus quick to meet the successive demands of high-speed communications. Beginning with the telegraph, through the telephone and radio to radar and sonar, the demands (posed mostly by military requirements) have been met. But, for their far-reaching effect on our way of life, television and now video must rate as the most revolutionary of all media of communication.

Water, road and rail

Just as human messengers on foot or on horseback provided the first means of communication of the spoken or written word, human beings and animals were once the sole means of motive power for transport. They required no specially prepared surfaces and were not restricted to any particular path, but having to support as well as move their load made them inefficient. The practice of supporting a load on a vehicle and using a force merely to move it soon became established.

Sledges and carts needed a prepared surface upon which to travel, and hence gave rise to a system of roads but it is no accident that many villages, some of which have since grown into great cities, developed on the banks of rivers. The river was the life-line of such communities and served not only as a source of water for drinking and agriculture but also as a means of communication. Along the river too, would have developed the technology of boat-building and other industries.

Life on the coast was no less progressive. The sea has always been a major source of food, and many communities exploited its advantages in times of war. From raft, reed boats and dug-out canoes to canal and river barges, transport by water was well established, but not until the invention of sails did it become international. The advent of sail must have been an economist's dream: the world's oceans as ready-made waterways and, at no extra cost, the power of the wind. It is easy to see how such freedom fired man's spirit of adventure and drove him on his many expeditions into unknown lands.

The convenience of waterways as a natural means of communication did not hinder progress in the development of roads and road vehicles. Just as the availability of sail power transformed water transport, so too the invention of the steam engine was to liberate men and animals from being power sources and open up the age of the railways, steam cars and steamships. Unfortunately, the miracle of wind power was not totally repeated in these instances. Not only did the motor car and the railways need their own highways but also the steam engine relied, firstly, on wood and, later, on coal – both exhaustable and indirect sources of energy – but conservation is a fairly modern consideration. Coal was not free, like the wind, but it was more reliable and almost as plentiful.

When the internal combustion engine was invented, the road vehicle was the first form of transport to benefit from the new source of motive power. The motor car has changed our way of life more than any other mode of transport. With it have come the benefits of fast reliable travel and, more importantly, freedom of the individual to travel where and when he or she desires. But the motor car is not without disadvantages, among them congestion, pollution and a drain of the world's dwindling reserves of oil. The motor car is unlikely to exist for much longer in its present form, but our love for it is so great that its total disappearance is equally unlikely.

Transport by air

As far back as 400 BC, the Greek Archytas is said to have made a steam-jet propelled model bird, but until an appropriate technology (in the guise of the light-weight internal combustion engine) became available, powered flight remained a dream. So devoted has man been to the development of flight that in the eighty years since the first sustained, controlled flight by the Wright Brothers, he has advanced from lighter-than-air craft to the Jet Age and the new frontiers of space travel. No other form of transport has grown so fast and done so much to improve communications. Journeys that used to take days or even weeks have been reduced to the insignificance of a few hours. The economic results of this revolution have unquestionably been enormous in terms of the speeding up and sophistication of world trade.

Transport engineering

The search for new vehicles to meet the ever-growing demand for faster and better transport continues relentlessly. Equally important is the need to improve the standard and capacity of the highways, including roads, railways and waterways, along which the vehicles travel. To this end, the civil engineer has been indispensable to the development of a comprehensive transport system. The roads of the past bear little resemblance, visually and structurally, to those needed for a 40-ton, 60mph lorry or a constant stream of 70mph cars. Similarly, the tracks along which the first steam trains travelled are inadequate for a modern 125mph express train. This pattern is repeated throughout the whole transport system including roads, bridges and tunnels, harbours and docks, dams and waterways, and airports. It is appropriate, therefore, that *Modern Technology* should include a fascinating section on the various types of civil engineering that are essential to modern transport systems.

History of transport

Transport is arguably man's oldest technology, predating both house building and agriculture. There is no reason to doubt that prehistoric men and women carried burdens in their hands, on their backs and on their heads, and the use of specially constructed litters, sleds and rollers for transport may also be much older than the generally accepted date of about 10,000 years ago.

Water and rail transport

The oldest artefacts that could be described as transport vehicles were crude boats of prehistoric times; men progressed to the dugout canoe about 20,000 years ago. At the same time members of early civilizations in many parts of the world must have developed ways of building rafts of local materials.

Rafts are still made in more or less the same way, using bundles of reeds, logs, grasses and other material, sometimes with added flotation from skin bags or sea-kelp bladders. From the raft, many peoples progressed to making boats with built-up hulls, sometimes using a framework covered by skins or bark (eucalyptus bark was the favourite in the countries of Australasia).

About 5,000 years ago canals were being constructed, at first to link close river channels and eventually to carry people and supplies over considerable distances. In much more recent times canals were dug throughout Britain and much of western Europe as primary transport routes, largely because of the inadequacy of roads. From 1770 to 1840 canals were almost unchallenged in these areas as the means for the slow but cheap transport of a rapidly growing volume of manufactured goods.

One great advantage of the canal was its ability to move very heavy loads for a minimal expenditure of energy. Compared with the canal barge, no land vehicle could move such loads until the coming of railways.

The first crude railways were used for commercial rather than private or passenger transport. Metal rails had been used in local works such as mines [9] since medieval times, but by about 1800 their use began to spread. By 1830 it had been realized that a uniform kind of track should be adopted and the two-rail system was introduced with smooth steel rails at agreed spacings and with flanges on the inner edges of the wheels.

Like a canal, a railway could carry heavy loads with minimal resistance to motion. Competition between the two forms of transport in many regions was intense, railways usually enjoying an advantage because of the ease of extension (branches and spurs could be built to serve almost every town) and because they were unrivalled in hilly areas. At the same time progress was made in the design and construction of roads, which in Europe until 1800 had been inferior to the roads built by the Romans.

Transport by road

In theory roads have always had an advantage over railways because of greater flexibility. They cost less to build, which means that a national road network can serve almost every factory and house. They can carry a wide range of vehicles up and down steep gradients. On the other hand, the resistance to motion is much greater than on a railway because the resistance of wheeled vehicles is dependent on the intensity of loading where

1 Tree trunks were probably man's earliest vehicles. More than 20,000 years ago he began to use wood and other materials to make rafts and the precursors of the later kayaks, coracles and canoes.

2 Egyptian ships date from c. 2500 BC. The broad spoon-shaped hull was made from acacia, a tree yielding only short, irregular timbers. The ship was steered by two oars on each side of the stern.

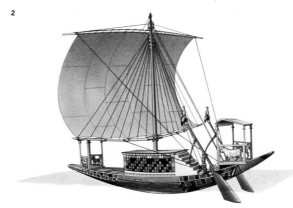

3 The travois was possibly the earliest land vehicle. Used by the Plains Indians of North America it comprised two poles joined to a man, a dog or a horse and dragged along the ground.

4 The chariot is illustrated on one of the tombs at Thebes (c. 1500 BC). Although the Egyptians never perfected the harness, they used many horse-drawn vehicles with wheels of spoked construction.

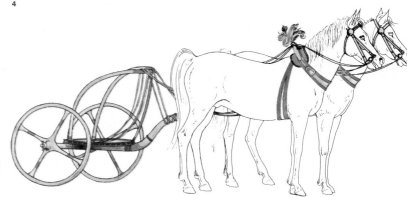

5 The first hydrogen balloon carried Jacques Charles and M. N. Robert from Paris to a field 40km (25 miles) away in December 1783 in under two hours. It looked like a modern balloon with a "boat" beneath.

6 Henri Giffard's airship could sustain an airspeed of 8km/h (5mph) on its steam-driven propeller. In 1852 Giffard navigated it from Paris to Trappes, making the first powered cross-country flight. Progress was delayed by lack of good engines.

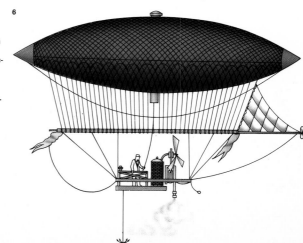

the wheels meet the fixed surface. With a railway this intensity is high and the surface smooth and regular. With a road the intensity is low and until quite recently the surface was irregular. Until late in the nineteenth century roads were marred by ruts, bumps and pot-holes, which not only slowed vehicles but often caused damage and even serious accidents. In many places it was accepted procedure to take coaches or goods carts to pieces and use teams of men to carry them over the worst sections of road surface.

Mechanically powered vehicles

All the earliest forms of propulsion had relied on natural forces such as wind and river currents or muscle power. By the early years of the nineteenth century mechanical power was being applied to move vehicles – at first steam engines in railway locomotives and ships. Then mechanically propelled road vehicles gained importance with the advent of the internal combustion engine after 1885. Motor cars multiplied in an amazing way, as did those convenient muscle-driven vehicles, bicycles. A key innovation with both of them

was the introduction of pneumatic tyres. The replacement of the horse and horse-drawn carriage by the rubber-tyred car forced governments to build smooth, all-weather roads both within and between cities.

Today's rail and road systems are more complex and many have automatic traffic-control systems involving computers, electronic communication and display systems, as well as methods for dealing instantly with sudden demands or emergencies.

There have also been several revolutions in marine transport. At one time merchant ships had to be equipped to fight off pirates. By 1800 many kinds of true cargo vessels were built and for 100 years they monopolized inter-continental transport.

The newest form of transport, the aeroplane [11], swiftly supplanted the ship as the vehicle for long passenger journeys, while economies of scale led to a startling growth in the size of oil tankers, bulk carriers and other cargo ships. The pressure on shipping lines to reduce journey time has also been relieved because over short distances hydrofoils [8] and hovercraft travel four times faster.

The Air Cushion Landing System (ACLS) enables aircraft to operate from any kind of surface. This is a converted Buffalo short-field transport plane that helped to prove the concept. The result is a vehicle able to land on concrete, ice, snow, crops, sand, water or any level part of the earth.

7

7 This river boat typifies hundreds that served US southern states in the 19th century. Paddle-driven, often with a stern wheel, they had shallow draught and yet could carry heavy loads.

8

8 The hydrofoil of V. Grunberg ran in 1934. Driven by tandem air propellers, it had two forward floats and a central submerged foil, which was adjusted automatically. It was 30 years before the modern foil.

9

9 This wooden tramway truck ran on wooden track in a German mine (c. 1510) and is probably typical of an early form of railway transport vehicle. By 1670 wagons had flanged iron wheels.

10

10 This Daimler car (1897) was built by the English Daimler Co, formed initially in 1893 to import cars from the factory in Germany. It had a two-cylinder engine and four forward and reverse speeds.

11

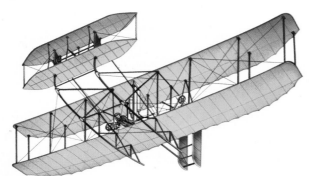

11 The Wright Flyer III was an improved version of the first aeroplane to make a successful flight. The Wright brothers learned how to control a glider, and then added a lightweight petrol engine.

12 Paul Cornu, the French inventor, made the first heavier-than-air machine to take off vertically in free flight. Tethered to the ground by a rope, his primitive helicopter rose 1.5m (5ft) on 13 November 1907, but lacked stability.

12

Sailing ships

No one knows when or where man first invented the sail, but it was probably one of the earliest attempts at harnessing a natural force and putting it to work. The earliest evidence of sailing craft comes from Egypt and dates back to the third millennium BC. Ancient Egyptian ships [5] had single square sails spread by two wooden spars, a yard at the top and a boom at the foot; they could sail only downwind but since the wind in the Nile valley is nearly always from the north, this allowed them to sail upstream. Going downstream did not require a sail.

Sailing against the wind

It was some time before man realized that sails could be made that would propel a ship against a wind – not directly into it, but at an angle of less than 90° – and it is only recently that the aerodynamics of such sails has been understood [1]. Another early breakthrough was the invention of the keel, a long plank running from stem to stern, from which the rest of the hull could be built up.

The square-rigged ships of the Middle Ages could not sail much closer to the wind than 90° and even the latest square-riggers cannot sail closer than about 70°. The "fore-and-aft" sail (in which the forward edge is secured to, and pivots around, a mast or stag), such as the Mediterranean lateen and the triangular Bermudan sail of modern yachts, can hold a course as close as 45° to the wind [4].

The fore-and-aft idea appears to have evolved in the Indian Ocean from the Egyptian square sail in the third century AD – leading to the lateen sail of the Arab dhows and to the lug-sail of the Chinese junk. The square sail did, however, survive until the end of commercial sailing ships because it was more efficient than the fore-and-aft sail on long voyages with following winds.

The Romans improved on the Egyptian rig by adding the *artemon* (spritsail) and a triangular topsail [6], but as in the Egyptian ships before and the Viking ships later, steering was done with an oar lashed near the stern. The Chinese, however, had known the axial rudder and the compass since about the first century AD. The former allowed better steering and was more robust than the steering oar; the latter allowed navigation out of sight of land without fear of overcast skies hiding the stars. These discoveries reached Europe only in the later years of the eleventh century and had great consequences in the development of European seafaring.

Development of ship and sail

The multi-masted ship originated in China and the idea was brought to the West at the time of Marco Polo in the thirteenth century. Before this time, vessels such as the single-masted double-ended cog had been used extensively for trade around Europe and the Mediterranean. By the end of the fifteenth century three-masted ships had become a common feature of European waters. The deep, broad carrack [7] was one such common trading vessel and the caravel was also developed at this time. Used mainly by the Portuguese, the caravel was a simpler and lighter vessel. It carried lateen sails (fore-and-aft) but sometimes the foremast was square-rigged.

The galleon [9], which appeared in the mid-sixteenth century, was a cross between the heavy carrack and the slim Venetian

1 Sailing against the wind is possible because the wind acting on a sail creates a lift [L] and a drag [D]. These are equivalent to a driving force [F] and a leeway force [S].

2 "Wearing" is making a downwind turn, a method often used by square-rigged ships, such as carracks and galleons, when sailing into wind. This method loses some ground to windward.

3 "Tacking" is turning into and across the wind. This is a manoeuvre more easily done by fore-and-aft vessels than by square-riggers and loses less ground to windward than wearing.

Wind direction
Lateen rig
Square rig

4 Fore-and-aft rigs are able to point much closer to the wind than square-rigs when tacking in a zigzagging course to windward. After sailing the same number of miles the fore-and-aft vessel is thus much farther ahead.

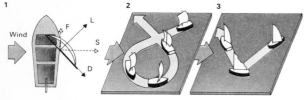

5 Egyptian ships of c. 1300 BC had a square sail and were steered by oars. The hull shape derived from reed boats.

6 The Roman grain ships of the 2nd century AD had a foresail, the *artemon*, and a topsail above the mainsail.

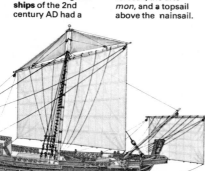

7 The shape of ships' hulls changed considerably between 1400 and 1600. The nef of 1400 [A] was double-ended, with a "pointed" stern, and had "castles" added at both ends. Multi-masted ships (inspired by Chinese junks) appeared with the carrack [B] (1450) and [C] (1465). The flat or *transom* stern appeared with the 1520 great ship [D] whose hull was also pierced for guns. Streamlining and bringing the forecastle inboard produced the galleon [E] (1545) and [F] (1587).

8 Clinker [A] and carvel [B] built hulls were characteristic of North European and Mediterranean ships respectively. From 1520 onwards all large ships adopted the carvel build with the butting of planks end to end.

galley. Galleons had slimmer hull lines [7] than the carracks, a square stern where the carracks were "double-ended" and a forecastle well inboard instead of hanging over the bow.

The transition from the carrack to the galleon was the last big technological "jump" for sailing ships. The difference between a sixteenth-century galleon and a nineteenth-century packet ship, such as the Blackwall frigate, was one of detail although the performance of the latter was far superior. The gradual evolution since the early galleons involved an increase in the size and number of sails, and the introduction of fore-and-aft staysails between the masts and jibs in front of the foremast.

From the mid-eighteenth century onwards, the Western sailing ship branched out in a variety of rigs, from two masts to six or even seven in the instance of a pure fore-and-aft schooner, the *Thomas W. Lawson*.

The last of the sailing ships

The fastest, the most beautiful and the most short-lived of the great sailing ships was the clipper [11]. She was developed in the 1820s in the USA, reached the height of her fame in the 1850s and 1860s and by the end of the century was obsolete.

The clipper was built primarily for speed. She was slim and light, with a limited cargo space, and carried an enormous area of canvas. She fulfilled a variety of needs. The Californian and Australian gold rushes (1849 and 1851), the China tea trade and, from the 1870s, the trade in wool and grain from Australia were all served by clippers. The competition between ships' companies in the race to make fast passages and high profits produced crews of the highest quality.

Such factors as steamships, the opening of the Suez Canal and the transcontinental railways made the clippers obsolete. They were replaced by larger windjammers that were built of steel and where cargo-carrying capacity and labour-saving devices were given precedence over speed. Despite their much greater tonnage (up to 5,800 tonnes) they did not require larger crews than the clippers. Even these ships were eventually killed by steamship competition.

The sails of the 3-masted, fully square-rigged ship are fore skysail [1], fore royal [2], fore top-gallant sail [3],

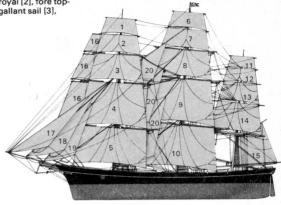

fore topsail [4], foresail [5], main skysail [6], main royal [7], main top-gallant sail [8], main topsail [9],

mainsail [10], mizzen skysail [11], mizzen royal [12], mizzen topgallant sail [13], mizzen topsail [14],

spanker [15], studding sails [16], outer jib [17], inner jib [18], fore staysail [19], and staysails [20].

9 Drake's *Golden Hind* was a medium-sized Elizabethan galleon. Her deck was about 28m (90ft) long. The rig consisted of the square bowsprit sail, 2 square sails on the foremast and 2 on the mainmast and a lateen on the mizzen. The hull was characterized by a slim underbody, a projecting head (derived from the galley's ram), a forecastle forming an integral part of the hull and a transom stern with a stern gallery. Steering was done with a whipstaff (the wheel only appeared during the 18th century). There were 2 full-length decks. Such ships were used both for war and commerce.

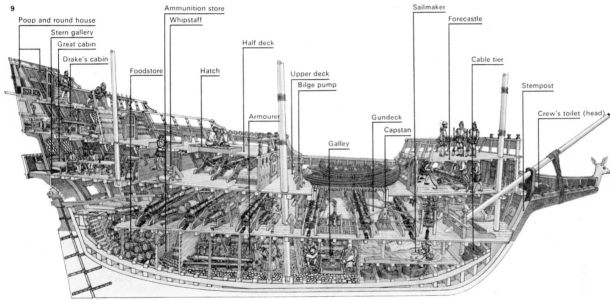

9

Poop and round house
Stern gallery
Great cabin
Drake's cabin
Foodstore
Ammunition store
Whipstaff
Half deck
Hatch
Upper deck
Bilge pump
Armourer
Galley
Gundeck
Capstan
Sailmaker
Forecastle
Cable tier
Stempost
Crew's toilet (head)

10

11

12

13

13 The barkentine (19th-20th century) has three masts with a square rig only on the foremast, thus reducing crew size and hence running costs.

10 The Dutch East Indiaman (1720) was larger than the *Golden Hind*, but of the same basic pattern. Two new sails appear: the sprit-sail topsail and the mizzen topsail. These heavily armed and extremely robust merchant ships could be used as men-of-war.

14

14 The brig (18th-20th century), a common coastal craft, has two masts, both of them square-rigged, and fore-and-aft staysails.

11 The clipper of the mid-19th century was a particularly efficient sailing ship. Its phenomenal speed made trading between Australia, China, USA and Britain much more economical. The name clipper came from the way the ships could "clip off" the miles.

15

15 The brigantine (18th-20th century) has two masts with a square rig on the foremast and main-sails and staysails on the mainmast.

12 The four-masted steel barks of the late 19th century were built of steel and they carried manufactured goods, grain and nitrates round the world. Their aftermasts had no yards. The bark rig appeared in the late 18th century and steel hulls in the 1870s.

16

16 The topsail schooner (18th-20th century) is a fore-and-aft rigged vessel with one or more square topsails set on the foremast.

5

Modern ships

Ships have changed vastly since the first iron-hulled steamer powered by a screw propeller, the *Great Britain* [1], crossed the Atlantic in 1843. Towards the end of the nineteenth century, iron gave way to steel as the standard material for hulls and sail-power declined in usefulness. At first indispensable as an auxiliary to the early crude steam engines, sail was ousted as steam machinery became more reliable. By 1918 there were very few sailing ships trading on main ocean routes.

Types of shipping

Since the introduction of steam there have always been three main divisions of non-naval shipping: passenger-carriers, cargo-carriers (merchant ships) and service craft. The largest passenger-carriers are ocean liners, particularly the North Atlantic record-breakers of the twentieth century. Competition from cheap and speedy air travel has driven big passenger liners out of business. But they survive as cruise liners, carrying holiday-makers to foreign ports instead of travellers on scheduled routes. Many famous liners have ended their careers by becoming

cruise liners and now specially designed ships [11] cater for the packaged holiday market. "Short sea" passenger ships and ferries have proved far more resilient in meeting the competition from air travel. Improvements in ship design have enabled road vehicles to drive on and off a ferry [10], allowing faster turnaround and reducing labour costs.

The passenger liner was once the largest type of non-naval ship, but since the 1950s it has been surpassed by the oil tanker [6]. As world consumption of petroleum products has risen, so has demand for tankers. Individual ships have increased in size from an average of about 50,000 tonnes deadweight in 1955 to 500,000 tonnes in 1976 (deadweight is the carrying capacity of a ship, including cargo, ballast, fuel, water, crew and passengers). The "supertanker" is relatively slow but can be operated by a small crew and it is the most economical way of shipping crude oil. The growth in size is likely to be limited only by safety factors and the risk of pollution from accidental spillage.

The cargo-carrying ship is still the mainstay of world trade, but here too there has

been a striking expansion in size. In order to save on operating costs, bulk-carriers handling dry cargoes of iron ore, grain or coal have grown to deadweights of more than 100,000 tonnes. Some are equipped to unload their own cargo, but carriers of grain, salt and coal, for example, still need dockside facilities.

The most important development in cargo-handling is the container ship [5], which loads cargo in prepacked, weathertight containers by means of special dockside cranes. The main advantage is that time in port is reduced and containers are easily handled by an integrated road or rail system. Loading and unloading of diverse cargoes, with its risk of damage and theft, is eliminated. The disadvantage is that container ships can operate only on fixed routes with specially equipped terminals, and in this respect they suffer from the same limitations as the old transatlantic liners.

Smaller vessels

A few general-purpose cargo vessels still "tramp" from port to port seeking any cargo they can find. Or their owners allow the

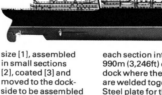

1 The first iron screw steamship, the SS *Great Britain* (1843), was not an immediate commercial success but showed that iron ships could carry more cargo more safely than wooden ones.

2 The *Lusitania* was torpedoed in 1915 by a German U-boat with the loss of 1,198 lives. Introduced in 1907, she helped to establish the Parsons steam turbine as a means of propulsion for big, fast liners.

3 Production line assembly of giant oil tankers is carried out in dry-dock shipyards like the extensive Mitsubishi yards at Koyagi in Japan [A]. Treated steel plate is cut to

size [1], assembled in small sections [2], coated [3] and moved to the dockside to be assembled into sections which can weigh up to 600 tonnes. Powerful gantry cranes [B] are used to lift

each section into a 990m (3,246ft) dry dock where they are welded together. Steel plate for the stern and bow is handled on another assembly line. The steel for these sections leaves a

treatment shop [4], goes to sub-assembly [5] and large assembly shops [6], and is built up in a pocket dock to be added as the ship is slid to the seaward end of the main dock. Final fitting out

is done afloat. Yards like the one at Koyagi build the 500,000-tonne supertankers needed to meet world demands for oil. The Japanese have the world's biggest tanker-building industry.

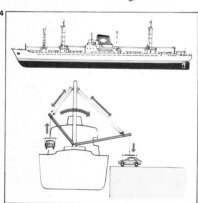

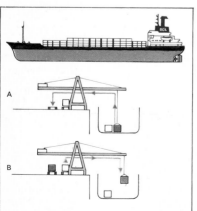

4 The *Lanka Devi* is a conventional cargo ship of a type still widely used. She can load or unload cargo with her own derricks if cranes are not available on the dockside. Though the *Lanka Devi* has her machinery placed amidships, a more recent trend in cargo vessels is for the bridge superstructure and the propulsion unit to be positioned either at or near the stern.

5 A container ship like the *Encounter Bay* must use special terminals to handle her 1,500 containers, each measuring 36 cubic metres (1,280 cubic feet). Unloading [A] and loading [B] can be carried out simultaneously. Like most container ships, the *Encounter Bay* has a high freeboard and an unobstructed deck, allowing containers to be stacked there. Bigger ships can carry up to 3,000 containers, close-packed because they are a standard size.

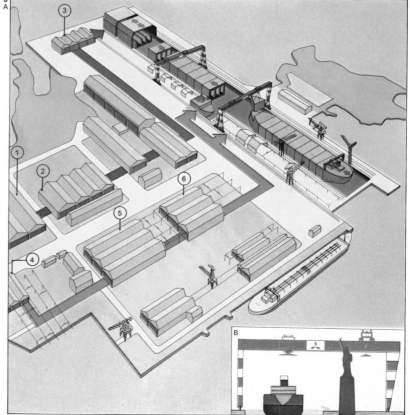

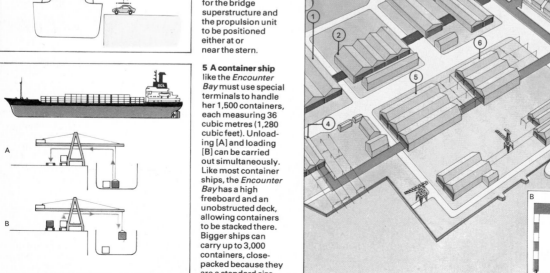

whole vessel to be chartered for a single cargo, like a conventional cargo vessel [4]. Now it operates on routes where container ships would be too costly, or it acts as a "feeder" to container routes. The "reefer", or refrigerated cargo liner, also remains important because it handles perishable cargoes such as fruit and meat. Smaller coasters and coastal oil tankers, which trans-ship cargo between ports, act as vital links both as distributors of cargo to lesser ports and as feeders to the major ports and container terminals. Roll-on/roll-off ships are used to carry truck trailers and low-loaders from point to point. Another variant is the LASH, or Lighter Aboard Ship concept, with barges or lighters hoisted aboard a large ship. After being dropped at the mouth of a river, the barges are towed upriver without any trans-shipment of cargo, as with containers.

Shipping could not function without a host of service craft. Foremost among these is the tug [9], which exists primarily to man-oeuvre larger ships in confined waters. Tugs are also used to salvage damaged ships on the high seas and to fight fires, and special "pusher" tugs handle barges on rivers and canals. Dredgers keep the channels in har-bours and estuaries open to deep-sea ship-ping, and a variety of small craft are emp-loyed on pilotage and maintenance of buoys and other navigational aids.

Marine engines

The main propulsion systems of ships are either diesel or steam engines, driving screw propellers. Diesel engines are favoured for their simplicity and economy, and they have steadily driven out the one-time workhorse, the vertical triple-expansion steam engine. Larger ships requiring high speeds rely on steam turbines. The new container ships and bulk-carriers designed for fast running have drawn for the first time on naval experience with high-speed steam propulsion. Gas tur-bines have been used experimentally, although they have not yet proved suffi-ciently cheap and reliable. Similarly nuclear power is still uneconomical, and the very small number of nuclear-powered merchant ships is not likely to increase until a cheap and compact reactor plant becomes available.

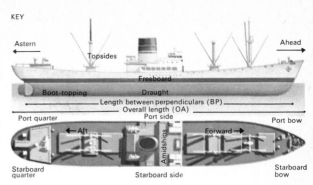

Terms used on ships include the fol-lowing: **Ahead** In advance of the bows. **Amidships** Near the middle of the ship's length. **Astern** Behind the ship. **Athwartships** From one side of the ship to the other. **Beam** Greatest breadth of the ship. **Boot-topping** Paint on hull between load line and water-line when ship is empty. **Bows** Foremost part. **Draught** Depth to which ship sinks in the water. **Forward** Towards the bows. **Freeboard** Distance from main deck to waterline. **Lee side** sheltered from the wind. **Port** Left side looking forwards. **Quarter** Direction between stern and beam. **Rake** Slope of funnel, masts or stem. **Sheer** Fore-and-aft curve of a hull rising towards bow and stern. **Starboard** Right-hand side looking forwards. **Topsides** Outer sur-face of vessel above water-line. **Trim** The way a vessel sits in the water. **Windward** Direction from which wind is blowing.

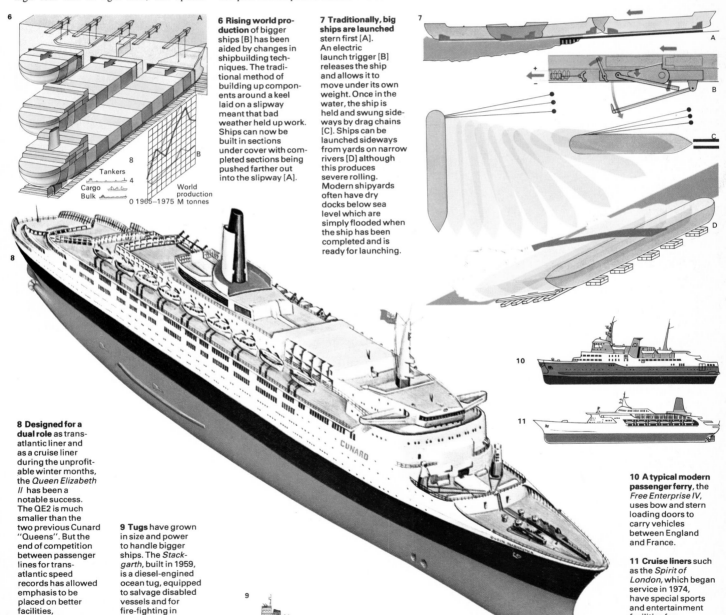

6 **Rising world pro-duction** of bigger ships [B] has been aided by changes in shipbuilding tech-niques. The tradi-tional method of building up compon-ents around a keel laid on a slipway meant that bad weather held up work. Ships can now be built in sections under cover with com-pleted sections being pushed farther out into the slipway [A].

Tankers

Cargo

Bulk

World production
0 1965–1975 M tonnes

7 Traditionally, big ships are launched stern first [A]. An electric launch trigger [B] releases the ship and allows it to move under its own weight. Once in the water, the ship is held and swung side-ways by drag chains [C]. Ships can be launched sideways from yards on narrow rivers [D] although this produces severe rolling. Modern shipyards often have dry docks below sea level which are simply flooded when the ship has been completed and is ready for launching.

8 **Designed for a dual role** as trans-atlantic liner and as a cruise liner during the unprofit-able winter months, the *Queen Elizabeth II* has been a notable success. The QE2 is much smaller than the two previous Cunard "Queens". But the end of competition between passenger lines for trans-atlantic speed records has allowed emphasis to be placed on better facilities, especially for lower-fare passengers.

9 **Tugs** have grown in size and power to handle bigger ships. The *Stack-garth*, built in 1959, is a diesel-engined ocean tug, equipped to salvage disabled vessels and for fire-fighting in addition to normal towage work.

10 **A typical modern passenger ferry**, the *Free Enterprise IV*, uses bow and stern loading doors to carry vehicles between England and France.

11 **Cruise liners** such as the *Spirit of London*, which began service in 1974, have special sports and entertainment facilities for holiday-makers.

Hydrofoils and air-cushion vehicles

Hydrofoils and air-cushion vehicles [Key] are machines that reflect today's demand for greater speed and flexibility in transport. In common with aeroplanes and helicopters these craft use energy for both upward and forward motion. A hydrofoil's hull is raised out of the water to reduce drag (friction) and thus enable it to travel faster than a conventional ship. An air-cushion vehicle (ACV) lifts itself in order to become independent of the surface over which it travels, which can be water, snow, marsh or sand. Today, each type of vehicle has a different use.

Hydrofoils and their uses

The first hydrofoils were built at the beginning of the twentieth century. Designers calculated that a sea wing (a lifting plane designed for running through water) [2] could be made much smaller than an air wing capable of generating the same lift force. Early experiments used foils stacked in the form of "ladders" [1A] so that, as the craft accelerated and lifted, fewer foils remained in the water.

By 1940 the more efficient surface-piercing foil [1C] had become preferred. In this type of hydrofoil a large foil slopes up on each side of the centre line, looking from the front like a V with the tips emerging from the water. These foils provide built-in stability in banked turns or through waves.

Most modern hydrofoils are of this type, although two other designs are also current. Many Soviet hydrofoils have depth-effect foils [1B], which stabilize automatically an inch or so below the surface of the water. They are ideal for use on shallow draught vessels for inland waterways but are useless in a rough sea. For this application, submerged foils [1D] are the best solution and these are the type used on most high-speed military hydrofoils. Small foils run deep in the water, supporting the vessel on streamlined struts. The angle of the foil can be varied by an autopilot, enabling the craft to run true even in heavy seas.

Most hydrofoils are fairly small, few civil types reaching 150 tonnes and the largest military version being 320 tonnes. As inshore ferries they can travel at high speeds without damaging river banks or disturbing smaller

craft with their wash, and they give a smooth ride across choppy water. Naval hydrofoils provide manoeuvrable platforms for guns, missiles and anti-submarine search and attack systems. At slow speeds, a hydrofoil behaves like a conventional ship and floats with its hull in the water. Control remains precise and the craft can ride out storms.

The story of the hovercraft

A hydrofoil is restricted to water and at low speeds needs deep water to float in. By contrast, a hovercraft – the most common kind of air-cushion vehicle (ACV) – is able to go practically anywhere.

In the nineteenth century engineers such as John Thornycroft (1843–1928) tried to reduce drag by pumping bubbles out of holes in a ship's hull. Later ACV developments sprang from the experimental work in the 1950s of Christopher Cockerell (1910–), who realized that some sort of "curtain" to contain the air cushion under the vehicle was essential to provide sufficient lift within the practical limits imposed by engine size.

Modern ACVs ride on a single bubble or

1 **Almost all hydrofoils** belong to one of four classes. Ladder foils [A] emerge progressively from the water as speed is increased. Depth-effect foils [B] are suited to shallow water without waves. Surface-piercing foils [C] are the most common form for passenger hydrofoils, while submerged foils [D] are preferred for rough seas. The foils are adjustable and their angle is controlled by an autopilot.

2 **Foils are sea wings.** At speed they generate enough lift to raise the vessel out of the water, thus reducing drag.

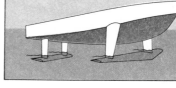

3 **Propulsion** poses problems because a hydrofoil's screw is lower than the engine. The sloping drive [A] is simplest but the thrust acts at a sharp angle. The Z drive [B] is best for deeply submerged foils, but requires two sets of bevel gears. The V form [C] is general on surface-piercing foil boats. An alternative is to use the engine to drive a pump, which squirts a water jet out at the stern to provide thrust.

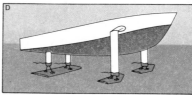

4 **The first full-scale hydrofoil** was built in 1906 by Enrico Forlanini (1848–1930). Lifted on three sets of ladder foils and propelled by front and rear air screws, it successfully ran at 71km/h (44mph). In 1918 a foil boat built by Alexander Graham Bell (1847–1922) reached 114km/h (71mph). Commercial development of the hydrofoil began in the 1930s.

5 **The Swiss** surface-piercing hydrofoil known as the PT 150-DC is one of the largest afloat. It is 37.9m (124ft) long overall with a maximum beam of 7.5m (25ft) and can carry 250 passengers at up to 67.5km/h (42mph) for 400km (248 miles). The vessel has air conditioning and heating which maintains the cabin temperature between 20 and 25°C (68–77°F). In addition to the surface-piercing front foil there is an air-stabilized submerged rear foil.

Twin propellers are sited below the rear foil. There are four passenger saloons, two on the main deck and two on the lower, and passengers can be served with drinks and refreshments in their seats. The Malmo-Copenhagen ferry uses a PT 150DC hydrofoil.

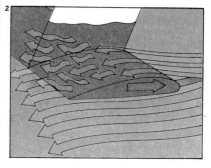

1 Radars
2 Liferaft
3 Front foil
4 Rear foil
5 Propeller
6 Two 3,400hp diesel engines
7 Bridge

cushion of air blown by fans through slots or jets round the underside of the hull [6]. The main part of the hull serves as a buoyancy tank, enabling a water-borne ACV to float when the lifting power is switched off. Air pumped by the lift fans raises the ACV on a cushion of slightly pressurized air, which leaks away round the edges at the same rate as it is fed in. The propulsion and lift systems may be driven either by one power plant or by separate units.

Early ACVs had flat undersides and daylight was visible beneath them when they were operating, although clearance was often only a few inches. To improve their performance over waves and other obstacles, later ACVs were fitted with flexible skirts [7]. These skirts contain the cushion of air but pass easily over obstructions. This facility makes them truly amphibious and they can operate equally well in or out of water. Unlike hydrofoils they are not limited in size and large passenger-carrying craft and car ferries are being used. Various types of propulsion and steering systems have been tried [8], some combining both functions.

Early optimism about the future of the ACV was not borne out by subsequent development. The craft has not yet shown itself to be completely economical for commercial use, probably because today's vehicles are too small.

Other uses of ACVs

Apart from conventional passenger transport ACVs have proved their value in the military sphere and the principle of the air cushion has been applied successfully to other modes of transport. The ACV system can be used on a train running over a smooth track, the air cushion reducing friction while propulsion is obtained from ducted fans or linear induction motors. As heavy load carriers ACVs are able to transport machinery weighing 500 tonnes over surfaces that could not possibly be traversed by wheeled or tracked vehicles. Air-cushion pallets for industrial use are easy to move and reduce strain on floor surfaces. The ACV principle has also been used in the design of hospital beds to lessen the discomfort of patients suffering from burns and for a "land-anywhere" aeroplane.

Hydrofoils and air-cushion vehicles are lifted and supported by the expenditure of energy – unlike water-borne ships or land vehicles resting on wheels. A hydrofoil [A] lifts itself to reduce drag, so as to run at high speed and travel smoothly across rough water. A hovercraft [B] does the same, but has the ability to traverse almost any kind of surface, including swamps, mud, river rapids and ice. The skirt fitted to amphibious hovercraft helps retain the supporting air cushion and lifts the rigid structure higher above the surface.

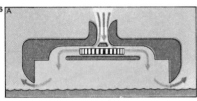
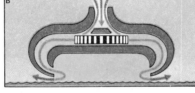
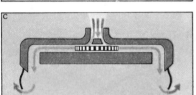
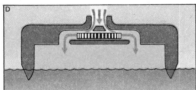

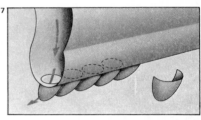

6 There are four basic types of ACV, each with a central lift fan. The simple "plenum chamber" [A] blows in air which escapes beneath the downturned edges. The peripheral jet [B] blows air inwards from a surrounding slit. With a skirt [C] the rigid body is raised above waves and solid obstructions. ACVs designed solely for use over water have side walls [D], saving lift power but adding extra water drag.

7 The skirt of an amphibious ACV is made of tough, rubberized fabric to withstand heavy wear. Air inflates the inner and outer walls, escaping through inward facing ducts or "fingers". These inflate the main cushion. They are designed for quick and easy replacement, since they are the parts most likely to be damaged.

8 ACV propulsion and steering is often by swivelling propellers [A]. To reduce noise and danger, ducted fans [B] may be used, or the propulsive jets may be provided by the same fans that inflate the cushion [C]. Like the fast hydrofoil, the seagoing ACV may be propelled by water jets [D]. Unless the propulsion system swivels, deflectors or rudders are needed to control the craft at speed or at rest.

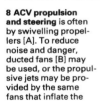

9 The first commercial hovercraft [A], SR-N1, (1959) was initially powered by a 450hp piston engine driving a fan, which fed the cushion as well as control propulsion ducts on each side. SR-N1 was later fitted with a skirt and a jet engine for high speeds. The

VT1 [B] was a large commercial ACV built in 1969 by Vosper Thornycroft. Designed to carry 10 cars and 146 passengers, it was propelled by water screws, yet had a skirt and could run out of the water up a slipway for loading. This design combined advantages of high speed with economy and low noise levels. Subsequent civil and military versions of the VT1 were fitted with a new propulsion system, the water screws being replaced by large ducted air propellers.

Submarines and submersibles

The invention of the submarine is usually credited to an Englishman, William Bourne. In 1578 he described a vessel that could take on and expel water to vary its buoyancy and that used a snorkel-like tube for its air supply. There is no evidence that Bourne's craft ever sailed and the first submarine was probably a leather-covered rowing boat built by a Dutch engineer Cornelius van Drebbel (1572–1634), in about 1620. According to the British chemist Robert Boyle such a boat took King James I (1566–1625) for a ride beneath the River Thames and even had some kind of "liquor" for renewing the air inside. Unfortunately no drawings or detail of this remarkable craft have survived.

Submarines in wartime

The *Turtle* [Key], a one-man submarine invented in 1776 by an American, David Bushnell (c. 1742–1824), was the first underwater vessel to be used in war. It pioneered two essential features of the modern submarine – a closed hull and screw propulsion, although the latter was worked by hand. But two further developments were necessary

before the submarine could become an effective fighting machine: a good undersea weapon and a source of power.

The Confederate navy used submarines during the American Civil War. Small craft known as Davids – named after the biblical David who vanquished the giant Goliath – were each armed with an explosive charge at the end of a long spar and powered by hand or steam. In 1864, a David, the *Hunley*, rammed the Union ship *Housatonic* off Charleston harbour; both vessels sank and the crew of the *Hunley* were killed. A self-propelled torpedo was also invented.

By the turn of the century the American inventor John P. Holland (1840–1914) was designing submarines powered by petrol engines. Holland's vessels were the first modern submarines and contained all the basic features of those that fought in both world wars. German submarines (U-boats) during World War I were highly effective as raiders of unarmed merchant ships, thereby threatening to cut Britain's vital supply lines. In World War II submarines took a toll of warships as well [6].

The effectiveness of the submarine remained limited by the slowness and short duration of undersea travel when vessels depended on electric motors powered by batteries. The batteries soon became exhausted and submarines had to surface frequently to obtain air for the diesel engines and recharge the batteries (through a dynamo driven by the engines). The diesel engines were also used for surface propulsion. In World War II a snorkel tube was developed to supply air to the diesel engines, which could be run just below the surface. This helped the submarine to escape detection.

How submarines work

Part of a submarine's hull is double-skinned. Water admitted into ballast tanks in the hull lowers the buoyancy of the vessel; diving planes on the sides of the hull control the angle at which the vessel sinks and level it out. Buoyancy is restored by expelling the water from the ballast tanks with compressed air. The central structure – the conning tower or sail – contains a periscope, radio and radar aerials and a snorkel tube. Tracking of an

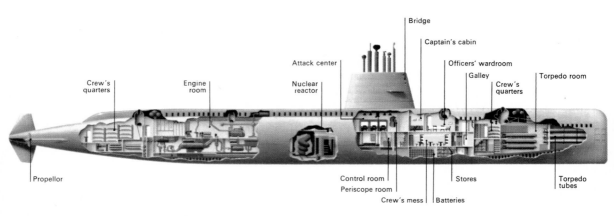

1 A nuclear submarine is a deadly weapon on an unprecedented scale. Each of its 16 guided missiles can carry up to 10 separate nuclear warheads, each sufficient to destroy a city. It need not surface and can fire its missiles from beneath the sea, thus remaining invulnerable. The USA and the USSR each possess more than 100 nuclear submarines. Air-conditioned (for the electronic systems as well as the crew), they can travel 644,000km (400,000 miles) without refuelling. The nuclear reactor powers a steam turbine that drives the propellers directly or by means of an electric generator and motors.

Crew's quarters / Engine room / Attack center / Nuclear reactor / Propellor / Control room / Periscope room / Crew's mess / Batteries / Stores / Bridge / Captain's cabin / Officers' wardroom / Galley / Crew's quarters / Torpedo room / Torpedo tubes

2 Locating submerged submarines from a ship, or locating surface vessels from a submarine, is achieved by listening for echoes of supersonic sound pulses transmitted through water. The system, originally called ASDIC by the British Royal Navy, is now called sonar. Submarines can be located using sonar buoys, which transmit signals back to a nearby mother ship, or by using a "dunking" sonar suspended from a helicopter and dipped just below the surface of the water.

3 The torpedo, invented by Austrian engineer, G. Luppis in 1864 and developed by Robert Whitehead (1823–1905), made the submarine into an effective fighting force. It is fired from a tube inside the submarine. Torpedo attacks on merchant shipping, as shown here, were successful in both world wars, but the torpedo is now primarily an anti-submarine weapon. Accurate positioning is no longer necessary, as modern torpedoes home in on their targets acoustically or are guided by wire. Short-range missiles for use against other vessels have been developed for firing from torpedo tubes.

4 Rising from the sea on a test flight, the *Polaris* missile has a range of nearly 4,630km (2,875 miles) and carries three nuclear warheads. The *Poseidon* missile has ten warheads. The missiles are ejected from their launching tubes by compressed gas and the two-stage solid-fuelled rocket motor fires at the surface. They are computer guided and the warheads separate on re-entry.

enemy vessel is accomplished by sonar (underwater) and radar (when surfaced) and communications are by radio. A submarine can receive messages underwater but has to have at least its radio aerial clear of the water in order to transmit signals, although methods of direct transmission are being investigated. Navigation is by a computerized inertial guidance system, assisted by sonar and radar in coastal waters or beneath ice floes. The periscope is used for photographing and for checking navigation by sextant.

The nuclear submarine [1] is a true undersea craft. It needs no air for its motors and can make long undersea voyages without refuelling. The first of these vessels, the USS *Nautilus*, was also the world's first nuclear-powered warship of any kind. Launched in 1954, its capabilities drastically changed the military strategy of the Great Powers. Instead of raiding surface vessels, nuclear submarines carry long-range intercontinental missiles armed with nuclear warheads that can be launched underwater. The submarines constitute a strike force that is practically invulnerable because they cannot

easily be located when submerged. They are intended to respond to the first strike against a country and thus deter any nation from making such an attack.

In addition to intercontinental missiles [4] the submarine can carry torpedoes [3] that either home acoustically or are guided by a wire trailed behind the torpedo. Weapons that are part-torpedo and part-missile can also be carried for use against distant vessels.

The role of submersibles

The term submersible may be used to describe any underwater vessel but today it usually indicates a non-military vessel. Small electrically-powered submersibles [7] are used to inspect and carry out maintenance of underwater structures, especially oil and gas drilling heads and pipelines; to check undersea cables and bury them in the mud on the sea floor; to search for minerals on the seabed; and to carry out oceanographic research. They have even been used to search for the Loch Ness monster. The submersibles have bright lights and sensitive manipulators so that they can work on the sea-bed.

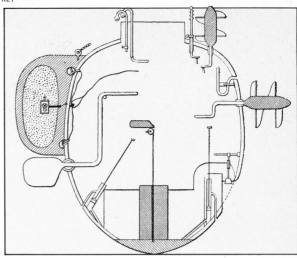

The Turtle, an American submarine, was in 1776 the first to operate in a war. The single crew member worked all the controls – lateral and vertical propellors, rudder and pumps – by hand. The packet of explosives [left] was detachable and designed to be fixed to the hull of an enemy vessel.

5

6

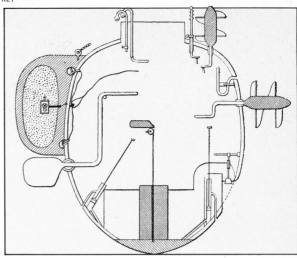

5 The largest submarine of World War I was the K-class of the British Royal Navy. It was 103m (338ft) long and had a crew of 55. The war proved that submarines were not greatly effective against warships but could be used to sink merchant ships and disrupt supply lines. Germany had no ocean supply lines but the Allies lost 32 ships for every German submarine they succeeded in sinking.

6 The German U-boat (*Unterseeboot*) was responsible for sinking millions of tonnes of Allied shipping during the early stages of World War II. Working in packs and armed with fore and aft torpedo tubes, the U-boats stalked convoys by day and attacked by night. The Allied development of radio direction finding and radar made surfaced submarines vulnerable to aircraft attack.

7 *Star III* is a submersible capable of operating to a depth of 610m (2,000ft). Powered by batteries it is 7.7m (25ft) long and carries a crew of two sealed inside the spherical steel pressure hull amidships. *Star III* is highly manoeuvrable as it has horizontal and vertical motors. It operates from a support ship and has been used to investigate the deep scattering layer of plankton that is so important to ocean ecology. Submersibles have also been used to locate deep-swimming schools of fish to help improve catches. They are capable of delicate undersea work on cables and oil rigs.

8

7

Aft trim tank   Vertical propulsion motor   TV cameras

Main ballast tank   Forward trim tank

Main propulsion motor   HP air flasks   Batteries   Pressure hull   Viewing ports   Bow thruster

8 Modern submersibles are important in oceanographic research. Using them scientists can search the ocean floors for evidence of oil, manganese nodules and other minerals. Similar vessels are used to inspect and maintain underwater structures such as offshore drilling rigs (for natural gas and oil) and submarine telephone cables. Mechanical "hands", controlled from inside the submersible, are used to collect samples or to hold tools. The vessel can also be equipped with powerful lights, television cameras and underwater cutting torches. At shallower depths, a submersible can act as a base and even living quarters for divers, who leave and enter the craft through an air-lock. Communication to the surface may be by telephone along a cable or a sonar (supersonic sound) beam may be used to transmit suitably coded voice messages or even slow-scan television pictures. All equipment is worked by electricity from storage batteries.

Carts, coaches and carriages

When early man was a hunter he found that he could transport his kill more easily if he dragged it on a crude sled [1] rather than carrying it on his back. Soon he found that lengths of tree trunks used as rollers could move even heavier loads.

A solid wheel fixed to a platform by a simple axle was a logical development of the roller system [2]. The first reported use of a wheel was in Mesopotamia, the land between the rivers Tigris and Euphrates, some 5,000 years ago. Oxen-hauled wheeled transport then developed and its use spread slowly to the Mediterranean, Europe and China. When the Romans turned their attention to the building of wheeled vehicles their fine roads permitted fast travel in horse-drawn chariots – an important factor in the administration of a vast empire.

In the period between the fall of the Roman Empire and the fifteenth century, progress in the development of vehicular transport lapsed. Most travellers were soldiers, pilgrims or pedlars who relied largely on horses or pack animals. Farm carts used for local haulage were drawn by heavy horses

specially bred for the work and in later times used as battle chargers. The few wheeled vehicles of the Middle Ages had no springs [4] and a long journey through Europe could take several uncomfortable months.

Wheeled transport develops

As communication between peoples increased, carriage transport began to develop. The first vehicles used rigid axles until suspensions in the form of flexible wood laths, then leather straps, were introduced. Early sixteenth-century carriages, often extravagantly decorated, were much resented. The public envied those rich enough to afford them, the Church considered private conveyances sinful and the authorities kept a close watch, thinking them ripe for taxing – attitudes very similar to the ones of those who opposed the introduction of the automobile some 400 years later.

By the seventeenth century, the period of mechanical and scientific awakening in Western Europe, some coaches and carriages had metal spring suspensions. Large rear wheels allowed the vehicles to travel at

higher speeds over the poor roads and also provided a more comfortable ride.

During the seventeenth century Britain changed, mainly because of trade, from a farming community to a commercial nation with the need to convey goods and people over long distances. Smaller, lighter vehicles were developed for rapid short trips. But for longer journeys the early stage-coaches could travel little more than 48km (30 miles) a day, stopping periodically at staging posts. A journey from London to Edinburgh – a distance of 675km (420 miles) – took 12 days even by fast coach.

From mail coach to rail travel

The first coaches to carry both mail and passengers travelled from Bath to London in 1783. Mail coaches were so reliable that clocks could be set by their 16km/h (10mph) schedule. Coaching inns, some of them able to cater for up to a hundred coaches a day, provided passengers with meals and accommodation along the main routes.

The nineteenth century saw great changes, including the brief introduction of

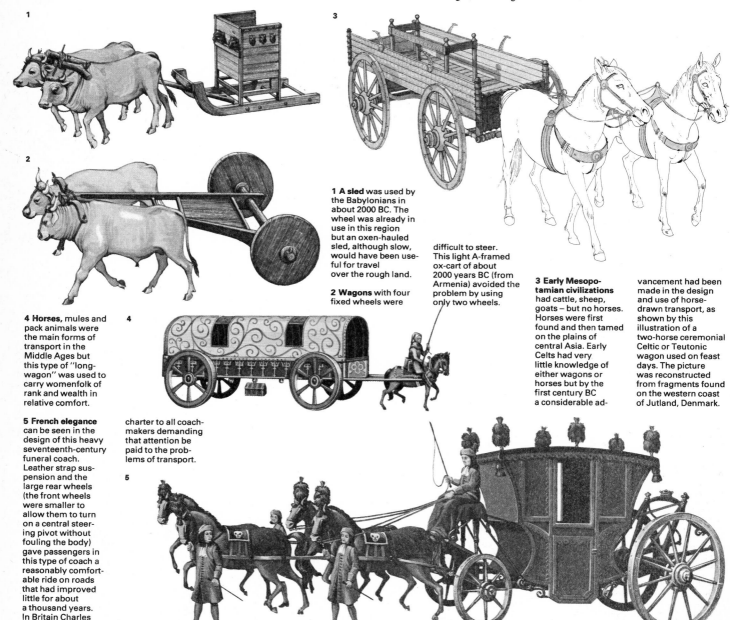

1 A sled was used by the Babylonians in about 2000 BC. The wheel was already in use in this region but an oxen-hauled sled, although slow, would have been useful for travel over the rough land.

2 Wagons with four fixed wheels were

difficult to steer. This light A-framed ox-cart of about 2000 years BC (from Armenia) avoided the problem by using only two wheels.

3 Early Mesopotamian civilizations had cattle, sheep, goats – but no horses. Horses were first found and then tamed on the plains of central Asia. Early Celts had very little knowledge of either wagons or horses but by the first century BC a considerable advancement had been made in the design and use of horse-drawn transport, as shown by this illustration of a two-horse ceremonial Celtic or Teutonic wagon used on feast days. The picture was reconstructed from fragments found on the western coast of Jutland, Denmark.

4 Horses, mules and pack animals were the main forms of transport in the Middle Ages but this type of "long-wagon" was used to carry womenfolk of rank and wealth in relative comfort.

5 French elegance can be seen in the design of this heavy seventeenth-century funeral coach. Leather strap suspension and the large rear wheels (the front wheels were smaller to allow them to turn on a central steering pivot without fouling the body) gave passengers in this type of coach a reasonably comfortable ride on roads that had improved little for about a thousand years. In Britain Charles II issued a royal charter to all coach-makers demanding that attention be paid to the problems of transport.

steam coaches. Travelling became more comfortable with the development of elliptical leaf springs made of several thin, flat springs bound together and these are still used for many purposes today. The design of carriages and coaches became more elegant and light following the improvement of roads by the engineer John McAdam (1756–1836) whose type of road surfacing, designed to compact by the weight of passing traffic, greatly facilitated travel.

The Victorians used numerous types of horse-drawn transport for short journeys, ranging from the light gig to the family brake. Wealthy families kept staff to drive or maintain a private coach or drag, a dog cart for sportsmen and gun dogs, a governess cart for the children, a phaeton for rapid journeys, a victoria for park and town use, a brougham for privacy and perhaps a stately landau for formal occasions.

In America the stage-coach enjoyed a longer span of life and helped to open up the West through a vast network of scheduled services operated by coaching companies such as Wells Fargo. The lightweight high-wheeled buggy [7] and canopied phaeton or surrey were extensively used for private transport. Both were distinctively North American vehicles. A buggy seated two people whereas a surrey was essentially a family transporter with two rows of seats.

Cabs, trams and buses

In Europe the hire-cab designed by Joseph Hansom (1803–82) in 1834 (and bearing his name) plied the streets of almost every city and horse-drawn trams and omnibuses provided reasonably inexpensive travel for the masses. The box-like omnibus, French in origin, was first introduced to London in 1829 by George Shillibeer at the time of the demise of the coach. By the 1840s the single-decker bus had developed into the double-decker with seating along the length of the top deck [8]. With further development improvements were added and the double-decker became the design adopted by bus companies when motor-driven transport began to replace horse-drawn vehicles. The last London horse bus in regular service continued to operate until 1914.

KEY
The brougham, a type of small, closed carriage for town and winter use, was first made in 1839 for Lord Brougham (1778–1868). It was unique in Britain and led to a revolution in carriage design, although similar vehicles were already in use in Paris. Eventually the brougham became one of the most common town carriages. The original version, known as the single brougham, was drawn by one horse and carried two people. Later models, known as bow-fronted and double broughams, were drawn by two horses and carried up to four people.

6 The charabanc [A] was useful in large establishments for communal transport. A private omnibus [B], driven by a liveried coachman, was used to carry small groups on excursions. The drag [C] was a private coach based on earlier mail coach designs. The wagonette [D], with seats down each side and a rear entrance, was fashionable for family outings. The dog cart [E], originally designed to carry sportsmen and their dogs, became widely used for everyday transport.

7 European carriage design influenced many early American models. But the buggy had a very definite North American character, although the word "buggy" was originally an English word meaning a hooded gig. The distinctive American buggy, which made its appearance in about 1850, was a light, fast carriage with two or four high wheels and a thin frame supporting the carriage and canopy. It was drawn by one horse and seated two passengers.

8 The word "omnibus" (meaning "for every one") originated in France in about 1825 for a transport service operating in Nantes. Introduced to London in 1829 by Englishman George Shillibeer (1797–1866) the omnibus was an immediate success. The initial service, which ran between Paddington and the Bank for a fare of one shilling, was provided by a horse-drawn vehicle carrying 18 to 22 passengers. A liveried conductor stood guard by the rear entrance door. Soon people adopted the practice of perching on the roof of these single-deckers, leading to the development of the double-decker "knifeboard" bus with no weather protection on the upper deck (fares on top were half price). By the 1880s it had developed into the two-horse "garden seat" bus pictured here, in which forward-facing seats replaced the long bench. Horse-bus services operated in London until 1914.

History of bicycles

Bicycles driven by cranked pedals date from the 1860s and since then the machines have become popular throughout the world, particularly in Britain, France, Italy, the Netherlands and other European countries. Troops riding bicycles were employed by the major powers in World War I and, more recently, by the Vietcong in Vietnam.

The first bicycle
The history of the bicycle begins with non-powered machines developed in France in the late 1700s. In 1791 the Comte de Sivrac built his *célérifère*. It was a wooden machine consisting of two wheels in line joined by a bar that carried a seat. The rider straddled the bar and "walked" the machine along. Similar machines were made by J. Nicéphore Niépce (1765-1833) (also the inventor of an early photographic process) in 1816 and by the German Baron Karl von Drais a year later. Drais' *Laufmaschine* soon became popular in Britain and Germany as the *draisine* or hobby-horse.

In 1839 the Scotsman Kirkpatrick Macmillan produced a "powered" hobby-horse

propelled by pedals at the front which worked backwards and forwards driving connecting rods to turn the rear wheel. Rotating pedal-cranks, driving the front wheel directly, were introduced by the French brothers Pierre and Ernest Michaux in about 1861. They called their machines *Vélocipèdes* and within four years were manufacturing 400 bicycles a year. By 1869 bicycle racing was established on the roads of France.

The "ordinary" or "penny-farthing" bicycle [Key] had a large front wheel driven directly by pedal-cranks and a small rear wheel. Invented in 1871 by the Englishman James Starley (1831–81), it rapidly became the most popular type of bicycle. The size of the large wheel was chosen to suit the length of the rider's legs and varied from 1m (39in) to 1.5m (59in) across.

Chain-driven bicycles
The first chain-driven machine was built in 1874 by H. J. Lawson. Pedal-cranks mounted on the frame turned a large sprocket wheel which drove an endless chain round a smaller sprocket on the rear wheel.

Bicycles again had wheels of roughly equal sizes. The Rover safety bicycle of 1885 was mass produced and within a few years completely replaced the penny-farthing. All these early bicycles had solid rubber tyres mounted on steel-rimmed wheels.

The modern machine
A milestone in the history of the bicycle came in 1888 when John Dunlop (1840–1921) invented the air-filled or pneumatic tyre. The diamond-shaped frame became standard and there were no major changes in bicycle design for the next 70 years. In the 1960s various manufacturers produced small-wheeled bicycles – some of which could be folded to fit into the boot of a car – for town use. Earlier unusual designs included the tandem, a long-framed bicycle for two riders, and the three-wheeled tricycle which became important as the type of machine into which Karl Benz (1844–1929) and Gottlieb Daimler (1834–1900) fitted petrol engines to make the first motor cars in 1885.

A modern bicycle has mudguards, electric lamps powered by batteries or a dynamo and

1 The Whippet of 1885 was designed by Lindley and Briggs. It had a pivoted and sprung frame designed to make the handle-bars, saddle and pedals independent of the rest of the frame and wheels.

2 The Dursley Pederson bicycle of 1893 was designed by M. Pederson and built at Dursley in England. The frame members were of twin narrow-section tubes, side by side for rigidity, giving a lighter frame.

3 The Raleigh Safety bicycle of 1901 had an all-steel frame joined by a new brazing process using pressed steel sockets brazed to the frame tubes by dipping the joints in molten brass.

4 The Swift ladies' bicycle of 1926 had no cross-bar on the frame, making it easier for a woman wearing a skirt to get on and off. The lightweight frame was an advance over early heavy designs.

5 The Velocino bicycle, made in Italy in the mid-1930s, was an attempt at a compact design that was easy to store and carry. Its inventors also claimed it to be easier to dismount in an emergency.

6 The Moulton bicycle, produced in the UK in 1962, had small wheels, rubber suspension and a low centre of gravity. The frame could be adjusted to "fit" the build of almost any rider and was strong enough to carry heavy loads.

lever or calliper brakes acting on the rims of both wheels [7]. It may have variable gear ratios and a guard to enclose the chain and transmission. Accessories include extra carrying capacity in the form of a rear-mounted rack, a basket in front of the handlebars and a saddlebag or a pair of panniers mounted on each side of the rear wheel.

The frame is generally made of seamless steel tubing brazed or welded together. In the brazing process pre-cut lengths of tubing are fitted over angled sockets and secured in place with molten brass. In welding there are no sockets and the tubes are joined with molten steel to give a joint stronger than the tubes themselves. Using special light alloys manufacturers can make racing bicycles weighing as little as 7kg (15lb).

Between 24 and 40 wire spokes join the wheel hub to the rim. The rim end of each spoke is threaded and a nut or nipple is screwed on to it to keep the spoke in tension. The rim may be made of aluminium alloy, stainless steel or chromium plated stainless steel. Hard rubber brake-blocks, worked by levers (called stirrups) or callipers (which act

like pincers to nip each side of the wheel) press on the rim for braking. An alternative type of brake acts by pressing inside the hub of the rear wheel and is brought into action by back-pedalling.

The rear wheel of a bicycle rotates faster than the large sprocket wheel turned by pedalling. There are generally about 48 teeth on the large sprocket wheel and about 18 on the smaller rear sprocket. This provides a gear ratio of about 2.66 to 1. Variable gears allow different speeds for a constant pedalling effort. There are two main types. In a *dérailleur* gear there are up to six rear sprockets of different sizes plus up to three on the cranks to provide a variety of gear ratios.

An epicyclic gear, developed by Sturmey and Archer, is more complicated. A small cog called the sun wheel inside the rear limb is rotated by the rear sprocket. A ring of teeth line the inside of the hub and the drive is taken to these from the sun wheel via a set of planet-wheel cogs. Three different gear ratios are available. Sturmey-Archer and *dérailleur* types can be combined on one hub to provide the rider with eight gears.

The penny-farthing or ordinary bicycle first appeared in England in the early 1870s, invented by James Starley. The rider pedalled cranks that were mounted at the centre of the large front wheel, which he also turned to steer the machine.

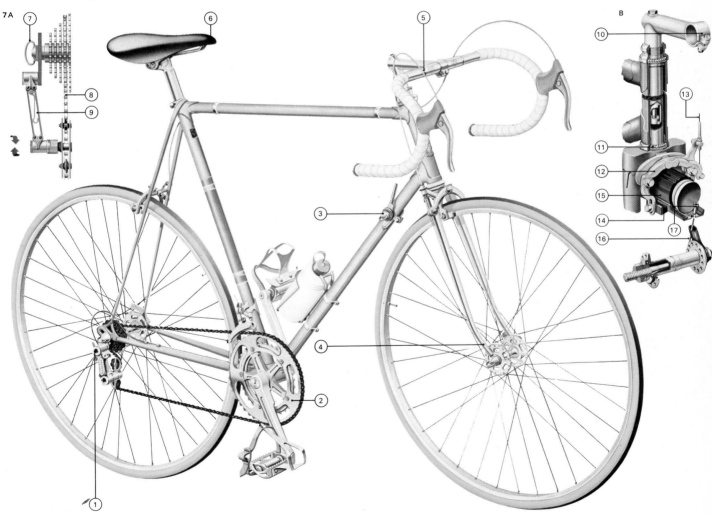

7 A modern racing bicycle has a short wheelbase for manoeuvrability and is made of light-weight alloys to reduce the weight of the machine. It has two sets of *dérailleur* gears, one [1] on the rear hub and the other [2] on the main

sprocket, giving it up to 28 different gear ratios. The gears are changed by means of two levers [3] on the frame. The front forks [4] are nearly straight, to reduce the wheelbase, but have enough curvature to act as springs. The handlebars [5] and saddle [6] are both adjustable and the saddle is fixed so that the distance from it to the handlebars is about the same as the length between the rider's elbow and fingertips. The height of the saddle above the lowest

point of the pedal is ideally 9% longer than the rider's inside leg length. The *dérailleur* gear [A] on the rear hub has up to six sprockets, of increasing sizes, mounted on a quick-release hub [7]. Small sprockets give high gears and

larger ones low gears. The drive chain [8] can be shifted from one sprocket to another by a parallelogram arrangement [9] held in sideways tension by a spring. The stem and fork assembly [B] of a modern bicycle has to bear much of

the weight and still pivot freely for steering the machine. Handlebars are fitted to an angled sprocket [10] at the top of the stem. A ballrace [11] provides a friction-free bearing. Most modern machines have brakes consisting of a cal-

liper [12] operated by a bowden cable [13]. When the cable is pulled the calliper nips brake-blocks [14] against the wheel rim. The tyre [15] has a canvas carcass covered by synthetic rubber tread. Each spoke [16] is tensioned by a nipple [17].

History of motor cycles

The motor cycle is an older invention than the motor car. Two Frenchmen, Pierre and Ernest Michaux, built the first motor cycle – a steam powered "boneshaker" in Paris in 1869, sixteen years before Karl Benz (1844–1929) and Gottlieb Daimler (1834–1900) made the first cars. But the advantage of Daimler's petrol engine was soon put to use by motor cycle designers.

Early developments
Other technical innovations soon improved these early machines. The pneumatic tyre of J. B. Dunlop (1840–1921), invented in 1888, helped to absorb some of the bone-jarring shocks from the road surface. The final drive was generally a leather belt, which tended to break or slip in wet weather. The engine was started by pedalling, to turn over the engine, or by "bump starting" in which the rider pushed the machine, running alongside and jumping into the saddle when the engine fired. The Butler spray carburettor of 1889, modified and refined by Wilhelm Maybach (1847–1929) in 1893, was the forerunner of those still used today.

Motor tricycles also date from about 1880. Some were little better than motorized wheelchairs. But the De Dion Bouton of 1898 had a rear-mounted engine, a differential, and was capable of the then staggering speed of 40km/h (25mph).

In Britain the Road Acts of 1861 and 1865 had required that all motor vehicles be preceded by a man carrying a red flag. The repeal of these laws in 1896 removed the restrictions that had cramped British designs for so long. In the same year Colonel Capel Holden patented a motor cycle with a four-cylinder opposed engine. This had a commutator-type distributor powered by a coil and a battery, as on a modern car. External connecting rods drove the rear wheel directly by means of overhung cranks.

Wider applications of motor cycles
The motor cycle movement was also growing in the United States where by 1905 the main manufacturers were Harley Davidson and Indian. Both companies pioneered the use of twist-grips [1] on the handlebars to control the throttle and advance and retard of the

ignition timing. The 1.75hp Indian of 1905 had a single-cylinder engine with a steel cylinder machined from a solid casting. Harley Davidson produced their first V-twin cylinder engine in 1909 and have used the same layout in most of their engines ever since. By 1914 the motor cycle speed record has risen to 150.5km/h (93.5mph). In the same year, the first of World War I, the British army began to use motor cycles for dispatch riders and used machines fitted with sidecars that could also carry a machine gun.

By the 1920s nearly all large-engined machines had a chain or shaft as final drive. Overhead valve engines began to appear and some, such as the 1,000cc units in Harley Davidsons and Indians, had four valves to each cylinder. In Germany BMW produced their first motor cycles with a horizontally opposed twin-cylinder engine, an arrangement that has also survived to the present.

As the volume of traffic increased, particularly in the United States, police forces began to use motor cycles for patrol duties. Large four-cylinder machines produced by companies such as Henderson and

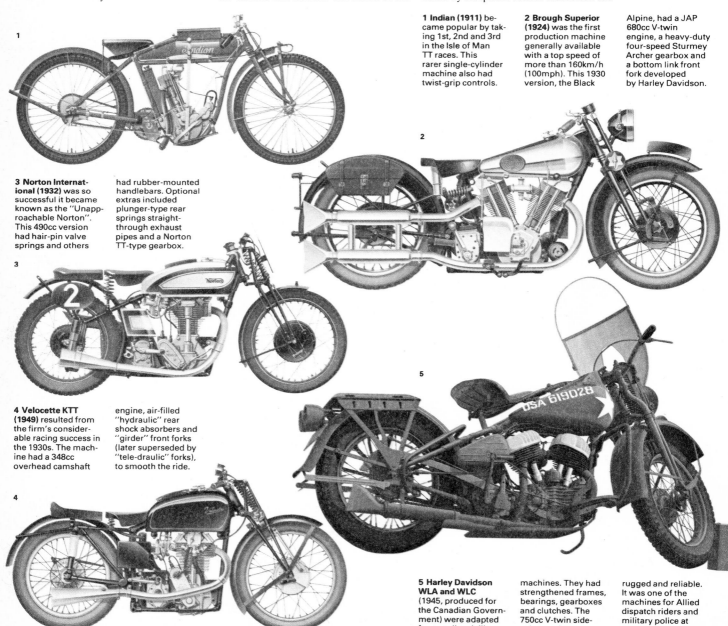

1 Indian (1911) became popular by taking 1st, 2nd and 3rd in the Isle of Man TT races. This rarer single-cylinder machine also had twist-grip controls.

2 Brough Superior (1924) was the first production machine generally available with a top speed of more than 160km/h (100mph). This 1930 version, the Black Alpine, had a JAP 680cc V-twin engine, a heavy-duty four-speed Sturmey Archer gearbox and a bottom link front fork developed by Harley Davidson.

3 Norton International (1932) was so successful it became known as the "Unapproachable Norton". This 490cc version had hair-pin valve springs and others had rubber-mounted handlebars. Optional extras included plunger-type rear springs straight-through exhaust pipes and a Norton TT-type gearbox.

4 Velocette KTT (1949) resulted from the firm's considerable racing success in the 1930s. The machine had a 348cc overhead camshaft engine, air-filled "hydraulic" rear shock absorbers and "girder" front forks (later superseded by "tele-draulic" forks), to smooth the ride.

5 Harley Davidson WLA and WLC (1945, produced for the Canadian Government) were adapted from earlier civilian machines. They had strengthened frames, bearings, gearboxes and clutches. The 750cc V-twin side-valve engine was rugged and reliable. It was one of the machines for Allied dispatch riders and military police at the end of the war.

Indian were particularly suited for driving on the long, straight American roads.

Two-stroke engines

A two-stroke petrol engine has fewer moving parts than a four-stroke and is easier to maintain. By 1930 Villiers and other companies were producing a wide range of single-cylinder two-stroke engines. During the late 1920s and the 1930s the motor cycle underwent a social change. It ceased to be a luxury machine and evolved into a relatively cheap and utilitarian form of transport. A pillion passenger could be carried behind the driver and a sidecar gave the "combination" a carrying capacity of up to four (two adults and two children).

By 1937 a Brough Superior fitted with a 1,000cc JAP engine had pushed the world speed record up to nearly 275km/h (170mph). Once again the motor cycle industry was preparing for war. In 1938 BMW produced the R75 model, with a sidecar, for the Germany army. Both sides made collapsible motor cycles for paratroops.

Post-war development was characterized by smaller, higher-revving engines and in Europe thousands of motor scooters were produced. Between 1950 and 1965 manufacturers of dearer "luxury" machines such as the Vincent and Sunbeam (which used rubber-mounted engines) were forced to close down in the face of competition from mass-produced machines from Triumph, BSA, Norton and AMC. A wide range of purpose-built machines became available for scrambles, trials and road-racing.

During the early 1960s the Japanese Honda company began to enter Western markets with their small, 50cc four-stroke machines. Followed by Suzuki and Yamaha producing two-strokes, they soon dominated the market with models ranging from 50cc "monkey bikes" to 750cc four-cylinder machines capable of 210km/h (130mph).

Most motor cycles sold today are economic and comfortable machines. Electric starters and hydraulic disc brakes are becoming standard. The late 1970s may see the introduction of more rotary engine motor cycles, such as those which are already being produced by the DKW company.

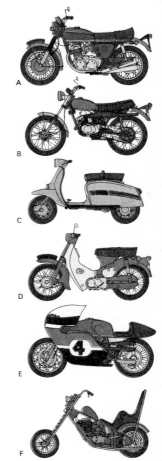

The first recorded motor cycle was built in France in 1869, based on an existing Michaux velocipede – a type of "boneshaker" pedal bicycle. It had a small single-cylinder steam engine. A flexible leather belt linked a pulley on the engine with a larger one on the rear wheel, thus gearing down the speed of the engine. Within 20 years other inventors constructed steam bicycles and tricycles and in 1886 the German engineer Gottlieb Daimler fitted his air-cooled petrol engine into a wooden bicycle, also of his own design. At about the same time the English inventor Edward Butler (1863–1940) patented his "Petrocycle", a three-wheeler with spoked wheels and a two-cylinder water-cooled engine. The first commercially successful petrol-engined motor cycle was produced in 1893 by Henry and Wilhelm Hildebrand in Munich.

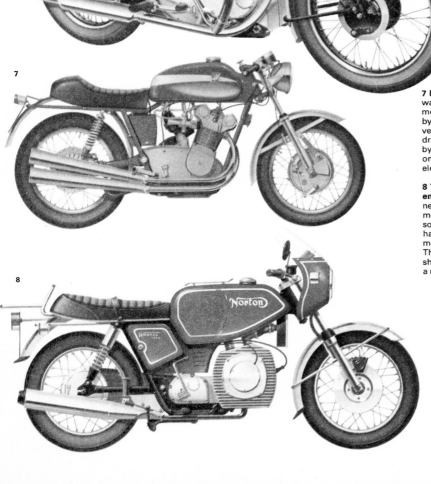

6

7

8

6 Vincent Rapide (Series C, 1950) was based on a 998cc machine of 1937. It had twin carburettors and twin brakes on each axle and in 1955 held the solo and sidecar records.

7 MV Augusta (1950) was a four-cylinder motor cycle designed by Ing Remor. First versions had a shaft drive, later replaced by a chain. It had one of the first electric starters.

8 The rotary Wankel engine may be the new power unit for motor cycles and some manufacturers have experimental machines using it. This illustration shows how such a machine may look.

9

A

B

C

D

E

F

9 Types of modern motor cycles include [A] standard 750cc road-going sports, capable of carrying two people at speed; [B] trials bike with high-mounted engine, wide handlebars and knobbly tyres for cross-country riding; [C] Italian-pioneered motor scooter with good weather protection; [D] "step-through" motor cycle with small engine and automatic clutch for use in towns; [E] fully modified road racer with a highly tuned engine in a special frame giving a 280 km/h (175mph) machine suitable for only the most experienced riders; and [F] the "chopper" using a standard engine in a highly modified frame with upswept handlebars and a sit-back saddle.

History of automobiles

The automobile was not invented overnight. It took shape from an accumulation of technical advances that resulted in a light and efficient engine. The accepted "fathers of the modern motor car" are two Germans, Karl Benz (1844–1929) and Gottlieb Daimler (1834–1900), who built their first petrol-fuelled motor vehicles within a few months of each other (1885–6).

More than a hundred years earlier, the first self-propelled road vehicle had rumbled through the streets of Paris at nearly 5km/h (3mph) when Nicolas Cugnot (1725–1804) demonstrated his steam-driven wagon [1].

The first automobile

The German Nikolas Otto (1832–91) made the first four-stroke internal-combustion engine in 1876 and in 1885 Daimler had installed a small four-stroke engine in a cycle frame. He drove his first four-wheeled petrol-driven vehicle round Cannstatt in 1886. In neighbouring Mannheim, Benz had tested his three-wheeler car.

Daimler licensed the French firm of Panhard and Levassor to build his engine.

Levassor placed it at the front of his crude car [2] and it drove the rear road-wheels through a clutch and a gearbox. Thus in 1891 the first car to use modern engineering layout was seen. Within three years of the appearance of the first Panhard France was staging motor races on public roads.

At the turn of the century, petrol, steam and electric power shared almost equal popularity for powering automobiles. Steam was well-tried and reliable and electric vehicles held the land speed record. France had several established motor manufacturers – Panhard, Peugeot, Renault, Daracq, Delahaye and others; in Germany Benz had made the world's first standard production car, the Velo (1894), and the Daimler company was just about to present the Mercedes to the public (1901) [3].

In the United States the automobile would develop along different lines. There the car was seen not as a rich man's toy, but as a new method of communication in a continent in which travel had been restricted by a lack of roads and great distances.

Great Britain, slow to start, had legislated

for the car in 1896 when the road speed limits were raised and soon such companies as Lanchester, Daimler (of Coventry), Wolseley and Napier were producing cars.

Motoring in Britain

Encouraged by the keen interest shown by King Edward VII, motoring in Britain became an accepted method of travel – for the rich. Some British manufacturers began to contest French car supremacy and among them the partnership formed in 1904 between Charles Rolls and engineer Henry Royce was one of the most significant [4]. At that time Henry Ford was preparing the motoring world for his Model T, which was introduced in 1908 [5].

By 1910 automobile design had become fairly settled, with a side-valve four- (or six-) cylinder front-mounted engine. Weather protection had been developed, and the electric starter from America (1912) had encouraged women to take to the wheel by removing the physical hardship of the starting handle. Interchangeable parts made to fine limits opened the gates to mass

1 The first self-propelled road vehicle, built by Cugnot in 1769, was a tiller-steered, two-cylinder, steam-powered tractor. Its "engine" was on the single front wheel and was designed to pull guns. It involved its inventor in the world's first motor accident when it hit a wall.

2 Panhard and Levassor (1894) was developed from the 1891 design. It had a Daimler engine mounted at the front of the car, with the drive passing through a clutch and gearbox to the rear road-wheels. This French design was to be adopted as the standard modern layout.

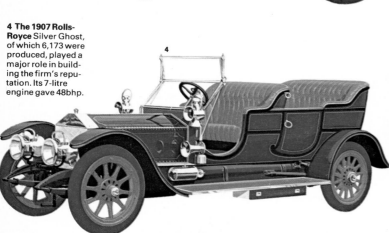

3 The Mercedes, built by Daimler, appeared in 1901. Technically advanced for its day, it had a 35bhp, 5.9-litre engine and gate change.

4 The 1907 Rolls-Royce Silver Ghost, of which 6,173 were produced, played a major role in building the firm's reputation. Its 7-litre engine gave 48bhp.

5 Ford's Model T (1908), a simple easy-to-drive car, brought motoring to the world. Nicknamed "flivver", more than 15 million were sold by the end of its run in 1927.

production. The Edwardians had laid down the working principles and the following years saw more refinement than innovation. "Balloon" tyres, pressed-steel wheels and four-wheel brakes appeared. Heavy and unstable coach-built saloon bodies encouraged the trend to wood-and-fabric and later to the rigid, welded pressed-steel body.

Cheaper cars

Greater demand by the public in the 1920s brought cheaper cars on to the market from such manufacturers as Morris, Citröen, Opel, Austin and Fiat, although such exotic models as Hispano-Suiza, Maybach, Voisin and Delage still commanded respect – and a deep purse. The economic depression of the late 1920s closed down many companies of both classes, from Clyno to Bentley, and forced the production of even more basic cars.

By the 1930s most cars were being made for the new middle-class "family" driver, uninformed in motoring matters and requiring a near foolproof vehicle. There were some technical milestones, however. In 1934 Citröen produced the Traction Avant [7], the first medium-sized car to have front-wheel drive and independent suspension, and in 1938 the German car that was to become the Volkswagen (people's car) was finalized and tested – the only car to have spanned four decades [8].

The first postwar cars were similar to prewar models, but in 1948 two British cars destined to influence future design appeared – the wide-tracked Morris Minor and the 193km/h (120mph) Jaguar XK120 sports car. In 1955 the hydro-pneumatic suspension system of the Citröen DS 19, a sophisticated successor to Citröen's 1934 car, astonished the motoring world. The end of 1959 saw the introduction of the Morris Mini-Minor/Austin Seven, now universally known as the Mini [9]. It had a transversally mounted engine, front-wheel drive, rubber suspension and short wheelbase.

Since then the automobile has played a more and more important part in modern life, until now its numbers have become a threat to health, to energy resources and to mobility itself – hence the renewed interest in pollution-free electric cars.

Gottlieb Daimler (1834–1900) in 1883 made one of the first relatively fast-running, lightweight engines using gasoline. Developed in the experimental laboratory he had set up in 1882 in Cann- statt, Germany, with Wilhelm Maybach, he had built it into a wooden motor cycle by 1885 and within a year produced his first car. At almost the same time, but independently, Carl Benz built his first car. This three-wheeler had a 1.5hp single-cylinder, water-cooled petrol engine mounted horizontally at the back of the car. Final drive was by means of a chain to a gear on the back axle.

6 A classic of the vintage era, the Vauxhall 30/98 was famous for its successes in sprints and hill-climbing competitions.

7 The revolutionary front-wheel drive Citröen of 1934 was the model for this 1939 15CV and subsequent models.

8 The Volkswagen, a car for the people, was designed by Ferdinand Porsche (1875–1951). First planned in 1934, the design of the air-cooled rear-engined "Beetle" has changed very little since that time.

9 The Mini, launched in 1959, was an instant success. Designed by Alec Issigonis, (1906–), it had a transverse engine with integral gearbox, front-wheel drive, and an all-independent suspension

10 The Fiat 128 is typical of the European car of the 1970s. It follows the world trend forced by the shortage and higher price of fuel and has a small high-revving engine for economy (with an overhead camshaft), mounted transversely at the front, and driving the front wheels. It has several built-in features and there are many variations on the basic design. It is available with two or four doors, as an estate car, and in "Rallye" and sports-coupé versions.

Classic cars

The history of the automobile spans less than 100 years from the spluttering experiments of pioneers such as Benz, Daimler and Panhard to the mass-produced, energy-conserving designs of the 1970s.

Between the two world wars, the fundamental principles of the machine had become well established. Henry Ford (1863–1947) in the United States had proved the economic common sense of mass production and motoring became available to an ever larger section of the population.

Yet during this time there emerged a few really great cars. They were carefully, almost lovingly, built – generally one at a time, to individual customers' orders. Some incorporated radical innovations, although most merely represented the best available combination of design and engineering skills. Their names became synonymous with quality and status. Some, such as Alfa Romeo, Rolls-Royce, Cadillac and Mercedes, survive as names. A whole list of others has gone. But these classic cars were the thoroughbred bloodstock whose descendants form one of today's major industries.

1 Mercedes (Germany, 1914) was designed by Paul Daimler for that year's Grand Prix. Its 4.5-litre engine gave it a maximum speed of 180km/h (112mph). It had two magnetos and three sparking plugs per cylinder. Front-wheel brakes were a post-World War I addition.

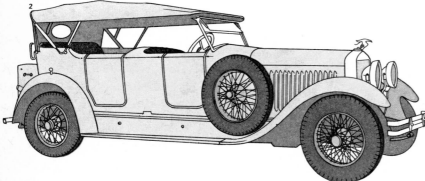

2 Hispano-Suiza (France, 1922) had a steel and aluminium engine, based on earlier aero-engines by the Swiss designer Marc Birkigt, of 6.6-litre capacity. It was the first car to have servo-assisted four-wheel brakes, and had a maximum speed of 137km/h (85mph).

3 Isotta-Fraschini A (Italy, 1929) had twin carburettors to feed petrol into its 7.4-litre eight-cylinder engine, giving an output of 120bhp. Its Italian manufacturer pioneered the use of four-wheel brakes.

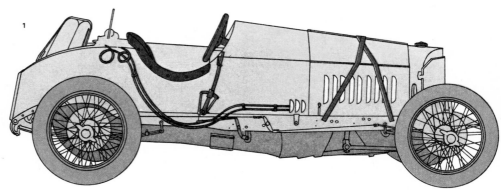

4 Duesenberg (United States, 1930) was one of America's most expensive cars. Its "straight-eight" 6.9-litre engine had more than 260bhp to give the car a top speed of more than 175km/h (110mph).

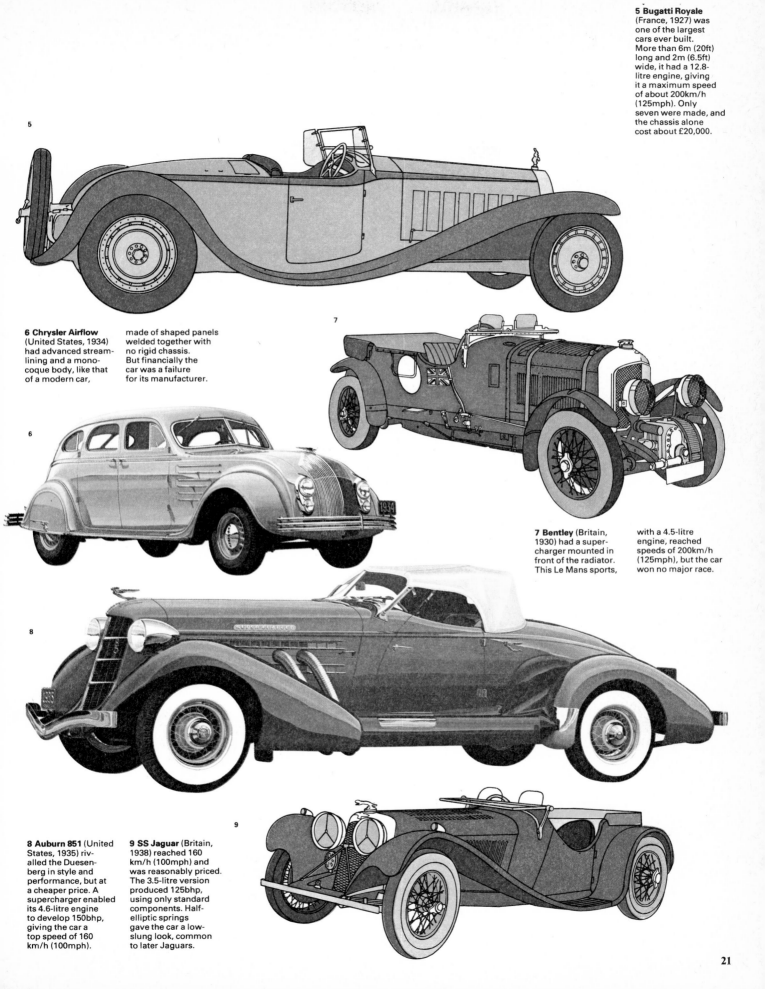

5 Bugatti Royale
(France, 1927) was one of the largest cars ever built. More than 6m (20ft) long and 2m (6.5ft) wide, it had a 12.8-litre engine, giving it a maximum speed of about 200km/h (125mph). Only seven were made, and the chassis alone cost about £20,000.

6 Chrysler Airflow (United States, 1934) had advanced streamlining and a monocoque body, like that of a modern car, made of shaped panels welded together with no rigid chassis. But financially the car was a failure for its manufacturer.

7 Bentley (Britain, 1930) had a supercharger mounted in front of the radiator. This Le Mans sports, with a 4.5-litre engine, reached speeds of 200km/h (125mph), but the car won no major race.

8 Auburn 851 (United States, 1935) rivalled the Duesenberg in style and performance, but at a cheaper price. A supercharger enabled its 4.6-litre engine to develop 150bhp, giving the car a top speed of 160 km/h (100mph).

9 SS Jaguar (Britain, 1938) reached 160 km/h (100mph) and was reasonably priced. The 3.5-litre version produced 125bhp, using only standard components. Half-elliptic springs gave the car a low-slung look, common to later Jaguars.

How an automobile works

A typical modern car can be divided into four main component systems: the engine, producer of the power; the transmission, which feeds the power to the road wheels; the electrical system; and the body/chassis, including steering, brakes and suspension [Key]. Wherever the engine is placed – at the rear, driving the rear wheels, in front, driving the front wheels, or even amidships – the working principle is basically the same. In the conventional front-engined, rear-drive car (the construction that is cheapest), the engine feeds rotary power via the clutch, gearbox, propeller shaft and differential to, finally, the back axle and road wheels.

Transmission

By using the clutch [6], the driver is able to connect or disconnect the engine's power from the road wheels, to engage gears, to start smoothly, and to stop the car without stopping the engine. When the driver depresses the clutch pedal while the car is in gear, the drive (power) is disconnected from the gearbox and the rest of the transmission; releasing the pedal reconnects the drive.

Generally located just behind the clutch, the gearbox (either manual or automatic) is designed to vary the ratio of speed between engine and road wheels. The normal petrol engine works best at between 2,000 and 5,000 revolutions a minute (the rate at which the crankshaft turns). To permit this while the car is moving at anything from 15 to 150 km/h (9 to 90 mph), the usual manual gearbox has a selection of four different forward gear ratios, through four pairs of gears [5]. Selecting low (first) gear allows the engine to turn at its working speed while driving the road wheels slowly, resulting in a greater torque or turning effort needed to overcome inertia, heavy loads or a gradient. When the car gathers speed and less effort is needed to power it, successively higher gears are engaged until top may be used.

The propeller shaft, running under the floor along the length of the car, is attached at its forward end to the gearbox and at the rear to the differential. The differential has two functions [7], to "bend" the driving power at right angles and feed it to the rear axle and wheels and, when the car is steered round corners, to allow the outer wheel to travel faster than the inner one.

Electrical system and brakes

In pre-1907 motoring days, the sole function of the battery was to produce the spark for plugs (which ignite the petrol-air mixture in the cylinders), but today the car depends on several electric devices for its operation [4]. These are all powered by the battery, which is re-charged by a dynamo (or alternator), driven by the crankshaft through a belt which also turns the cooling fan. The 6- or 12-volt battery supplies the coil (an induction coil), which produces high-tension electricity for the plugs via a distributor. The battery also provides current for the horn, lights, heater, windscreen wipers, radio and, the heaviest drain of all, the starter motor.

Almost all modern cars, benefiting from racing practice, have disc brakes on the front wheels and drum brakes on the rear. Some cars have discs all round. Metal discs which rotate with the wheels are gripped by stationary pads when the footbrake is applied [8]. As the discs are open to the cooling air, heat

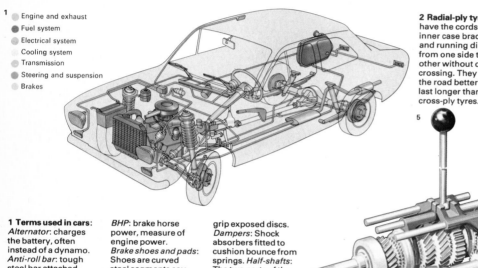

1 Engine and exhaust
Fuel system
Electrical system
Cooling system
Transmission
Steering and suspension
Brakes

1 Terms used in cars:
Alternator: charges the battery, often instead of a dynamo. *Anti-roll bar*: tough steel bar attached to the suspension which minimizes roll when cornering.

BHP: brake horse power, measure of engine power. *Brake shoes and pads*: Shoes are curved steel segments covered with lining which press on the brake drums. Pads

grip exposed discs. *Dampers*: Shock absorbers fitted to cushion bounce from springs. *Half-shafts*: The two parts of the rear axle, taking drive from the differential.

2 Radial-ply tyres have the cords of the inner case braced and running directly from one side to the other without criss-crossing. They hold the road better and last longer than cross-ply tyres.

vides equal stiffness to both the walls and the tread. It is highly dangerous to use cross-ply and radial-ply tyres together, and in many countries this practice is illegal.

3 Cross-ply tyres are manufactured with their cords crossing one another trellis fashion. This pro-

4 The 6- or 12-volt car battery must, through the coil, deliver 10,000 volts at up to 300 times a second to the plugs, and must also provide current for starting, heating, lighting and electrical accessories. The diagram shows only the starting, ignition and recharging electrical systems.

1 Battery
2 Ignition key
3 Electromagnetic relay, activated by the key when starting, connecting the battery to the starter motor
4 Starter motor
5 Dynamo or alternator, driven by the engine to recharge the battery
6 Control box
7 Ignition coil
8 Primary coil
9 Secondary coil
10 Distributor
11 Contact breaker
12 Rotor arm
13 Spark plug

5 The gearwheels of the gearbox (except reverse) are always in mesh. Those on the output shaft [1] revolve around it and those on the layshaft [2] are fixed. When a gear is selected, the appropriate gearwheel is locked to the output shaft. In first gear, the widest ratio is used for low-speed driving; second and third gears use progressively narrower ratios, and top gear is obtained by coupling the input shaft directly to the output shaft. Overdrive is a separate and higher top gear fitted to some cars to reduce wear and tear and petrol consumption. It may be engaged automatically or by the driver.

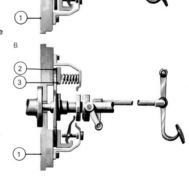

6 The clutch is basically made up of three plates: the flywheel [1], which is fixed to the engine shaft and rotates with it; the driven plate [2], which is connected to the gearbox shaft; and the pressure plate [3], which clamps the

driven plate to the flywheel when the clutch is engaged by releasing the clutch pedal [B]. Disengaging the clutch by depressing the pedal [A] separates the plates so that the flywheel and driven plates rotate independently.

is quickly dissipated, avoiding brake-fade, the bogey of overworked and overheated drum brakes. All four brakes are operated by the brake pedal via hydraulic lines. The parking (hand) brake operates on the rear wheels only, usually by a mechanical linkage.

Suspension and construction
Suspension is designed to give the passengers a comfortable, smooth ride, and to protect the body and parts of the car by reducing the shocks from the uneven surface of the road [10]. However, springs alone would give a bouncing ride, and shock absorbers are fitted to "damp" down the oscillation that the springs themselves produce. Traditional elliptical or semi-elliptical springs have in many cars been replaced by helical or coil springs, torsion bar springs (in which a twisting action is used as springing), gas-and-fluid (combined springs and shock absorbers) or rubber springs, or several types combined.

The front wheels of a car are each mounted on separate short axles, so that when the steering wheel is turned and the movement passed to them, each wheel turns on its own

axis (the inner one describing a slightly tighter arc than the outer). Rack-and-pinion steering [9], the most popular of several systems, has a pinion on the end of the steering column that engages a transverse toothed rack. The rack, connected at its ends to track-rods attached to each road wheel, is moved right or left by the action of the steering wheel, steering the wheels in the required direction. Power steering makes this easier.

Until the 1930s, the traditional way of building a car was by making a rigid chassis (the wheels, machinery and frame). Everything else was bolted on to the chassis. Now many manufacturers use the body itself as the frame. When welded together, the pressed-steel body panels form a rigid "box", each unit contributing to the strength of the structure. Using unit-construction (monocoque) methods, cars can be made more cheaply, and are considerably lighter than earlier models built on a separate chassis. A number of small manufacturers produce cars using light alloy or fibreglass bodies, which need a separate chassis, often a tubular "space-frame" on which to build the car.

KEY
A typical modern car has the engine mounted at the front driving the rear wheels through a gearbox and propeller shaft. The engine, suspension and steering system are all fixed in to the main body of the car, which is constructed as a welded rigid "box" from separate curved body panels. Many manufacturers design cars which can be adapted for right- or left-hand steering, for worldwide sales.

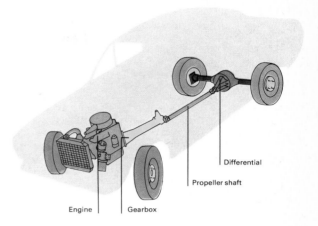

Differential
Propeller shaft
Engine   Gearbox

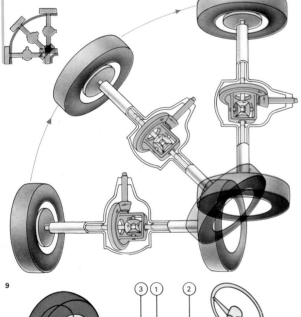

7 The differential allows one of the half-shafts and its road wheel to rotate more slowly than the other when the car is turning, although both are still being driven, thus improving the cornering and reducing tyre wear. The two half-shafts take the drive from the differential to the road wheels. The diagram shows that when the driver is turning the steering wheel, the rear inner road wheel describes a tighter, shorter arc than the rear outer wheel. Turning a corner would result in tyre scrub and loss of handling qualities without the differential. A pinion on the end of the propeller shaft turns the crown wheel in the differential, which rotates four bevel pinions, allowing the half-shafts to be driven at different speeds.

8 When the brake pedal is depressed, a piston in the master cylinder forces fluid along hydraulic pipes to slave cylinders on each wheel, pushing shoes or pads into contact with drums or discs. (Brake-shoe pads are curved steel platforms covered with tough fibrous shoes which act on the inside of the brake drums. Pads act on exposed discs holding them in a vice-like grip.)

1 Brake pedal
2 Master cylinder
3 Hydraulic pipe
4 Brake shoe and lining
5 Brake drum
6 Slave cylinder
7 Drum brakes on
8 Drum brakes off
9 Disc brakes on
10 Disc brakes off
11 Brake pad
12 Disc

9 Two main types of steering systems are commonly used. Rack-and-pinion steering has a toothed pinion [1] at the end of the steering column [2], which engages with a transverse rack [3] moving it right or left as necessary. Track rods [4] at each end transmit the movement to the wheels. The steering box system (not shown) has a box which houses a worm reduction gear. The gear drives a drop arm, and, via a transverse link, a slave arm. The power-assisted system is a modern refinement of steering, which facilitates driving larger cars by using power steering worked by hydraulic pressure.

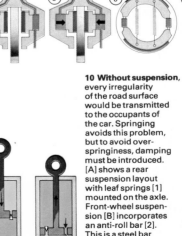

10 Without suspension, every irregularity of the road surface would be transmitted to the occupants of the car. Springing avoids this problem, but to avoid over-springiness, damping must be introduced. [A] shows a rear suspension layout with leaf springs [1] mounted on the axle. Front-wheel suspension [B] incorporates an anti-roll bar [2]. This is a steel bar attached to the suspension to minimize roll by its torsion or twisting resistance when a car corners rapidly. It is not the bar fitted to some cars to prevent the occupants being crushed if the car turns over. Coil springs [3] absorb road shocks. Telescopic shock absorbers [C] are often called dampers and are fitted to the chassis and suspension to cushion bounce from springs. Oil is forced through the constricting valves and slows down the recoil movement.

Cars and society

The internal-combustion engined automobile has been in common use for less than 70 years. At first a toy, then a mode of transport for the rich, and later part of the pattern of living, it was designed as man's mechanical servant. Together with the lorry, it revolutionized the world's trade and social life by its speed and mobility.

The introduction of cheap, mass-produced cars, pioneered by Henry Ford's Model T of 1908, brought personal transport to ordinary people. They could go almost anywhere and the new-found freedom created the beginnings of domestic tourist industries. More expensive cars became status symbols, often representing the wealth or importance of their owners.

The threat to society
Now it is a question of the car's survival or demise. Today, with 220 million vehicles on the world's highways, many people think that the answer to the rapidly increasing problem of pollution and fuel shortages can at last clearly be seen. They consider that sometime in the future society must forget the

automobile as we know it – a five-passenger, four-wheeled vehicle up to 5m (16ft) long and 2.5m (8ft) wide using the appallingly inefficient internal combustion engine, pouring toxic wastes into the air, damaging people's ears and minds with its noise, congesting cities, creating fuel shortages and beginning to take away the very freedom of movement for which it was developed. There may have to be a radical change in size, power unit and people's approach to their personal transport.

What type of engine?
All combustion, from that in a bonfire to a car engine, produces undesirable by-products – carbon monoxide, various unburned hydrocarbons and, from cars, nitric oxide, lead salts, iron oxide and soot in exhaust smoke. New regulations governing the toxic content of exhaust fumes have done much to reduce air pollution. But they cannot (even with the most stringent emission curbs such as those laid down for the future in the United States in 1975, which demand reduction of around 95 per cent) hope to eliminate

automobile-related pollutants entirely. Similarly, the most vigilant noise-abatement organizations cannot hope effectively to damp the roar of heavy, under-powered vehicles working under stress. And even the most ambitious planning of city centres can at best clear only a fraction of shopping space – at the cost of adding to the numbers of vehicles on the roads elsewhere.

In the short term, current and planned regulations will help in certain areas. But automobile designers have long been investigating the day-after-tomorrow, particularly with regard to engines, fuels and overall size reduction, in addition to various public transport systems such as monorail, hover and "bullet" trains.

Modern steam road vehicles have been tested for more than 25 years; their basic problems are weight and water supply. Research continues on low-emission systems such as the stratified-charge engine [1], gas turbine, Stirling (hot-air) engine and hybrid-electric [Key] (in which such an engine powers a generator to charge batteries used for cruising). Other possible power units

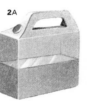

1 The stratified-charge engine is in effect a conventional petrol engine with a modified cylinder head and induction system. In an ordinary engine, the petrol-air mixture is of similar density in all parts of the combustion chamber. In the stratified-charge unit, it is richer near the plug and weaker elsewhere. The rich mixture near the plug ignites readily and the weaker mixture burns more completely.

2 Diesel-fuel exhaust emission from a correctly adjusted engine pollutes the air much less than does a petrol-fuelled unit. Of all the toxic fumes discharged by any type of internal combustion engine, invisible and odourless carbon monoxide is the most damaging. A petrol engine produces thirty times as much as a diesel engine. Can A represents petrol engine emission, B diesel.

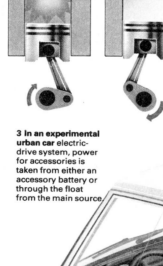

3 In an experimental urban car electric-drive system, power for accessories is taken from either an accessory battery or through the float from the main source.

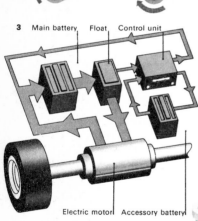

4 Short-range personal transport is provided by this experimental urban electric car. A direct-current electric motor mounted on the rear axle is driven by a special 84-volt lead-acid battery, which gives the car a greater range than conventional batteries. A built-in charger can be plugged into a household socket and recharges the battery in 7 hrs. This General Motors car has a range of 93km (58 miles) at 40km/h (25mph).

Electric motor   Batteries

are pure electric (one of the great goals, because electricity supplies can be made almost unlimited, but still handicapped by heavy batteries and the need for frequent recharging), and fuel cell power, which would convert conventional fuel energy directly into electric power without burning it. This would be one of the most significant developments of our time, but is not likely to be practicable for some years. More than 250 designs of small electrically powered "city" or urban cars have been produced; if the cars were made commercially they could help congested cities and relieve parking problems (three can be parked in one normal bay), although light and heavy traffic would probably have to be segregated.

The future of the car engine

Current research has already produced technical advances aimed at improved economy and ecology, although most of them would, at best, provide only temporary relief. The car industry has produced the catalytic converter [6], a type of de-polluting silencer for use with low-lead petrol. Fuel economy has been improved by electronic ignition, by steel-ply radial tyres which have less rolling resistance, by lower rear-axle ratios, scaled-down engine capacities and, mainly in the United States, the reintroduction of overdrive.

There are three immediate goals. First, future engine design (internal combustion engines will probably remain for at least the next 15 years) must aim at conserving fuel and reducing exhaust pollutants. Second, a way of controlling traffic density in cities, and its flow elsewhere, must be found. Third, and most urgently, greater safety must be built into structural design and additional equipment provided (such as collapsible steering columns, rigid "boxes" and deflecting properties), not only to combat the injuries likely to be received in a collision but also to prevent accidents (improved tyres, brakes, lights, suspension and visibility).

Long-term aims must be to find an alternative power system now that oil supplies – even offshore supplies – are unpredictable. And a fundamental reappraisal in society's attitude to all road transport, its appearance and its function, must be made.

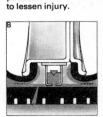

Batteries ____   Electric motor   Petrol engine

The hybrid city car was developed as a possible answer to pollution in towns. For city and suburban use the car runs on its electric motor, but on out-of-town journeys the small internal combustion engine is started. The electric unit is used on its own only where there must be no pollution and the petrol engine charges the batteries at other times.

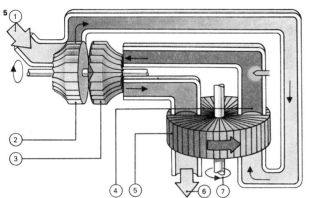

5 The gas-turbine car engine was developed originally by the British Rover Company, which tested the first gas-turbine car in March 1950. It is quiet, powerful, has low maintenance costs and runs on low-grade, lead-free fuel. But it is expensive to manufacture.

1 Air in
2 Radial compressor
3 Compressor turbine
4 Fuel in
5 Power turbine
6 Exhaust
7 Power out

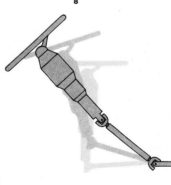

6 Catalytic converters, built into silencers, have been used as a partial solution to present exhaust pollution. Nitrogen oxides are reduced to ammonia at the first catalyst bed and hydrocarbons and carbon monoxide are converted to carbon dioxide and water at the second. The most suitable catalyst is platinum but this is extremely expensive. The system has proved to be efficient enough for some manufacturers to re-calibrate their engines for higher peak performance, using catalytic converters to "clean up" the extra pollution in the exhaust gases.

7 The ideal safety car [1] has a rigid compartment protecting passengers restrained by seat belts and head rests. The car body is designed to absorb impact and, in a collision, the engine deflects downwards, and the steering column collapses. The injuries sustained by unrestrained passengers [2] depend on the speed of the collision (here 97km/h [60mph]), but the location and type of injuries are similar.

Moment of impact

Full impact

8 A collapsible steering column is hinged mid-way along at a universal joint. With an ordinary rigid steering column, a head-on collision can make the wheel break off and impale the driver on the column. The collapsible column hinges on impact, absorbs some of the force and swings away from the driver's chest. The lower arc of the wheel should be padded or flat to lessen injury.

9 Deaths in road accidents are quoted here as the number per million vehicles in various European countries during 1971. The USA had 493 per million, and Japan about twice as many as Belgium.

10 A puncture at speed is extremely dangerous – the tyre collapses. A recent development uses a ring of containers [A] that burst when the tyre deflates [B], releasing fluid that seals the hole [C] and vaporizes to re-inflate the tyre [D].

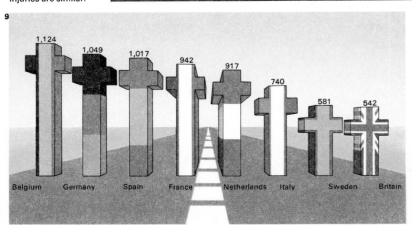

1,124 Belgium
1,049 Germany
1,017 Spain
942 France
917 Netherlands
740 Italy
581 Sweden
542 Britain

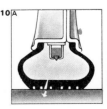

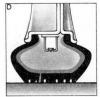

Trams and buses

Industrialization – the transformation of scattered cottage industries into centralized factories and offices – demands good commuter transport. In the early stages of industrialization people moved in from rural areas to live within walking distance of their places of work. But as the developing cities sprawled outwards an efficient system of passenger transport became necessary to feed industry its manpower.

The motor car is inefficient for such a purpose because it takes up far too much road space for the average number of passengers it carries and produces congestion. And it was invented too late to form the basis of a good system. Bicycles are a possible solution, but few people are willing to ride them in all weathers or over long distances. Systems of public transport are essential.

Early passenger transport systems

Cities in Europe and America began to grow large enough to need passenger transport systems in the early 1800s, when the only feasible source of motive power available was the horse. The horse-drawn bus might have seemed the obvious choice of vehicle, being a logical development of the stagecoach, but roads were in such poor condition in cities that coach-like vehicles gave a very uncomfortable ride. The first extensive transport systems used horse-drawn trams rather than buses because rail-borne vehicles not only carried people smoothly but also allowed a horse to pull twice as many passengers, because of easier rolling. Medieval miners transported minerals by pushing wheeled tubs along primitive rails made of wooden beams. The word tram reflects this origin, being derived from the Low German *traam*, meaning beam, although Americans use the more descriptive word "streetcar".

From tram to trolleybus

Trams and railways developed together. The first city tram network spread through New York in the 1830s, at the time when steam railways began to appear in Britain. Steam soon came to the tramway too and the first steam engine to pull a tram chugged its way around New York in 1837. Europe lagged some way behind – the first horse-drawn tram network did not open in Britain until 1860 and steam trams did not appear until 1872. Europe pioneered the next and most important development, however, with electric trams [1] in Berlin in 1881.

Coincident with the development of the electric tram came the trolleybus. By the first years of this century commercial systems were operating in Europe and the first English trolleybus routes operated in Leeds and Bradford in 1911. Trolleybuses had twin poles and overhead wires because the rubber wheels insulated the vehicles from the ground. (Trams needed only a single wire for current pick-up, the circuit being completed through the metal wheels and rails.) The first trolleybuses collected current through a trolley slung on the wires, hence their name, but the sprung poles used on trams were soon found to be more efficient.

The trolleybus was a silent and fume-free form of transport capable of fast acceleration and greater manoeuvrability than the tram. Trolleybus networks were built where a city did not want to afford the expense of laying rails for trams and they were often set up in

1 The electric tram provided the first cheap and reliable urban transport. It travelled along rails set flush with the surface in the centre of the road or along a track beside it. Current was collected either from a single overhead wire through a sprung pole that ran along the wire, through a bow-shaped collector or pantograph, or from the ground through a collector that slid along a conduit between the rails. The overhead wire formed one half of the circuit and the street rails completed it, whereas the conduit contained both positive and negative conductor rails. The trams often ran on separately powered bogies and they all had wooden scoops that prevented anyone from falling under the wheels of the vehicle. Both trams and trolleybuses made use of rheostatic braking in which the motors act as brakes.

2 San Francisco has the oldest cable tramway, which opened in 1873. Other hilly cities soon introduced cable-hauled trams. In 1884 the first cable tramway in Europe opened on Highgate Hill in London. Other cities noted for cable systems were Melbourne, Kansas City, Edinburgh and Wellington. Cable trams proved unreliable and are no longer in use except in San Francisco and Wellington.

3 An articulated tram makes its way through the streets of Stuttgart in Germany. Modern tramways often couple cars together in this way and thus achieve a more economic method of operation.

4 The first trolleybuses were introduced soon after the turn of the century by the tramway companies. At first current-collecting trolleys ran on top of a pair of overhead wires, but later ones contacted the conductors below them.

the suburbs to feed the inner tram routes.

Both trams and trolleybuses had to contend with buses and found the competition more and more intense. Buses have a long history, the first horse-drawn vehicle being run in Paris by Blaise Pascal in 1662.

Buses versus trams

The name bus – from the Latin *omnibus*, meaning "for all" – appeared shortly before the introduction of the first horse-drawn bus into Britain in 1829. Steam buses soon followed, but the first motorbus – an elegant petrol-driven coach built in Germany by Benz – did not begin service until 1895, by which time trams were well established.

Compared with trams the early buses were small, noisy and smelly and the solid tyres gave the passengers a bone-shaking ride. But buses soon improved and tramways began to decline. In the aftermath of World War II many disappeared as city councils decided to forgo the costs of re-equipping their tramways.

As motor traffic increased trams often impeded cars and severe congestion

occurred, exacerbated by dewirements and power failures. Buses became more economic and were more flexible in routing than either trams or trolleybuses, and consequently have now almost entirely superseded them. Trams still operate in several European cities and trolleybuses are to be found in the USSR and Switzerland. In Britain trams still ply the streets only in Blackpool and the Isle of Man and all trolleybuses have disappeared, the last to go being those of Bradford in 1972.

Modern tram designs include articulated vehicles [3] of several interconnected coaches, but flexibility of design has always been a feature more typical of motorbuses. The descendants of the elegant many-doored, open-air touring charabancs of the 1920s are the luxurious air-conditioned, toilet-carrying, reclining-seated, long-distance coaches of today [7]. The old "any-more-fares" city bus is giving way to the pay-as-you-enter, turnstiled bus with few seats and a large standing area. And minibuses and dial-a-bus services now carry passengers on less busy routes.

KEY

The first trams were pulled by steam "locomotives", generally with vertical boilers and side panels that totally enclosed the moving parts and wheels.

This tram ran in East London in 1887. Its engine used a steam pressure of 100lb per sq in and it burned about 9kg (20lb) of coal for an hour's working.

Passengers rode in a non-powered trailer, with no weather protection for those on the upper deck. Other trams had compressed air engines.

5 Motorbuses were introduced to the streets of Paris and London at the end of the nineteenth century. Their petrol engines were noisy and smelly, but the new buses soon demonstrated their advantage over the tram – the ability to go anywhere served by road. This type of bus, the AEC PS-type was developed after the end of World War I from the London General Omnibus Company K-series.

6 One-man operated buses are a recent development in urban public transport. Passengers either pay the driver or buy tickets from a coin-operated machine. The system saves on bus company staff but can cause delays while passengers are boarding the bus. For short, high-capacity routes in cities some transport companies use "standing-room only" vehicles.

7 The Greyhound Bus network covers the whole of North America, its coaches providing a cheap and reliable means of inter-city transport. Passengers may spend several days and nights aboard.

8 A tourist coach travels through the resort of Sitges in Spain. Such vehicles are often extravagantly arrayed to attract tourists and designed to provide a view of the town rather than as a means of rapid urban transport.

Special purpose vehicles

Conventional vehicles such as cars and trucks are designed to run on firm roads, normally with only slight gradients, and carry average loads. A special purpose vehicle has some extra features. It may be able to travel over unusual terrain or to carry a load that is beyond the capacity of ordinary vehicles.

For economy, speedy development and sometimes reliability, specialist vehicles are designed to make the best use of components already available. A standard truck chassis can be fitted with a special body or be used to tow various trailers [7]. Existing components can be built on to a new chassis or into a monocoque hull welded from flat sheets.

Basic design considerations

The first consideration must be the type of load to be carried. This may be two oil explorers and their instruments, 30 tonnes of timber, or a 120mm gun, ammunition and crew. In general, large vehicles are best for bulk loads. Off the road their size makes obstacles relatively easy to surmount – what would be an obstacle to a conventional vehicle becomes less significant. But on the road,

many special purpose vehicles are difficult to manoeuvre because of their excessive size.

The terrain over which loads are to be taken is another important consideration in the design of a special purpose vehicle. Soft ground calls for running gear that spreads the load over a large area to reduce the degree to which the vehicle will sink into the ground. There must be enough traction to overcome the resistance due to sinkage and to cope with slippery gradients. The two main choices are all-wheel drive or caterpillar tracks.

A wheeled vehicle tends to be less expensive and quieter than a tracked vehicle. Extremely large wheels are fitted to small vehicles, making them as good as tracked vehicles on soft ground and giving the added advantage that, with low-pressure tyres, they can float. In some so-called all-terrain vehicles (ATVs) the tyres are so broad that the wheels cannot be pivoted for normal steering. Instead they employ "skid" steering by driving the wheels on each side of the vehicle at different speeds.

For a given size and weight, caterpillar tracks grip better than wheels and distribute

the vehicle's weight more evenly, making them a good choice for cross-country use. Tracked vehicles aso have a lower fuel consumption in heavy conditions. They are skid-steered by driving the tracks at different speeds.

Suspension for cross-country work

The type of suspension is determined by the speed at which the vehicle has to travel over the roughest ground it is likely to encounter. Trucks and cars designed for smooth roads have only slight suspension resilience. If driven fast across country their suspension is liable to break. For this reason, vehicles adapted with only minimum modification for off-road use have a "hard" suspension giving the driver such an uncomfortable ride that he will not go too fast. Agricultural tractors and their derivatives normally operate so slowly they manage without any suspension at all, although wheeled tractors have resilient tyres, producing bounce. Tracked "crawler" tractors have no resilience; they are slow and are used only for heavy work.

The prime examples of fast cross-country machines are armoured fighting vehicles

1 Concrete carriers transport large quantities of concrete that has been mixed away from the site to where it is needed. The drum revolves slowly during the journey to keep the concrete properly mixed. The convenience of off-site mixing justifies the cost of transporting concrete by road.

2 Tracked commercial vehicles are used in snow and on marshy ground. In the Arctic areas of Alaska, Canada and the Soviet Union they are used by the timber industry and by oil and ore prospecting companies. They range from small tractors for hauling sledges, and slightly larger personnel carriers with heated cabins, to huge 40-tonne load platforms.

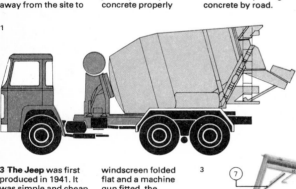

3 The Jeep was first produced in 1941. It was simple and cheap to manufacture; strong; had good cross-country performance; and yet was small, light and easy to recover if it became bogged down or immobilized. The name "Jeep" is shorthand for General Purpose – GP. The Jeep was adapted for many special tasks. With its

windscreen folded flat and a machine gun fitted, the Jeep made a good scout car; with locally produced frames to take stretchers it could be used as an ambulance. Most rivals to the Jeep are complex and heavier.

1 Hood in folded position
2 Ammunition
3 Machine-gun mount
4 Radio
5 Aerial mount
6 Windscreen
7 Hand-operated windscreen wiper
8 Pads for windscreen when folded
9 Capstan winch
10 Safety strap

(AFVs), such as tanks, with tracks and suspensions of high resilience. Vehicles such as earth-movers would benefit from suspensions when hauling "spoil" but at present an increased operating speed would not justify the extra cost that would be incurred.

A small European family car carrying the driver alone has power in relation to the vehicle weight of about 60bhp per tonne, whereas an expensive sports saloon might have 180bhp per tonne. At the other extreme the European limit for trucks is a minimum of 8bhp per tonne (6kW/tonne) and manufacturers have problems achieving this modest power for large trucks at the limit of 38 tonnes laden weight (requiring 304bhp).

For economy of operation, a diesel engine is supreme in commercial vehicles, unless the vehicle is small or high power output is needed for minimum weight, when a petrol engine is a better choice.

Generally the transmission – the linkage that connects the drive from the engine to the wheels or tracks – must suit both road journeys at relatively high speeds and slow, heavy work across country. It must also provide the power for winches and other equipment. Except in simple vehicles, the transmission is usually as heavy as the engine.

Steering a special purpose vehicle

Short tracked vehicles can be skid-steered. A long narrow vehicle is built in two parts, with a powered and articulated joint in the middle, and the vehicle steered by "bending" it sideways at the joint. Such vehicles have a good performance on soft soil such as clay or on snow. In the same conditions, a wheeled vehicle should have wheels of a large diameter rather than of broad section, but there is seldom enough room to fit them. A sharp tread on the tyres is necessary when the surface is weak. In dry sand fat tyres perform well, but the tread should not bite deep and make the sand grains flow from under the wheels of the vehicle.

Reliability is difficult to achieve in special purpose vehicles. Often their use cannot be simulated accurately in trials and over-insurance in design – making all parts stronger than necessary – must be avoided or the vehicle will be excessively heavy.

A tipper truck justifies a special design, because its body is so short. The loads it carries are massive yet consist of small particles, such as sand. The tipping mechanism allows rapid unloading by the driver working alone, so providing economy and a rapid turn-round time.

4 The Coles Colossus is a 28-wheeled truck designed as a crane carrier. It has hydro-pneumatic suspension and the engine is a Rolls-Royce 300hp turbocharged diesel. Sections can be added to the jib-strut crane in order to convert it into a tall tower crane.

5 The racing car's wedge shape and its fat tyres increase its speed through bends, but both raise wind resistance and thus lower top speed.

6 Swamp buggies like this Danish Seiga "Tortoise" use large, low-pressure tyres to carry men and materials over inland waters and soft mud.

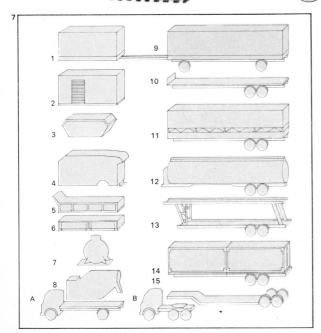

7 A basic truck [A] can have various types of vehicle bodies, such as a plain van [1], side-entry van [2], rubble skip [3], dust cart [4], tipper [5], open truck [6], liquid gas carrier [7] or cement carrier [8]. It can also be adapted to tow a trailer [9]. One tractor [B], with different semi-trailers to form articulated units, good manoeuvrability and allowing full and economic use of the vehicle. Such trailers include flat open type [10], closed wagon [11], tanker [12], car-transporter [13], container-carrier [14] and, to facilitate the loading of very heavy items, the low-loader [15]. Suitably adapted these can tow extra trailers in the long "road-trains" common in the United States.

8 This riot vehicle weighs 20 tonnes, has bullet-proof steel and glass for protection, and carries a 15-man squad. It is armed with a water cannon, special sprays and a high-intensity siren. It can assist authorities in controlling crowds and rioters in situations where minimum force is desired.

9 A combat engineer tractor, with tracks and an aluminium armoured hull and capable of 56 km/h (35 mph) on land, can perform a variety of digging and dozing tasks in the battlefield. Powered by water jets, it can travel through water and, using a rocket-propelled anchor, can winch itself up steep river banks and prepare ramps for other amphibious vehicles.

Small technology and transport

Physical communications – basically roads and railways to transport people from place to place – are an essential ingredient of progress. When irrigation canals were built in Indonesia more than half a century ago, the building of roads parallel to the canals did not seem worthwhile. But the lack of such roads led to a decline in standards of inspection and maintenance and as a result the canals steadily deteriorated. Today, to transport additional food for growing populations, the canals are being rebuilt – with service roads, and costing much more than they would have originally.

An adequate transport system is equally necessary for the distribution of food and for the more general trade without which there can be little continuing improvement in the quality of life in any community.

The basic ingredients of physical communication are products of technology. The richer the community, the more sophisticated the technology that develops. Progress is the result of man's mastery of the world he lives in and of his ability to use the resources within his reach. In regions in which modern mechanized road building and modern transport is too costly for the local communities, and where progress is limited by the lack of adequate physical communication, there are two ways in which the problem can be solved. The first is by foreign aid – the system in which the richer nations provide the poorer ones with money, materials or trained personnel. The second is by the use of simpler, less costly technologies. Even where outside aid is available, it may be more productive to use it for a wide range of schemes based on low-cost local technology than on a few highly sophisticated and correspondingly more expensive projects.

Building low-cost roads

The principles of road design are simple, and road building can also be a relatively simple process [1, 2]. Earth, and sometimes rock, must be moved and stones must be quarried, crushed, collected and spread according to a plan. The checking of levels is important because the drainage of the finished road depends on it. But even levelling does not require expensive instruments and techniques. A cheap but accurate method uses a length of transparent plastic tubing with its ends tied along a pair of wooden rods. The rods are placed upright on the ground and the tubing filled with water. If the rods are graduated, say in centimetres, from the bottom up, the difference in ground levels where each is placed can be quickly found by reading off the height of the water-level in each tube, and subtracting one from the other. The tube can be up to 30m (100ft).

The building of bridges

Some roads have to cross a watercourse. It may be possible to construct a shallow ford, but the roadway under the water will be quickly worn away unless it is made of well-cured concrete. In most cases therefore, a bridge is needed.

In the Western world a modern road bridge is generally a structure made of reinforced concrete or, for longer spans, steel. Both materials have advantages where the loads to be carried are frequent and heavy. But this does not mean that they are necessarily the best for a bridge carrying light

1 Low-cost methods of road construction vary according to the climate and availability of materials and labour. The basic principles are universal and the following alternatives to more generally accepted methods can often be adapted to suit varying situations. To build an earth road, the first step is to clear trees, shrubs and roots [1]. Trees are cleared to keep the road in sunshine and therefore dry. The topsoil is removed [2] and dumped not closer than 8m (26ft) from the centre of the road. Wide side ditches [3] are dug and soil from them spread to raise the road level between them. The road surface is compacted by rolling [4], ensuring a cross slope (for drainage) of not less than 1 in 20. The ditches must be graded along their length so that excess water can run away [5]. The original topsoil should be relaid on the ditch slopes to encourage the growth of grass [6]. A waterproof surface can be given to a compacted earth road [7] by spreading a layer of 5cm (2in) stones, then brushing and watering in finer grades of crushed stones to fill the spaces. A final rolling produces a dense surface [8]. Bridges can be built using a number of standard prefabricated timber sections supported on an iron beam and fixed together with interlocking metal plates (shown in inset).

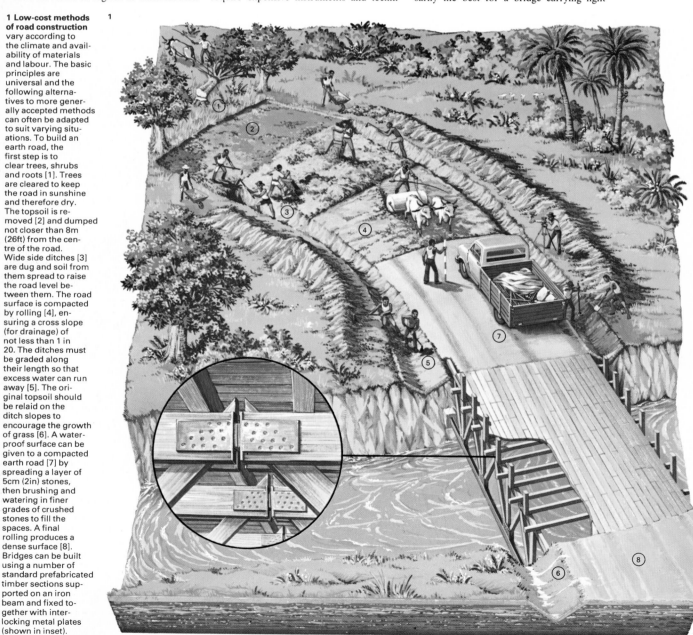

traffic in undeveloped areas where cement and steel has to be brought at considerable expense from distant sources of supply, and yet where suitable timber, quarried stone, and bricks may be available locally. Before the general use of iron (from about 1830) and concrete (from about 1890), most bridges were built of masonry or timber, or a combination of both.

The design of bridges is not usually considered a field for standardization. But a recent scheme by the forestry department in Kenya has shown that enormous savings in cost can be achieved by standardization. A British civil engineer working for the department has designed a standard 30m (100ft) timber truss panel made from Kenya cypress. The panels are prefabricated at a central workshop, carried to each site and joined together there to form a bridge with a carriageway running over the top cord. Two panels set parallel to each other, can safely carry a 20-tonne truck. If a route has to be upgraded for heavier vehicles, more panels can quickly be added to an existing bridge.

For longer bridges intermediate timber piers can be built up from the river bed to support two or more spans. A pilot project has been set up that produces an average of one bridge span every three days. Some steel is used for panel couplings and ties, but most of the bridge is built from local materials, using local labour. As a result, the proportion of imported (and hence expensive) materials is kept to a minimum.

Low-cost transport

Modern motor vehicles may be necessary for carrying heavy loads in rural areas, but medium-sized loads can be transported by traditional means provided friction and gradients are kept to a minimum. The systematic construction of roads provides an opportunity for avoiding steep gradients. It also ensures a smooth, hard road surface on which rubber tyres roll with a minimum of friction. Modern wheel bearings eliminate the other main source of friction. By such means [3] an ox-team can be used to carry heavier loads more efficiently. Other means of providing low-cost rural transport depend on the local environment and materials.

A well-designed road does not collect water [A] but allows it to drain off [B]. John McAdam (1756–1836) first applied the basic principles of a serviceable road – it is the subsoil that supports the traffic and any soil sufficiently compacted and kept dry can support any reasonable weight.

2 Earth- and water-bound roads can be built without costly modern machinery. The 2.4m (8ft) drag-grader [A] has metal edges and is drawn by two oxen. This form of grader was used on the construction of many early US roads. One man can shift a load of soil with a team of oxen and a fresno scraper [B]. It is made from a strong oil drum. The steel-nosed V-drag [C] is used for cutting ditches.

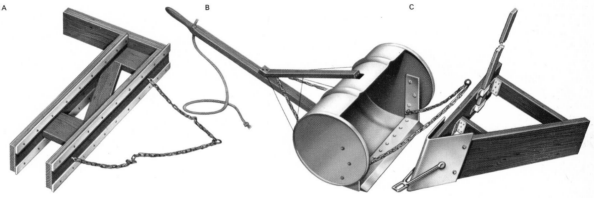

3 The ox-cart is still the most widely used load-carrying vehicle in the rural areas of most of the world's developing countries. Among its advantages is the fact that, unlike a motor vehicle, it is simple to maintain, easy to repair and uses the energy of fodder and not of oil. The ox causes no air pollution and provides manure as a valuable by-product. The main disadvantage of the traditional ox-cart is the energy wastage due to primitive wheel bearings and the friction between solid wheels and the road. By fitting the back-axle, wheel and tyre assembly of scrapped automobiles, the disadvantages of the ox-cart can be overcome at low cost to produce a more efficient vehicle.

4 Where there are water routes the barge provides an economical method of transporting heavy loads. In coastal China an experiment in the mass-production of reinforced concrete sampans has resulted in a cheaper product with a longer life. The six- and ten-tonne sampans are hand-built upside down over a pit, using prefabricated bulkheads over which steel rods and wire mesh are laid before cement platering.

5 The cycle rickshaw is a cheap and convenient form of transport in several South-East Asian cities where there are marked differences in earnings and much unemployment. It often competes directly with the more sophisticated buses and taxis. Opinions may differ about the moral desirability of public transport propelled by human energy, but cyclists such as the one seen here resting are able to work and support their families as well as providing a service.

Locomotives

The spread of railways, which transformed life in the nineteenth century, is linked inextricably with the steam locomotive. To its devotees the steam locomotive was one of the most romantic and beautiful machines ever built. It first appeared in 1804 in a simple version [1] invented by a Cornishman, Richard Trevithick (1771–1833).

Early rail systems
The first steam locomotives to do useful work were ordered and used by coal mines in northeast England in 1813–20. In 1825 a public railway was opened between the English towns of Stockton and Darlington. It had been planned for horse traction, but George Stephenson (1781–1848), a leading builder of colliery locomotives, persuaded the directors to operate a steam locomotive hauling trains heavier than horses could manage. The success of this line led to the much bigger and more important railway between Liverpool and Manchester. It was opened in 1830 after bitter opposition from landlords, coachmen, canal bargees and the large sector of the population that abhorred

any change and considered smoke-spouting locomotives to be engines of Satan. Against spirited competition, Stephenson's *Rocket* [2] was chosen to provide the motive power. It was small and light enough to run on only four wheels without breaking the flimsy iron track. Thanks to steady improvements in manufacturing, it became possible to make boilers stronger, cylinders and pistons more accurate and better fitting, and the whole locomotive capable of developing more power at higher speeds.

For a century steam locomotives provided nearly all the traction for the world's railways. There were no dramatic technical advances but size, power and speed grew constantly. In Europe many rail systems used excellent track, capable of bearing 100-tonne locomotives running at up to 160km/h (100mph). But in the United States in early days, and in most other young, developing countries, track was lighter, and often badly laid by men racing to complete more miles each day. This called for more wheels to spread the load. Engines came to be identified by their wheels, so that 4–6–2 desig-

nated the number of leading, driving and trailing wheels. Speeds were limited and seldom exceeded 80km/h (50mph), apart from one or two short record-setting runs.

The steam locomotive had reached its zenith by the 1930s. European "steamers" were clean, splendidly painted in the livery of their operating companies and, when designed for express passenger haulage, often capable of reaching 160km/h (100mph). American locomotives tended to be more utilitarian. Demands for greater power led to increases in size until they became the biggest land vehicles in history.

Electric locomotives
The first rival to steam came in the form of the direct-current electric motor, adopted in cities (especially in underground railways), to avoid smoke pollution. The first electric train ran at an exhibition in Berlin in 1879. Soon countries such as Switzerland and Norway found that it was cheaper, with the development of hydroelectric power, to generate electricity than to burn brown coal or wood, and their networks became all-electric.

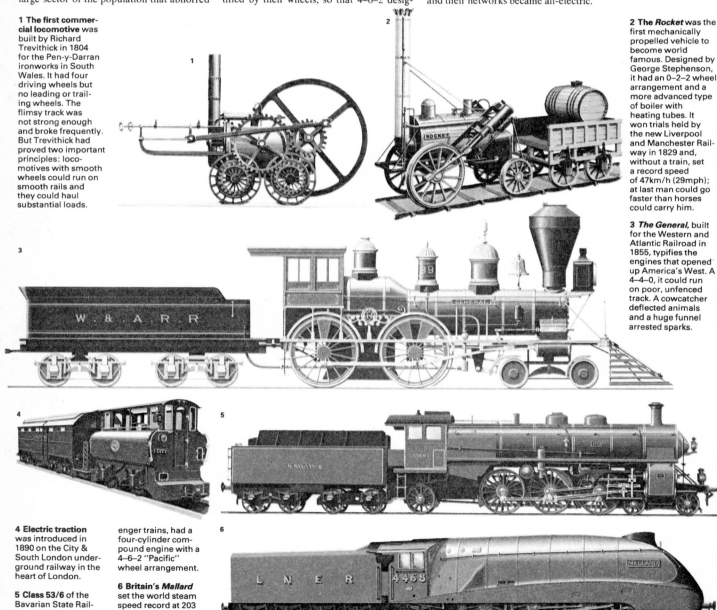

1 **The first commercial locomotive** was built by Richard Trevithick in 1804 for the Pen-y-Darran ironworks in South Wales. It had four driving wheels but no leading or trailing wheels. The flimsy track was not strong enough and broke frequently. But Trevithick had proved two important principles: locomotives with smooth wheels could run on smooth rails and they could haul substantial loads.

2 **The *Rocket*** was the first mechanically propelled vehicle to become world famous. Designed by George Stephenson, it had an 0–2–2 wheel arrangement and a more advanced type of boiler with heating tubes. It won trials held by the new Liverpool and Manchester Railway in 1829 and, without a train, set a record speed of 47km/h (29mph); at last man could go faster than horses could carry him.

3 *The General,* built for the Western and Atlantic Railroad in 1855, typifies the engines that opened up America's West. A 4–4–0, it could run on poor, unfenced track. A cowcatcher deflected animals and a huge funnel arrested sparks.

4 **Electric traction** was introduced in 1890 on the City & South London underground railway in the heart of London.

5 **Class 53/6** of the Bavarian State Railway, dating from 1908 and used to pull prestige passenger trains, had a four-cylinder compound engine with a 4–6–2 "Pacific" wheel arrangement.

6 **Britain's *Mallard*** set the world steam speed record at 203 km/h (126mph) in 1938, pulling a seven-coach train.

Today the electric motor, with its linear form under development, is regarded as the best form of traction for railways but the huge capital costs impede its introduction except on the busiest routes. As long ago as 1955, French Railways demonstrated that electric trains of conventional type [9] could run at more than 320km/h (200mph), but average speeds of public trains have risen only slowly. The Japanese New Tokaido line [10] achieved a sudden jump in speed because the line was laid for high speed. Even so, track and trains need constant maintenance.

Diesel power
About 1920, the first diesel locomotives and railcars came into general use, powered by compression-ignition oil engines developed by the German Rudolph Diesel (1858–1913). Though often noisy, diesel engines pick up speed faster and convert 25 to 45 per cent of their fuel energy into useful haulage, whereas the fuel efficiency of steam traction seldom exceeded eight per cent. Despite greater capital cost, diesel locomotives gradually ousted steam from 1935

onwards, until today steam engines are confined to a shrinking number of railways in Africa and Asia and a few local lines elsewhere. Diesels can be started and stopped easily, burn no fuel when not working, and can run at close to maximum power for hours at a time with no strain on either machines or crew (in contrast to the grimy slavery of the former stoker, or fireman, on the steam footplate). Many diesel locomotives run more than 160,000km (100,000 miles) a year and modern examples are highly reliable, versatile and relatively efficient, as well as being fast [11, 12].

Only in the smallest sizes does the diesel engine drive the wheels through a mechanical gearbox, as on a lorry. Generally the two are linked hydraulically or electrically. Hydraulic transmissions are arrangements of turbines linked by oil under high pressure, and they can transmit smoothly 2,000 horsepower with any ratio between input and output speeds. In the diesel-electric locomotive the engine drives a generator or alternator. This is used to supply current to traction motors similar to those of electric locomotives.

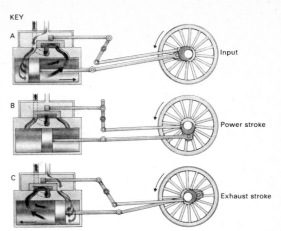

KEY

Input

Power stroke

Exhaust stroke

The double-action engine used to drive a steam locomotive uses superheated steam generated in a heating-tube boiler. Steam entering the cylinder [A] drives the piston back and exhausts steam from the other side of the piston. [B] shows the mid-position, with both inlet valves closed. In [C], steam is led to the other side of the piston and the cycle is repeated. The exhaust steam passes directly into the atmosphere, and this wasted energy, coupled with the design of the boiler, gives this type of steam engine the remarkably low efficiency of only eight per cent.

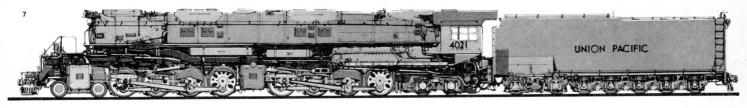

7

7 The "Big Boy" class of the Union Pacific were the heaviest locomotives built (540 tonnes). With a 4–8–8–4 layout, they hauled heavy freight trains in the Rocky Mountains at up to 120km/h (75mph).

8

9

10

10 New Tokaido trains began running between Tokyo and Osaka in 1964. With 12,000hp per train, the new electric route of 515km (320 miles) is covered in three hours, but costs are high.

11 Typical of the locomotives of today is a diesel-electric built in Montreal in 1972 for East Africa. Devoid of frills, it spreads its weight on eight axles in two pivoted bogies and can haul big loads.

8 The *Beyer-Garratt* (4–6–4 + 4–6–4) of Rhodesia Railways shows how articulated design can fit powerful locomotives to light track. The boiler supplies a pair of engines pivoted at their ends.

9 Class CC 7100 of the SNCF (French Railways), pulling a light train, ran at 331km/h (205mph) in March 1955. It was a standard electric locomotive modified with a high gear ratio.

11

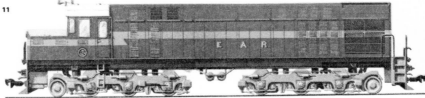

12

12 The High Speed Train, introduced by British Rail in 1973, set a world record for diesel trains when it reached a speed of 230km/h (143mph). Planned for general service from 1976, it has a light but powerful diesel at each end and with 4,500hp can carry passengers at 200km/h (125mph). To increase normal service speed to 250km/h without major alterations to track and signals, British Rail is developing an electrically propelled Advanced Passenger Train. A prototype is planned to run between London and Glasgow in 1978.

Railway transport

Man built railways long before he built steam engines and before he had even mastered the basic technology of engineering with iron and other metals. The earliest railways were constructed of timber and were in operation not later than the fourteenth century. They were built to overcome the severe limitations of other forms of land transport. The provision of a purpose-built track avoided pot-holes and ruts and deterioration due to the weather and simultaneously reduced the friction and rolling resistance of vehicles so that a given force could transport a heavier load.

The first railways

Most railways built before 1825 [1] were what might today be called tramways. They ran over distances of 3km (2 miles) or less and carried a single commodity such as coal or stone (for example between a mine or quarry and a loading wharf for ships). Wagons were pulled by horses or by human beings. Rolling stock was solidly made of wood, reinforced and joined by metal. Wheels were crude, but the smoothness of the track meant that they could be much smaller than those for carts and coaches running on roads. The track, variously of wood or iron, was built with inner, outer or double flanges to keep the trucks running along it.

At first trucks were pushed individually. Then growing traffic led to two or more being coupled together, by simple iron links or even by ropes, to operate as a train. Usually the horses or human beings had to push only over short sections or on the return journey, the falling gradient from a pithead to a wharf being mainly downhill. Often a horse would ride down in an empty truck, ready to pull the unladen train back to the mine again. There was no signalling or traffic control and the absence of brakes meant that coal-laden trains ran downhill completely out of control.

Improvements and standardization

Not until after 1820 were crude friction brakes fitted, but the really big advance was the invention of powerful air, steam and vacuum brakes. The air brake, introduced by George Westinghouse (1846–1914) in 1869 [6], cut the stopping distance needed on level track by as much as 90 per cent.

By 1820 several of the variable features had been firmly decided upon. Track was no longer of wood but of iron, with high-strength steel in standard sections following at the end of the 1860s. The flange was no longer on the track but on the inner edges of the wheels, which were fixed in pairs to the axles. Although not understood at the time this feature enabled trains to run faster and more smoothly.

Rolling stock had to be designed to fit the loading gauge of the line so that no part projected far enough outwards or upwards to strike a tunnel, bridge or signal. The restriction of the loading gauge meant there were capacity advantages in making vehicles longer, but they had to run round corners without forcing the flanges off the rails. Most early stock had only two axles. By 1845 three-axle goods and passenger stock was common, all axles being held in axle-boxes fixed to the vehicle frame. By 1875 the biggest coaches were fitted with pivoted two-axle bogies, which allowed increased length and reduced the minimum radius of curve that could be traversed.

1 Early trucks ran on wooden rails. Invariably the plain wooden wheels were kept on the track by flanges, grooves or other guideways built into the track. This truck hauled iron ore in the 1500s.

2 Railway gauges throughout the world range in width from 5ft 6in (1.68m) to less than 2ft (60cm). Most European countries, and North America, use the standard gauge of 4ft 8.5in (1.43m).

3 A   B   C

3 Early passenger cars established the idea that there should be three different classes of accommodation for rail travellers, priced at different levels. Third class [A] was simply an open truck, second class [B] had bench seats and first-class travellers were housed in something resembling three opulent horse carriages on a single chassis [C]. All these had to be designed to function together.

4 Underground trains have been carrying the workers of the world's major cities since London's Metropolitan line opened in January 1863. In its first year the line carried 9.5 million passengers. Today the entire London network carries more than two million passengers each day. Trains of some major cities are shown here.

4   New York   Berlin   Montreal   London

By this time trains often comprised 12-bogie passenger cars, or had standard couplers, and the different operating authorities gradually standardized on preferred systems.

In the twentieth century it became necessary to try to standardize rail gauges [2] and to fit all rolling stock with standard braking and control systems, vehicle heating and lighting supplies and, above all, with standardized couplers. Early couplers were merely heavy hooks and links, connected by hand, but by 1925 automatic couplers were beginning to come into use. These resembled strong claws that could snap shut by merely pushing vehicles together and prevented an individual vehicle from overturning if its wheels should come off the track [5].

Railway passenger transport
The early years of the twentieth century saw the growing construction of urban underground or rapid-transit railway systems. This led to a fresh class of rolling stock [4], designed for passenger transport only, often with a small loading gauge for underground lines and propelled by electricity (picked up from one or two extra current-carrying rails). Unlike most earlier trains these were powered by electric motors placed along the train, instead of having a separate locomotive to move the rolling stock.

Such "multiple unit" (m.u.) trains are completely flexible in that they can be made up of any number of small groups of cars and can run equally well in either direction. They are also capable of rapid acceleration and braking because they have a very high ratio of power to weight and powerful brakes. Some have been fitted with rubber tyres (to reduce noise) and almost all have power-driven sliding doors. The latest stock is fitted with automatic control so that if a driver rides with the train he does so only as a passive overseer. Similar technology operates on long-distance passenger trains for surface use. Propulsion is being applied to most or all axles right along the train and water-turbine brakes are fitted to slow trains down from very high speeds. The latest trains have bodies that can tilt smoothly on bends [Key]. Steel and wood have given way to light alloys and fibre-reinforced plastics.

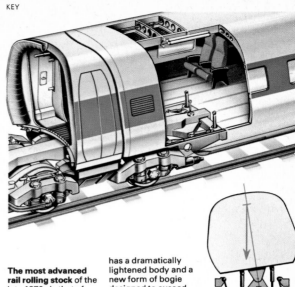

The most advanced rail rolling stock of the late 1970s is that of the British Rail Advanced Passenger Train (APT). It has a dramatically lightened body and a new form of bogie designed to exceed 250km/h (155mph) even round the bends of existing track.

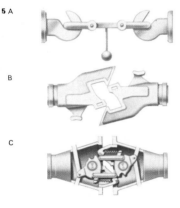

5 Couplings between railway wagons began as simple hooks and chains [A] with buffers to absorb the shock. Automatic couplers and uncouplers [B] were introduced in the USA in 1882 and led to today's buck-eye coupler [C]. Some include connections for the brakes, electrical controls and heating. Instead of buffers American wagons have "draft" gear that uses springs, friction or hydraulics to absorb operating shocks.

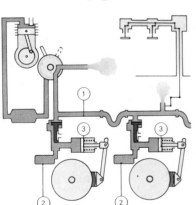

6 George Westinghouse's pneumatic brake, patented in 1869, is used more widely by railways than any other type. The brake pipes are kept full of compressed air. When the brake is applied air in the main pipe [1] escapes. Auxiliary reservoirs [2] that still contain compressed air are then automatically connected to the brake cylinders, in which the pistons [3] move outwards and force the brake-shoes on to the wheels.

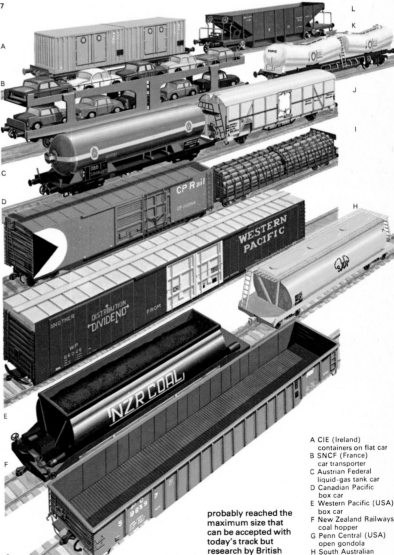

Stockholm

Paris

probably reached the maximum size that can be accepted with today's track but research by British Rail from 1963–8 opened the way for freight trains of the future to run with greater safety at speeds of at least 235km/h (145mph).

A CIE (Ireland) containers on flat car
B SNCF (France) car transporter
C Austrian Federal liquid-gas tank car
D Canadian Pacific box car
E Western Pacific (USA) box car
F New Zealand Railways coal hopper
G Penn Central (USA) open gondola
H South Australian bulk grain hopper
I Finnish State flat car (timber)
J Italian State refrigerated van
K British Rail bulk cement
L Indian Railways hopper

7 Modern freight stock is designed to carry particular kinds of commodities. Vehicles have now

Railways of the future

The railways of the future will probably not involve any spectacularly new principle but will be developments of those we use today. Most rail administrations have built their entire system to a stereotyped model, with two steel rails of a particular type separated by a "gauge" of about 4ft 8.5in (1.43m), 3ft 6in (1.07m), 1 metre (3.28ft) or 5ft 6in (1.68m). Sums of money equivalent to hundreds of millions of pounds were invested in this track and, in today's economic environment of inflation and rapidly rising material and labour costs, it is not easy to see how any major change can ever occur. Only in a place with no existing railway at all can new railway principles be adopted without the financial loss of scrapping an existing system. Yet already much is being done to improve efficiency of "traditional" two-rail systems.

Rewarding trends in railways

One of the most rewarding efforts is the elimination of traffic bottlenecks, level crossings, sharp bends and permanent-way restrictions of all kinds. Another improvement is to construct the track in a different way. Instead of laying rails and ties (sleepers) on a bed of ballast, which constantly needs attention, track could be made up into prefabricated concrete-based sections laid directly on to firm ground [2]. The maintenance cost of such track could be cut to less than one-tenth of that of a traditional track.

Another vital area for improvement is automatic train control. Today railways are introducing electronically based control and communications systems [1]. These involve fixed beacons or cables laid along the track for communication between trains and a control centre with a computer [3]. Trains can be started automatically, accelerated at an exact rate, held to precisely the best speed at all times and automatically guided on to the right track or made to comply with any special limitations. Any emergency can be instantly known throughout the system, the computer changing its program to re-instruct all traffic. Using early forms of such control, city transit systems such as San Francisco's BART and London's Victoria Line have, since their first day, been operating automatically, the driver riding as a pas-senger to keep an eye on things.

Use of such automatic control, coupled with arrangements for bringing trains to rest in a safe distance, has been allied with advances in the design of rolling stock to allow dramatic increases in speed. One alternative to the traditional railroad is the monorail [Key], which has been in use for most of this century in various forms. Its main advantage is not extra speed but the fact that it is easy to erect on stilts across a city.

With changes to the track, speeds greatly in excess of 250km/h (155mph), beyond the limit for conventional track, will be possible.

Wheels obsolete

The most radical new developments in the final quarter of this century involve the elimination of wheels. High-speed vehicles can run along smooth tracks by air-cushion lift or magnetic levitation [Key]. Although both methods demand the consumption of energy – doing what the wheel does for nothing – the wheel-less train can run much faster than a wheeled one and needs less costly track. By getting rid of any contact bet-

1 Marshalling yards offer a foretaste of the semi-automated railway of the future using the same track as today. Freight cars enter the yard over the hump in the foreground, roll down the slope beyond, are scanned by an electronic eye and switched to the correct track. They are slowed and halted by hydraulic retarders beside the rails which "squeeze" the wheel flanges. The whole process is under computer control.

Hydraulic retarder

Electric eye

Hump

2 Railway track cannot break away from the established form and spacing of rails, but it is continuously being developed to reduce costs, especially the cost of maintenance.

The British track in the foreground, laid on prefabricated concrete base sections, needs no ballast and in theory little attention for years. In a large rail system this type of advance would save a larger sum than the total annual bill for the cost of the energy to drive the trains. The possibility of eventually changing to a different form of track is remote.

3 Automatic train control – applying the brakes when a train is approaching an obstruction – has been employed on railways in Britain for many years. But this fully automatic system is still in the experimental stage. A set of "wiggly wire" conductors is laid between the running rails of the track and the electric currents in them detected (using induction) by coils suspended from the underside of the locomotive. The presence of a current is shown on equipment in the cab as a digit, say a number 1. If a second wire runs in the opposite direction to the first, its current effectively cancels that of the first wire and the equipment records the number 0. In this way, the pattern of wires can relay a series of coded instructions, in the form of a set of consecutive digits, standing for "reduce speed to 50km/h" or "stop train in 2km", and so on, controlling a train automatically.

ween train and track the need for maintenance would also virtually be eliminated, or so it is hoped. There would be no noise save for the rush of air past the vehicle and the only power used to drive the train at cruising speed would be that needed to overcome drag. The track, basically made of concrete box sections, would have to be rather straight in comparison with today's metals because at, say 800km/h (500mph) it would be impossible to climb gradients comfortably, to breast summits or to negotiate curves. The TACV (tracked air-cushion vehicle) [4] is a well-developed technology, although no extensive system has yet been built.

From present to future

The magnetic-levitation method (maglev) dates from as recently as 1968 and many systems are operating over short test stretches. The fundamental feature of maglev is the use of the same magnetic field both to lift and to propel the train (probably a single vehicle). Superconducting magnets are used to effect dramatic savings in consumption of current.

For the more distant future there is a wealth of fantastic possibilities. Undoubtedly the most rewarding, most frightening and least likely in the foreseeable future is the gravity tunnel train [6A]. If a tunnel were to be bored from, say, London to New York, it would seem at each end to dive quite steeply down into the earth. A vehicle placed in the tunnel would fall towards its destination. If the tunnel were empty of air the vehicle would reach a speed of many thousands of kilometres per hour at the mid-point, when it would appear to be travelling on level ground. It would then increasingly seem to climb, coming to rest at its destination (with no expenditure of energy, save that of pumping out the air). Man does not yet possess the technology to build such a "railroad", but he could build shorter gravity-vacuum systems that would dive down in curving tunnels between stations only a few miles apart, with atmospheric pressure behind the car and a near vacuum in front. Another "train" of the future might zoom along an air-filled tube by sucking in air in front, compressing it and discharging it as a propellant jet behind [6C].

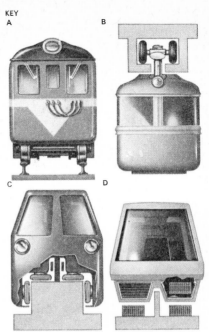

KEY
A
B
C
D

There are many kinds of railways already in use. Almost all the world's public rail track is of the two-rail variety [A], with steel rails spaced side by side. In urban areas the monorail is sometimes found, with the cars riding above the track or hanging from it [B]. Advocates of air cushion trains [C] claim that the track, made from re-inforced concrete box sections, is cheaper. One of the latest systems uses magnetic levitation [D] to support the train. Examples of all these have been tested. Various futuristic designs exist only on paper and nobody can foretell with certainty what the railways will look like even 25 years ahead.

4
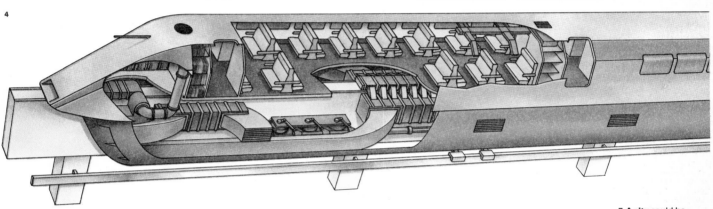

4 The hovertrain, a British tracked air-cushion vehicle (TACV), illustrates the kind of system that one day may supersede the steel two-rail. The track is assembled from cheap concrete boxes carried on short stilts. The only physical contact between vehicle and track is the sliding electric current pick-up that serves the linear motor. Electric blowers form an air-cushion to lift and guide the vehicle.

5
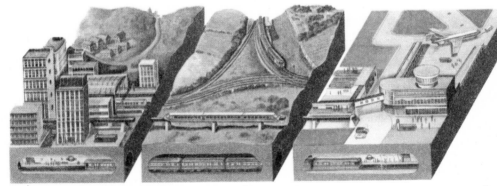

5 A city could be linked to a distant airport using three kinds of rail links. A conventional surface railway (diesel or electric) could serve the city and a junction to other rail routes. An underground railway could serve outlying suburbs and the centre, and a high-speed monorail could form a non-stop rapid link directly to the city. But only an underground can be built with little disruption to existing buildings.

6 Futuristic ideas for railways, not yet even in the experimental stage, include a vacuum train and an airtube system. The vacuum train [A] is "sucked" along by low pressure in front of it; gravity aids acceleration and deceleration because the tunnel slopes down steeply from one station and slopes upwards to the next [B]. The tunnel for the airtube train [C] is filled with air and air cushion pads keep the train centred. Airflow through the train propels it along.

6 A   C

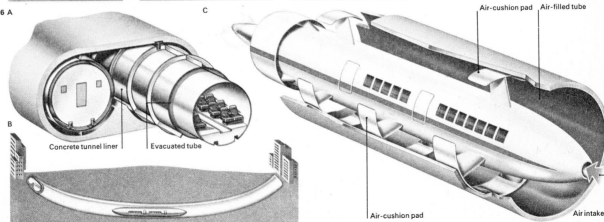

Air-cushion pad   Air-filled tube

Concrete tunnel liner   Evacuated tube

B

Air-cushion pad   Air intake

Balloons, blimps and dirigibles

When early men dreamed of flying they usually imagined "flying machines" that resembled artificial birds. It so happened that, more than a century before the technology existed to make flying possible in this way, a totally different method of flying was developed in France. This suddenly developed method – the use of balloons – is called lighter-than-air flight. The technical term for such aircraft is an aerostat. Aerostats are buoyant in the atmosphere and float at a particular level that depends on their mass, on the surrounding atmosphere and also on the volume of air that they displace.

Balloon construction

The concept of making a balloon from some light material and filling it with a gas having a density less than that of air dates from medieval times. In 1670 Francesco de Lana proposed an aerial ship to be lifted by four large copper spheres from which the air had been pumped out (he did not know that spheres strong enough not to collapse would weigh many times more than the mass of air they displaced). In the next century the bal-

loon came much closer with the discovery of the gas we now call hydrogen, the least dense of all the elements. The British chemist Joseph Black (1728–99), who studied hydrogen, thought of making a hydrogen-filled balloon, but probably did no experiments.

A few years later, in France in 1782, the papermakers Joseph and Etienne Montgolfier (1740–1810 and 1745–99, respectively) had been watching charred fragments spiralling upwards above a bonfire. Why, they wondered, did the fragments rise? Thanks to their skill with paper the Montgolfier brothers were able to build small balloons which, when filled with hot air from a fire, took off and sailed upwards. On 4 June 1783 they publicly flew an 11m (36ft) balloon of linen and paper that climbed to about 1,830m (6,000ft).

The balloon caused a sensation. Jacques Charles (1746–1823) had meanwhile set to work to build a hydrogen balloon, while the Montgolfiers constructed a hot-air balloon large enough to lift a man, carrying a fire beneath it. On 15 October 1783 Pilâtre de Rozier was carried aloft in the tethered bal-

loon, while five weeks later [Key] he and the Marquis d'Arlandes flew the first aerial journey in history, covering 8km (5 miles) in a gentle breeze in 25 minutes. Charles's hydrogen balloon made a manned flight the following week, on 1 December 1783. For the next 100 years lighter-than-air flight dominated man's attempts to fly, with balloons reaching heights of 6km (3.7 miles) and travelling hundreds of kilometres (for example, in 1859 John Wise flew 1,300km [804 miles] from St Louis to Henderson, NY). In 1870, during the Franco-Prussian War, balloons were the only link that existed between Paris and the outside world.

Uses of balloons and airships

It was natural for early aeronauts to wish to devise some means of locomotion to free themselves from the mercy of the wind. Some attempted to use oars and others tried propellers cranked by hand, but it was not until the invention, in 1852, of the steam-driven dirigible (meaning "steerable") by Henri Giffard (1823–1921) that the airship emerged as a vehicle. The earliest airships

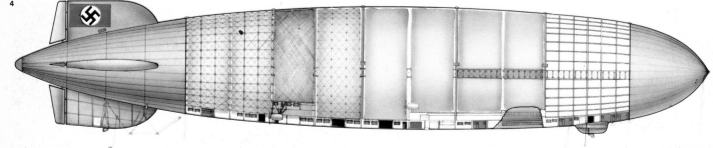

2 Non-rigid airships all have flexible envelopes that are stabilized by being inflated to a pressure slightly higher than that of the surrounding atmosphere. The load is suspended by a system of ropes or wires that distributes the weight around the fabric envelope. The sea patrol blimp illustrated dates from 1913 but closely resembles many used in World War II. Similar ships, filled with non-inflammable helium are still flying. Some are used for advertising and carry huge arrays of lights that can be made to display slogans or pictures. Others are being developed as freight carriers.

1 Ferdinand von Zeppelin (1838–1917) pioneered the rigid airship, which was to take his name. His first vessel, LZ1, flew in 1900 and was followed by a whole series, including this LZ13 of 1912. It was 141.5m (460ft) long and 13.8m (45ft) in diameter and could carry more than six tonnes of passengers and cargo. This airship, named *Hansa*, made nearly 400 flights carrying more than 8,000 passengers 45,000km (30,000 miles). LZ14 (remumbered L1) was ordered by the German navy; some commercial airships were taken over by the army, which used them in World War I for reconnaissance and bombing.

3 Semi-rigid airships are uncommon but the *Norge* was one of a series of Italian airships of the 1920s and achieved fame by making a voyage to the North Pole in May 1926. There was no rigid structure inside the gas envelope, but a rigid keel ran from bow to stern and served as a structure to which everything could be attached. Cords and cables extended upwards from the keel to secure the envelope, preserve its shape and enable it to lift the whole ship. Below the keel were braced frames carrying the control car and engine nacelles.

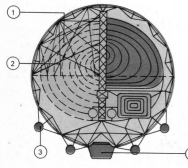

4 Rigid airships have a skeleton framework that contains the lifting gas in a series of bags. The largest ever built were the German LZ129 *Hindenburg* (1936) and LZ130 *Graf Zepplin* (1938), named after the earlier LZ-127 of 1928. Each had 200,000m³ (7 million cu ft) of hydrogen, giving a lift of about 232 tonnes, contained in gas bags [1]. These were housed inside the aluminium framework [2] from which were hung the four 1,050hp diesel engines [3] and the payload [4] comprising 50 passengers and their baggage and 12 tonnes of freight and mail. The *Hindenburg* exploded in flames in the US in 1937.

| 0 | 30 | 60 | 90 | 120m |
| 0 | 100 | 200 | 300 | 400ft |

5 Relative sizes of the three types of airship show the greater size possible with rigid [A] compared with semi-rigid [B] and non-rigid [C] ships.

were what are today called non-rigids [2]: each had an envelope of flexible fabric from which the load was suspended by cords. In the semi-rigid airship [3] there is a rigid keel and in the rigid type [4] the entire envelope is built round a rigid framework. All were fully developed by the start of World War I in which airships, tethered "kite balloons" and non-rigid "blimps" all played major roles.

The operation of all aerostats depends on balancing their mass against the volume of displaced atmosphere. With gas balloons and airships the normal technique is to vent gas from the envelope to descend and to release sand or water ballast to rise. Airships in cruising flight can also change their direction or height by using aerodynamic tail controls, but these are not effective at low speeds. With hot-air balloons the lift depends on the difference in temperature between the air inside and that outside the envelope.

The future of the airship

By the beginning of World War II the large airship was dead – killed by a series of major disasters. Among the last of these was the destruction by fire in 1937 of the German airship *Hindenburg* [4], with 36 deaths. Barrage balloons and blimps had their uses but after 1945 there remained very few devotees of the sporting hydrogen balloon. Then, in about 1965, the scene was transformed. The modern hot-air balloon gradually became a worldwide best-seller and today many hundreds are sold each year. They use immediately controllable propane burners with which climb and descent can be governed for a whole day if necessary.

The airship is also being recognized once more as a potential cargo carrier. All over the world designers and freight carriers are studying plans of completely new kinds of airships that would make use of modern technology to carry loads of hundreds or thousands of tonnes in safety and at low cost. Such giant cargo airships – the *Skyship* [8] is an example – could become a reality before the end of the century. They may be especially useful in opening up undeveloped regions and in carrying large freight containers and possibly even bulk cargo direct to their final destination.

KEY

Man's first balloon flight took place on 21 November 1783 when two men travelled about 8km (5 miles) across Paris. They rose aloft standing on a gallery of wickerwork suspended beneath the painted envelope of the Montgolfier brothers' largest hot-air balloon. Made of paper-lined linen and coated with alum to reduce the fire risk (although not with complete success) the envelope was 15m (49ft) high and the whole balloon weighed about 785kg (1,730lb). The air inside, a volume of about 2,200m³ (77,700 cu ft), was heated by a large mass of burning straw resting on a wire grid in the centre of the gallery.

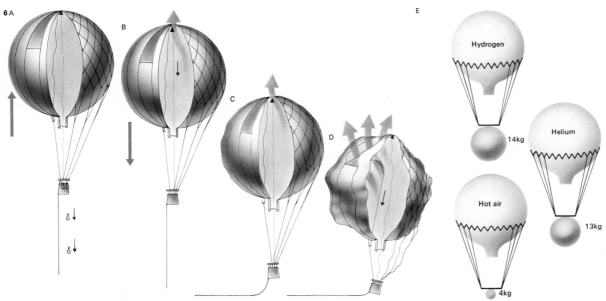

6 Balloons rise because the gas they contain is less dense than air. Control is limited to upward motion by releasing ballast [A] and downward by releasing gas [B]. A drag rope [C] gives stability and slows the balloon on landing, when the rip panel is opened [D] to let the gas out. The lifting power of 28m³ (about 1,000 cu ft) of gas is shown in [E].

Hydrogen
14kg
Helium
Hot air
13kg
4kg

8 *Skyship* is a proposal for a modern cargo airship. This 10m (32ft) model was demonstrated in Britain in 1975. A full-scale *Skyship*, 215m (700ft) across, would cruise at about 160km/h (100mph) and have a crew of 24 with a payload of 400 tonnes.

7 The British R101 airship crashed on a hill at Beauvais, France, in 1930. The ship was on a voyage from England to India when it crashed, killing all but six of the 48 people on board. Burning hydrogen created a fireball hot enough to melt the metal of which it was built. This and the fatal disaster to the *Hindenburg* seven years later sealed the fate of the hydrogen airship.

History of aircraft

Contrary to popular belief, the brothers Orville (1871–1948) and Wilbur Wright (1867–1912) were not the first men to build an aircraft that could fly. Otto Lilienthal (1848–96) in Germany, for example, had already made hundreds of flights in his gliders. The Wright brothers' place in history is assured by the fact that their aeroplane was the first powered, controllable heavier-than-air machine craft to fly, in 1903.

Louis Blériot's pioneering flight

After the Wright brothers one of the important contributors to aeroplane design was Louis Blériot (1872–1936). He introduced a number of new features in his design, including a tractor (pulling) propeller, single wing (monoplane) and rudder and elevator at the rear. His Type XI achieved world acclaim on 25 July 1909 by flying from France to England. As with almost all other flying machines of its day it was of mixed construction; the main spars of the stubby wing and the four longerons of the lengthy fuselage were made of ash and the whole structure braced by numerous wires. Like the Wrights,

Blériot covered both the top and bottom surfaces of his wings, although many other designer-aviators used only a single surface of fabric, stretched over the top of the wing.

By 1912 Deperdussin, helped by research in Scandinavia, had built a racer of monocoque (single-shell) construction, which made for strength, lightness and a completely new streamlined form. He built his fuselage from multiple thin veneers of tulip wood, wrapped to shape and finally glued and covered with doped (lacquered) fabric. Most of the 100,000 aircraft built in World War I used the traditional wire-braced wood structure, but then the monocoque design developed gradually and found new expression in metal. Some early military aircraft, such as the Voisin L series, had all-metal structures. Some were made of steel tubing assembled by welding, riveting or with bolted joints, and others used the new aluminium alloy Duralumin. Whatever the material, the basic method was to make a strong skeleton and cover it with fabric.

A few wartime machines designed by Hugo Junkers (1859–1935) were not only

all-metal in skeleton but were also skinned with metal. In 1919 Junkers flew his F13, the first all-metal monoplane in commercial service. The low-mounted wing was completely unbraced by struts or wires and, like the fuselage, was skinned with Duralumin sheets having fore-and-aft corrugations for rigidity. From this stemmed a family of transports used all over the world, the best known being the Ju 52/3m – the leading European airliner in the 1930s and an aircraft built in large numbers for Hitler's *Luftwaffe.*

The only other family of transports able to rival the Junkers all-metal monoplanes were those from the Dutch Fokker company. These were also monoplanes, but they had deep wooden wings mounted above the fuselage of welded steel tube with a fabric covering. Together these two companies dominated Europe until the mid-1930s.

The Schneider Trophy

Throughout the 1920s, much attention and money was lavished on the Schneider Trophy – an international competition for racing seaplanes. Seaplanes rather than conven-

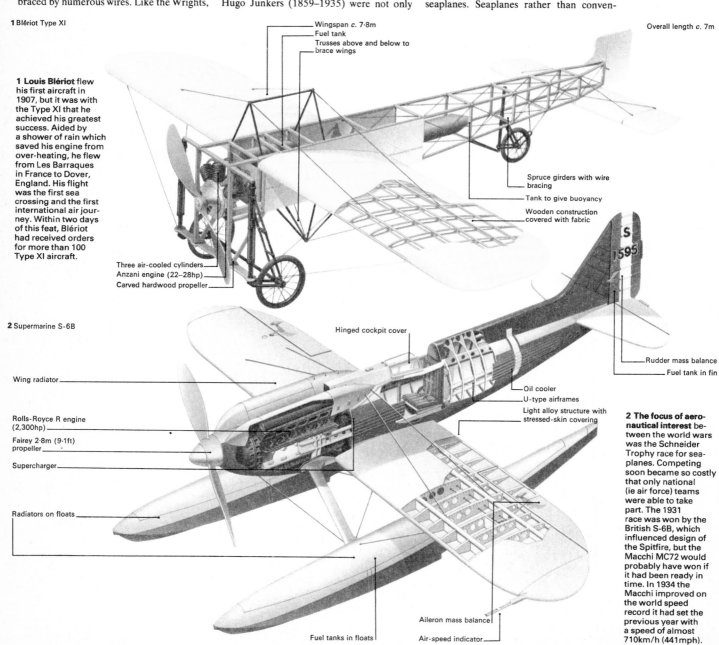

1 Blériot Type XI

Wingspan *c.* 7·8m
Fuel tank
Trusses above and below to brace wings

Overall length *c.* 7m

1 Louis Blériot flew his first aircraft in 1907, but it was with the Type XI that he achieved his greatest success. Aided by a shower of rain which saved his engine from over-heating, he flew from Les Barraques in France to Dover, England. His flight was the first sea crossing and the first international air journey. Within two days of this feat, Blériot had received orders for more than 100 Type XI aircraft.

Spruce girders with wire bracing
Tank to give buoyancy
Wooden construction covered with fabric

Three air-cooled cylinders
Anzani engine (22–28hp)
Carved hardwood propeller

2 Supermarine S-6B

Hinged cockpit cover

S 1595

Rudder mass balance
Fuel tank in fin

Wing radiator

Rolls-Royce R engine (2,300hp)
Fairey 2·8m (9·1ft) propeller
Supercharger

Oil cooler
U-type airframes
Light alloy structure with stressed-skin covering

Radiators on floats

2 The focus of aeronautical interest between the world wars was the Schneider Trophy race for seaplanes. Competing soon became so costly that only national (ie air force) teams were able to take part. The 1931 race was won by the British S-6B, which influenced design of the Spitfire, but the Macchi MC72 would probably have won if it had been ready in time. In 1934 the Macchi improved on the world speed record it had set the previous year with a speed of almost 710km/h (441mph).

Aileron mass balance

Fuel tanks in floats

Air-speed indicator

tional aircraft took part because Jacques Schneider thought that future international airline operators would make wide use of waterborne aircraft.

In addition to the public interest it stimulated, the competition had great influence on the mainstream of aircraft design. Also significant was the steady improvement in aviation technology, especially in the United States. The most important factor was the perfection of all-metal stressed-skin construction, in which the light-alloy skin was not just a covering but a crucial load-bearing part of the structure (so permitting a lighter skeleton underneath). Engines were improved and installed in better ways, with cowlings giving reliable cooling and reduced drag. Propellers were no longer fixed blades of wood or metal, but consisted of hub mechanisms carrying blades whose pitch (setting to the airflow) could be varied to suit the different demands of take-off and high-speed flight. Wings were fitted with flaps to give more lift at take-off and both lift and drag for landing. Landing gears were made retractable to reduce drag. Inevitably, air-craft acquired "systems" worked by electricity, hydraulics, compressed air and other methods, which grew ever more complex.

The Douglas aircraft

One of the first modern airliners was the Boeing 247 of 1933. In the same year Douglas flew the DC-1, only one of which was built, and took orders for the slightly improved DC-2. In 1934 Britain held an air race to Melbourne, Australia; the outright winner for speed was a special racer, carrying no load, but the second and third places were taken by a DC-2 and a Boeing 247. On 17 December 1935, the thirty-second anniversary of the Wrights' first flight, Douglas flew the DC-3. Over the next ten years this was to become the world standard airliner and the standard Allied transport in World War II, with some 11,000 being built in the United States and the Soviet Union. Large numbers are still in use and individual DC-3s have flown as many as 80,000 hours. Previously, few aircraft flew for more than 1,000 hours without either being wrecked or suffering from severe structural fatigue.

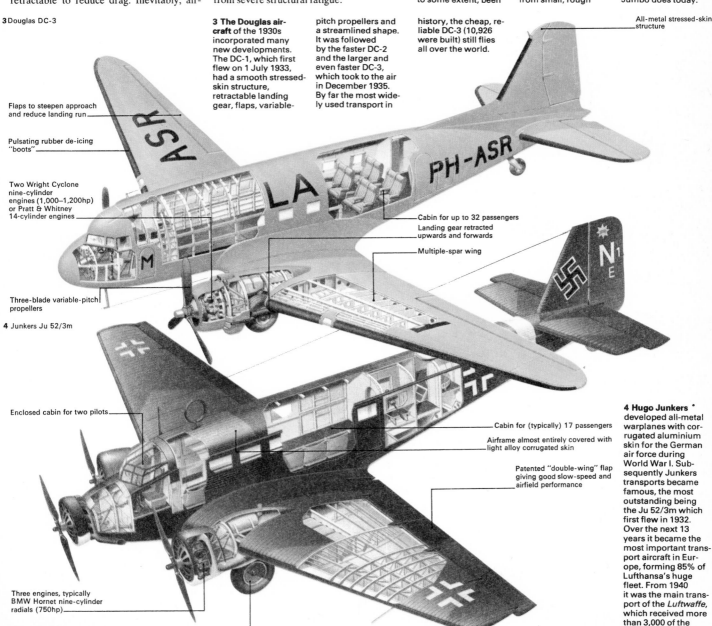

Boeing 747 "Jumbo"

Douglas DC-3

Junkers Ju 52/3m

Supermarine S-6B

Blériot Type XI

3 Douglas DC-3

The frailty and small size of early aircraft is emphasized by the comparison of their silhouettes with that of a modern Jumbo jet. This growth has, to some extent, been forced and made possible by huge improvements in propulsion and in airfields. Even the Ju 52/3m and the DC-3 had to operate from small, rough grass fields. These planes represented the most efficient compromise between conflicting demands that was possible in the 1930s, just as the Jumbo does today.

3 The Douglas aircraft of the 1930s incorporated many new developments. The DC-1, which first flew on 1 July 1933, had a smooth stressed-skin structure, retractable landing gear, flaps, variable-pitch propellers and a streamlined shape. It was followed by the faster DC-2 and the larger and even faster DC-3, which took to the air in December 1935. By far the most widely used transport in history, the cheap, reliable DC-3 (10,926 were built) still flies all over the world.

All-metal stressed-skin structure

Flaps to steepen approach and reduce landing run

Pulsating rubber de-icing "boots"

Two Wright Cyclone nine-cylinder engines (1,000–1,200hp) or Pratt & Whitney 14-cylinder engines

Three-blade variable-pitch propellers

Cabin for up to 32 passengers

Landing gear retracted upwards and forwards

Multiple-spar wing

4 Junkers Ju 52/3m

Enclosed cabin for two pilots

Cabin for (typically) 17 passengers

Airframe almost entirely covered with light alloy corrugated skin

Patented "double-wing" flap giving good slow-speed and airfield performance

4 Hugo Junkers developed all-metal warplanes with corrugated aluminium skin for the German air force during World War I. Subsequently Junkers transports became famous, the most outstanding being the Ju 52/3m which first flew in 1932. Over the next 13 years it became the most important transport aircraft in Europe, forming 85% of Lufthansa's huge fleet. From 1940 it was the main transport of the *Luftwaffe*, which received more than 3,000 of the 3,234 aircraft built.

Three engines, typically BMW Hornet nine-cylinder radials (750hp)

Fixed landing gear

Modern aircraft

The advent of the gas turbine engine late in World War II revolutionized aircraft design. The light plane – although still a recognizable descendant of earlier models – has been dramatically improved by fitting turbine engines. More advanced machines – airliners, heavy freighters and virtually all military aircraft and helicopters – have been utterly transformed. Of course the basic principles of wing lift, control, lift drag ratio and structural design necessarily remain unchanged. However, development of ever more complex and sophisticated control, navigation and guidance systems has continued to the point where the systems today often account for more than half the cost of an aircraft.

The early pace setters

This strange equation is true even for the class of aircraft bought by wealthy private owners and companies. In the 1930s the Percival Gull and Percival Vega Gull set several world records for long flights, establishing these planes as reliable private-owner and light business aircraft for many years. Built entirely of wood, they were neat low-wing

monoplanes powered by air-cooled piston engines of 130–200hp and seated three or four adults in a comfortable enclosed cabin. Such aircraft were among the first to be capable of undertaking long flights to distant parts of the world with some certainty of getting there. However, it is almost impossible to compare them with similar planes today, which are loaded with pilot-aids of all kinds. Intense competition means that modern aircraft, such as the Beechcraft Super King Air 200, have to be improved and up-dated constantly, resulting in a superior and more reliable product.

Instead of being made of wood, this Beechcraft model has a light alloy stressed-skin structure designed for fatigue-free use over perhaps 30 years (a factor never even considered 40 years ago). It is as large as several airliners of 1935, with seating for up to eight passengers. Maximum take-off load is 5,670kg (12,500lb), four times that of the Percival Gull. The two 850hp turboprop engines are almost nine times as powerful. Instead of flying for 1,130km (700 miles) at 225km/h (140mph) at a height of 4,880m

(16,000ft) the pressurized King Air 200 cruises at 9,850m (32,300ft), far above most bad weather, for up to 3,300km (2,050 miles) at over 510km/h (320mph). Yet perhaps the biggest contrast is in complexity of manufacture and operation; the number of items of equipment built into the aircraft that contribute directly to its flight – such as pumps, valves, radios, instruments and controls – amounted to 33 in the Gull. The total for the modern machine is 4,408.

The arrival of Comet I

When the British Comet I came into service in 1952, most airlines thought it premature and continued buying piston-engined machines for a while. But new jet aircraft offered the passenger a wholly new experience – flight that was not only faster but also significantly smoother and more comfortable. The early jets were, however, not so impressive to the man on the ground although they stimulated unprecedented and sustained growth and profitability for the airlines; they were outwardly extremely noisy and burned fuel rapidly.

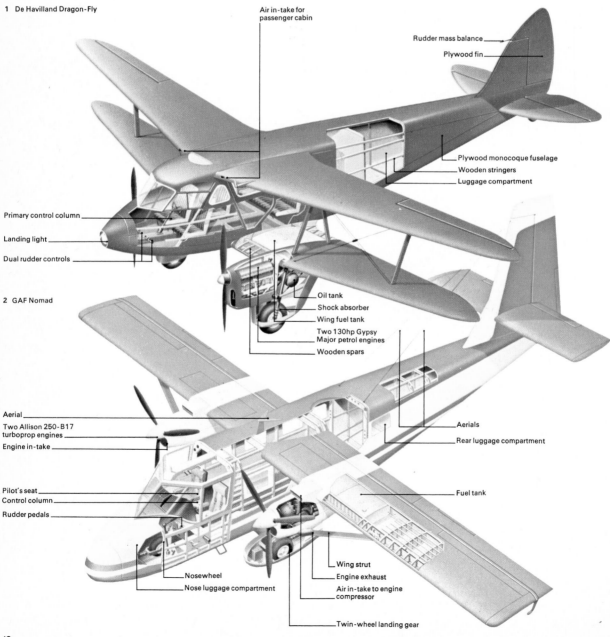

1 De Havilland Dragon-Fly

Air in-take for passenger cabin

Rudder mass balance

Plywood fin

Plywood monocoque fuselage

Wooden stringers

Luggage compartment

Primary control column

Landing light

Dual rudder controls

2 GAF Nomad

Oil tank

Shock absorber

Wing fuel tank

Two 130hp Gypsy Major petrol engines

Wooden spars

Aerial

Two Allison 250-B17 turboprop engines

Engine in-take

Aerials

Rear luggage compartment

Pilot's seat

Control column

Rudder pedals

Fuel tank

Nosewheel

Nose luggage compartment

Wing strut

Engine exhaust

Air in-take to engine compressor

Twin-wheel landing gear

1 **Low capital cost has always been of** paramount consideration in the manufacture of light aircraft, discouraging new technology; the wooden De Havilland Dragon-Fly, first sold in 1936, carried five passengers at 200km/h (125mph) for up to 966km (600 miles). The aircraft cost less than a modern four-door car. Today's light aircraft differ only in details – for example, the layout of the engine cylinders. By 1990, even small ones may be equipped with turbine engines.

2 **The latest technology** has transformed the larger of the light aircraft types. These are too costly for most private owners and are generally used by companies employing a professional pilot. The Australian GAF Nomad 22 is powered by two turboprop engines and can carry up to 13 passengers in great luxury. It can fly at a cruising speed of 325km/h (202mph) with a range at maximum payload of up to 930km (580 miles).

An answer to such problems was the large-diameter turbofan, a cross between a turbojet and a turboprop. Although the principle had been known since the early work of Frank Whittle (1907–), the inventor of the first British jet engine, and in 1947 Metropolitan Vickers had built such an engine – the F3 – aircraft of the period were not capable of carrying it. The large-diameter turbofan was rediscovered during the development of a US Air Force freighter in the mid-1960s. The losing bidder for that contract, Boeing, took four of the giant, yet quiet engines and used them to propel the Boeing 747, the first of the huge wide-body transports, popularly known as the "Jumbo".

Increasing public demand has resulted in a progressive increase in the size of transport aircraft. The DC-3 cabin is 1.7m (5.5ft) wide, and a Constellation of the immediate postwar years had a cabin 3m (10ft) wide at its widest point. The first of the big jets, the Boeing 707 of 1958, had a much longer cabin, which was 3.5m (11.5ft) wide throughout. In 1969 the first Boeing 747 was delivered, with a cabin nearly twice as long and 6.1m (20ft) wide.

The capability of such aircraft is much greater than mere size suggests, because they travel faster and fly far more hours a day than older machines. Several airlines have just one Boeing 747F freighter, but a single 747F can carry more cargo each year than all the world's airliners of 1939. And the turbofan-powered wide-bodied jet is, by comparison, relatively clean and quiet.

Supersonic transport
These "selling points" are not present in either the Concorde or the Tu-144, the first supersonic transports to enter commercial service. It is extremely difficult to make supersonic propulsion systems quiet, although the rapid and steep climb of these aircraft creates a local noise problem only around the airport itself. The move towards wider cabins is reversed in the SST (supersonic transport), because at Mach 2 (twice the speed of sound) aircraft must be relatively slim. On the other hand, journey time is greatly reduced so the SST offers as much extra to the passenger as did the first jets when they were introduced in the 1950s.

Boeing 747 "Jumbo"

AIR FRANCE

BAC-Aérospatiale Concorde

GAF Nomad 22

De Havilland DH90 Dragon-Fly

These aircraft silhouettes, reproduced to a common scale, illustrate the size of the Boeing 747 and the slenderness of Concorde. Supersonic aircraft must be relatively slender if they are not to be uneconomic, whereas the subsonic 747 can have a much wider cabin. The next generation of long-haul subsonic airliners will almost certainly be even larger. The differences between the two light aircraft are less apparent externally and involve mainly the structural materials.

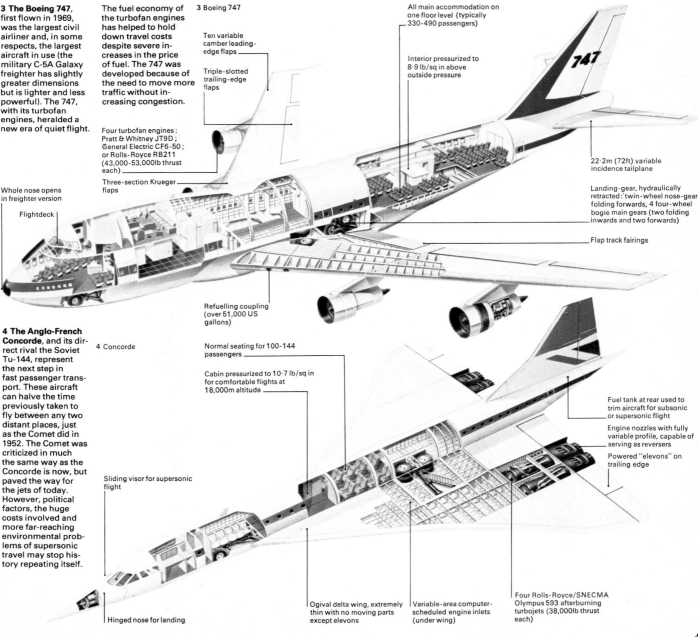

3 The Boeing 747, first flown in 1969, was the largest civil airliner and, in some respects, the largest aircraft in use (the military C-5A Galaxy freighter has slightly greater dimensions but is lighter and less powerful). The 747, with its turbofan engines, heralded a new era of quiet flight.

The fuel economy of the turbofan engines has helped to hold down travel costs despite severe increases in the price of fuel. The 747 was developed because of the need to move more traffic without increasing congestion.

3 Boeing 747

Ten variable camber leading-edge flaps

Triple-slotted trailing-edge flaps

Four turbofan engines: Pratt & Whitney JT9D; General Electric CF6-50; or Rolls-Royce RB211 (43,000-53,000lb thrust each)

Three-section Krueger flaps

Whole nose opens in freighter version

Flightdeck

Refuelling coupling (over 51,000 US gallons)

All main accommodation on one floor level (typically 330-490 passengers)

Interior pressurized to 8·9 lb/sq in above outside pressure

747

22·2m (72ft) variable incidence tailplane

Landing-gear, hydraulically retracted: twin-wheel nose-gear folding forwards, 4 four-wheel bogie main gears (two folding inwards and two forwards)

Flap track fairings

4 The Anglo-French Concorde, and its direct rival the Soviet Tu-144, represent the next step in fast passenger transport. These aircraft can halve the time previously taken to fly between any two distant places, just as the Comet did in 1952. The Comet was criticized in much the same way as the Concorde is now, but paved the way for the jets of today. However, political factors, the huge costs involved and more far-reaching environmental problems of supersonic travel may stop history repeating itself.

4 Concorde

Normal seating for 100-144 passengers

Cabin pressurized to 10·7 lb/sq in for comfortable flights at 18,000m altitude

Sliding visor for supersonic flight

Hinged nose for landing

Ogival delta wing, extremely thin with no moving parts except elevons

Variable-area computer-scheduled engine inlets (under wing)

Fuel tank at rear used to trim aircraft for subsonic or supersonic flight

Engine nozzles with fully variable profile, capable of serving as reversers

Powered "elevons" on trailing edge

Four Rolls-Royce/SNECMA Olympus 593 afterburning turbojets (38,000lb thrust each)

43

How an aeroplane works

If someone holds a sheet of paper in both hands and raises it in front of his face, tilting the near edge slightly downwards, most of the sheet (beyond the hands) arches down towards the floor. What happens if he blows across the top of the sheet? Oddly enough, it rises until it is stretched out horizontally. One might have expected this by blowing on the underside, but why is the sheet lifted by blowing over the top?

The answer lies in the effect that speed of flow has on the pressure of air. In the case of the paper, and the arched shape of an aeroplane's wing, air flowing over the top has to flow farther than that crossing underneath. The upper air therefore speeds up and as a result, its pressure falls. The higher pressure of the slower air below creates "lift". This effect is responsible for about 80 per cent of the lift on a normal aeroplane wing moving at less than the speed of sound [Key].

Wings and air flow
Modern aeroplane wings are not like sheets of paper but are more-or-less fixed in cross-section. A conventional subsonic section always has a strongly arching top. The underside may be fairly flat in slow aeroplanes, with the thickest part of the wing well forward (towards the "leading edge"). In fast aircraft the wing looks almost symmetrical, so that it would work either way up, and the thickest part is about half-way between the leading edge and trailing edge. In every case most of the lift is generated by reduced pressure as air curves faster over the top. A little lift is added by increased pressure underneath.

Factors affecting lift
For any given wing the lift depends on the angle of attack (the angle at which the wing meets the oncoming air). The greater the angle, the greater the lift – up to a point. Some modern aircraft with short but wide wing shapes, such as Concorde, can go on generating lift to seemingly impossible angles; but ordinary wings soon run into trouble. At an angle of about 16° there is little more lift to be had. By 18° the lift is erratic, the flow finds it hard to remain attached across the top of the wing and, suddenly, it breaks away. Instead of smooth, streamlined flow, the air billows away in great eddies. Lift is largely lost and any aircraft flown at such an angle of attack stalls [2].

Wing lift also depends on the square of the airspeed; lift at a given angle of attack may be 1,000kg at 100km/h, 4,000kg at 200km/h and 9,000kg at 300km/h. So how does an aeroplane take off? The pilot knows its gross weight, the airfield's height above sea-level and the air temperature (hot or high places have thinner air and give less lift). For each set of conditions he knows how fast the wing must move through the air in order that maximum lift (with a safe margin left to avoid stalling) shall exceed the weight. In all but the most simple aircraft the lift at low speeds can be greatly increased by extending flaps behind and below the trailing edge and, often, by using "Kreuger flaps" along the leading edge that serve to increase the curvature of the wing section. These devices change the apparent cross-section of the wing, making it act far more effectively on the airflow and greatly intensifying the difference in pressure between the underside and upper surface. At the correct speed the pilot

1 Control surfaces behave like miniature wings. These surfaces are: ailerons for roll [A] about the longitudinal axis, giving lateral control; elevators for pitch [B] about the lateral axis for longitudinal control; and a rudder for yaw [C] about the vertical axis for directional control. Each surface is hinged and is controlled from the cockpit. When deflected the surface's main effect is not to push the whole aircraft but to cause it to rotate about one of its axes. Sideways movement of the control column moves the left and right ailerons in opposite directions because, as one wing comes up the other must go down. Fore-and-aft movement of the stick deflects left and right elevators together because both act together in raising or lowering the tail for a dive or climb. In supersonic aircraft there are sometimes no ailerons and the left and right tailplanes can twist in opposite directions for roll control. The rudder is moved by foot pedals and one of the things a pupil pilot must learn is how to "harmonize" the various controls, working the stick and pedals together to just the right degree. In very large or fast aircraft, some or all of the control surfaces are hydraulically powered and an artificial "feel" is fed back to the pilot's controls in the cockpit.

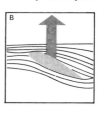

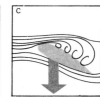

2 Stalling occurs when the angle at which the airflow meets the wing exceeds a critical value. At high speed [A] the angle is small. At lower speeds the nose must be pulled up more and more to maintain height [B]. Suddenly the aircraft stalls and a spin [C] may result.

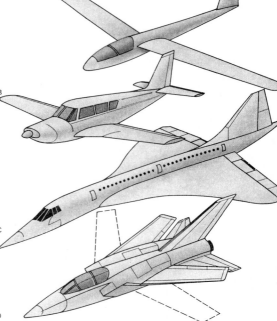

3 Wing shapes vary depending on their purpose. Sailplanes [A] and man-powered aircraft have long, narrow wings to optimize maximum lift and minimum drag at low speeds (80–145 km/h [50–90mph] for a high-performance glider). Light planes [B] have simple, thick wings that provide good lift at low speeds. A supersonic airliner [C] has a wing that is optimized for cruising at twice the speed of sound (Mach 2: 2,175 km/h [1,350mph]). It is rather like a Gothic window flying apex-first and is less efficient at take-off and landing. Supersonic combat aircraft [D] often need variable-sweep "swing wings" that can be folded back for operational flying or spread out sideways for cruising or "loitering".

pulls back on the control column [1]. This deflects the horizontal tail (elevators or, often, the whole tailplane) so that it is tilted sharply, with the leading edge pointing downwards. Immediately the airflow pushes the tail down, the whole aircraft "rotates", the wing reaches the angle at which lift exceeds weight and the aircraft climbs away.

Airborne control
As speed and height are gained the pilot "cleans up" the aircraft by retracting the various flaps. The wing can lift the aircraft without them and, as speed continues to increase, the angle of the wing becomes less and less and the aircraft levels out. At full speed the wing skims virtually edge-on to the airflow. But in any sudden manoeuvre, such as a tight turn, the wing has to generate vastly increased lift. In the most violent manoeuvres it is possible to reach stalling angle even at high speed. Normally a stall-warning system alerts the pilot of any approach to stall and this is especially important in thin air at great heights where wing angles are greater under all conditions. The "absolute ceiling"

that the aircraft can reach is, in fact, the altitude at which level flight demands the stalling angle even at maximum speed.

In straight and level cruising flight the control surfaces on the wings form an integral part of the lifting surface. Any movement of the cockpit controls deflects these surfaces or the tail rudder to make the aircraft rotate about one or more of its axes [1]. Roll and pitch commands are often needed; the rudder is used mainly in making a "co-ordinated" turn, with the nose of the aircraft moving left or right along the horizon, the wings tilted to give a lift force acting towards the centre of the turn and the rudder and elevators acting together. When landing the pilot places the aircraft in exactly the right position, aiming along the runway centreline, at such a speed that the wing (with all high-lift devices extended) reaches stalling angle just as the wheels make grazing contact with the runway. Many aircraft extend "spoilers" as they touch down to kill remaining lift. The same spoilers can be used with or instead of ailerons to produce roll motion in high-speed flight or as air brakes on a landing approach.

KEY

Streamlines (paths of particles of air) show airflow over a wing [1] giving lift [2]. The airflow rises across the leading edge [3], arches across the top of the wing and leaves travel- | ling sharply downwards. When high-lift devices such as leading edge slats and trailing edge flaps are extended, the effect is accentuated and the airflow over the wing | almost resembles an upside-down U. Designers try to achieve the highest possible ratio of lift to drag (aerodynamic resistance) by choosing the correct form of wing.

4 Aircraft propulsion is tailored for the job. The piston engine [A] is cheap and efficient for slow aircraft. The turboprop [B] also handles a huge airflow but it is better suited to larger aircraft. | Turbofans [C–E] are best for aircraft that fly at high subsonic speeds, such as airliners. In [C] the fan at the front of the engine displaces air round the main engine. In [D] several fans force air along by- | passes and into the tailpipe. Turbofan E has an afterburner. Extra fuel is injected to burn in the tailpipe and so provide more power. But it is noisy and generally used only for highly supersonic aircraft.

4 A

B

C

D

E

5 Vertical take-off and landing (VTOL) designs have included the HS 141, with lift jets for vertical take-off [1]; the propulsion turbofans started [2] and the lift engines shut off [3]. It was never built. The CL-84 had two turboprops on a | tilt-wing set at 90° for take-off [4]; the wing slowly rotated [5] and then completely straightened [6]. The Harrier has a directional thrust engine blasting downwards for take-off [7]; the nozzles then rotate for acceleration into | wing-lifted flight [8, 9]. The DHC 7, a short take-off and landing (STOL) machine, has four turboprops blowing across flapped wings, which deflect the slipstream down for take-off [10] before the aircraft levels out [11].

5

HS 141

CL-84

Harrier

DHC 7

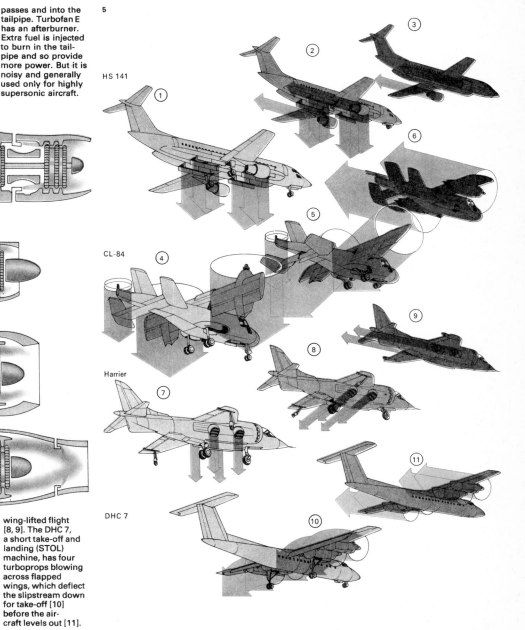

Helicopters and autogyros

The conventional aircraft copes efficiently with its main task, the moving of people and cargo from one point to another. But it is limited because it cannot hover above the ground to lift or set down an object in one precise position and it cannot land on ground too uneven for the building of an airstrip. For difficult terrain, and difficult jobs, a helicopter is needed.

Helicopters in history
All heavier-than-air flying machines stay in the air using the principle known as lift. As an ordinary fixed-wing aeroplane moves quickly through the air the shape of the wings makes the air pressure below them greater than that above. The difference in pressure "lifts" the aircraft and enables it to fly. If the wings can be made to rotate instead of being fixed, lift can be obtained without the machine itself moving forwards. This is the principle on which a hovering machine works.

The principle has been known for a long time. Leonardo da Vinci (1452–1519) sketched a design for a rotating-wing machine [Key] and dubbed it *helix pteron*,

which is Greek for "spiral wing". The name is in use today in slightly changed form in the word "helicopter".

No helicopter could fly until an engine could be made sufficiently light and powerful. With the development of the petrol engine about 1900, the power problem was solved and full-scale helicopters just managed to become airborne. These first rotating-wing machines ran into stability problems and test pilots were reluctant to try them out unless the machines were tethered. The problem of keeping a hovering machine aloft without tilting proved very difficult to solve and yet deliberate tilting proved to be necessary to enable the machine to fly in a particular direction.

Tilting a windmill
In 1923 the Spanish inventor Juan de la Cierva (1896–1936) successfully flew a machine that was a strange hybrid between a helicopter and a fixed-wing aircraft [4]. It had wings and a propeller, but it also had a freewheeling rotor on top. As the machine flew, the motion of the air past the rotor

whirled the blades like a windmill and provided extra lift, enabling it to fly slowly and to take off with a short run. Cierva called it the "Autogiro", from the way the blades automatically gyrated as it flew. This effect is called auto-rotation and it can enable a helicopter to land safely if it loses power.

A most versatile machine
By World War II the helicopter had been perfected, due principally to the work of Igor Sikorsky (1889–1972) [5], an American of Russian origin. One of the main difficulties was torque – as the engine turned the rotor in one direction, it also turned the body of the helicopter in the opposite direction. Torque is a consequence of action and reaction and has been overcome in two main ways. Either a small vertical rotor, fitted to the tail of the helicopter, acts as a propeller to oppose the torque or the helicopter has two horizontal main rotors that spin in opposite directions, thus cancelling out the torque. By adjusting the tilt of the various rotors the helicopter can be held steady or made to turn. Another solution to the problem of torque is to power the

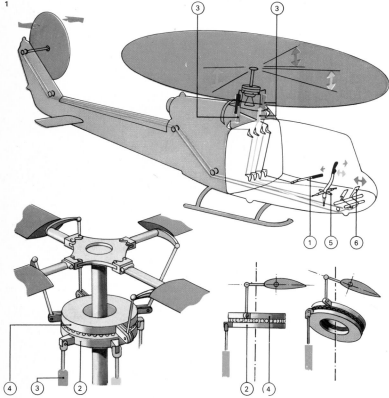

1

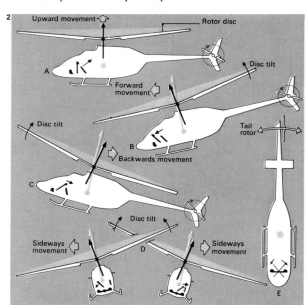

2

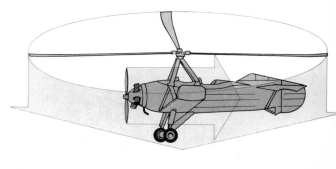

2 Vertical and hovering flight occurs when the axis of rotation of the rotor is in line with the centre of gravity [A]. Moving the collective pitch stick increases or decreases lift. Pushing the cyclic pitch stick forwards tilts the rotor disc (the space swept out by the blades) forwards and moves the helicopter forwards [B]. Pulling the stick back [C] makes the helicopter move backwards and pushing it to the right or left enables it to "crab" sideways [D]. The tail rotor is controlled by the rudder bars [E]. This swings the helicopter round in order to allow the pilot to change the direction of flight.

1 A tail-rotor helicopter has a cyclic pitch stick [1] that operates jacks [3]; these tilt the lower swashplate [2]. The upper swashplate [4] also tilts, tilting the main rotor to propel the helicopter. The collective pitch stick [5] raises or lowers the swashplates, thus changing the pitch of the rotor blades and altering the lift of the main rotor. The foot pedals [6] change the pitch of the tail rotor blades, swinging the helicopter round.

3

3 Rescue is a task at which the helicopter excels. Injured mountaineers, shipwrecked sailors, stranded tourists and flood and earthquake victims often owe their lives to helicopters.

4 The autogyro was designed by Juan de la Cierva in order to make flying safer. The free-wheeling rotor (as well as the wings) provided lift. The propeller produced forward motion. Ironically, Cierva himself was killed in an aeroplane crash.

rotor by having a jet engine at the tip of each blade; the blade's motion is the reaction to the jet's thrust and no torque occurs. A small ram jet may be used or exhaust air ducts may be connected to a gas turbine in the body of the helicopter.

Once stable in the air, a helicopter can fly easily in any direction. The rotor produces a downwash of air and the reaction to this downwash forces the machine upwards. If the lifting force equals the weight of the helicopter, then the craft remains stationary in the air. If the lifting force is lessened by slowing the rotor or if the angle at which the blades sweep through the air is changed, the machine descends. If the rotor is tilted slightly as it whirls, part of the downwash of air is directed to one side and the helicopter moves in the opposite direction.

Forward speed, however, is not very great and manufacturers are experimenting with aircraft that have the manoeuvrability of the helicopter and the speed of the fixed-wing machine. Winged aircraft with tilting rotors that can face upwards or forwards are being tried, although the use of jet engines with swivelling exhausts has so far been more successful in aircraft such as the Harrier "jump-jet".

Helicopters are used for passenger transport – for example, as a rapid service between airports and city centres and to link islands without airstrips. But helicopters are expensive to buy and to run and thus have generally failed to compete economically with other forms of passenger transport. They are used mainly in special applications for which no other machine would be suitable. Only helicopters can be used for many kinds of rescue work [3] – to lift people trapped in burning buildings, to rescue sailors from shipwrecks or holiday-makers swept out to sea and to remove people from areas devastated by earthquakes or floods. Helicopters are invaluable for transferring both workers and materials to remote places and are also used as cranes to hoist heavy objects into position on top of buildings – some modern churches have their spires placed in this way. The flexibility of the helicopter also makes it a versatile war machine for carrying men and weapons, and for hunting submarines.

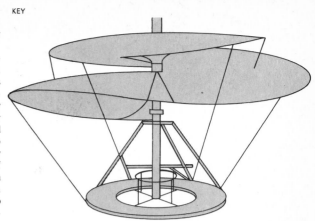

Leonardo da Vinci made this design in 1483 for a rotating-wing aircraft. The spiral wing, which Leonardo suggested should be made of starched linen, would have lifted the machine in much the same way as the rotor of a helicopter. But it is certain that Leonardo's machine never flew. There was no engine in existence that was capable of powering the device and even if there had been it would have spun wildly out of control, for Leonardo did not realize that the engine would also rotate the body in the opposite direction to the wing. This turning effect is known as torque.

5 The VS-300, built by Igor Sikorsky, was the first practical helicopter. It first flew in about 1939, but went through many modifications before being perfected. At one stage it could fly in every direction except forwards. These problems were overcome by 1941 and production models were tested in World War II. Its single main rotor and small tail rotor became the predominant helicopter design.

6 A twin-rotor helicopter achieves twice as much lift as a single-rotor machine with a similar rotor. The Soviet Mi-12 is the world's largest helicopter. Built by Mikhail Mil, it set a world record in 1969 by lifting 40 tonnes to a height of more than 2,000m (6,560ft). It has a span of 67m (220ft) across its rotors, which spin in opposite directions. The Mi-12 is a transport aircraft.

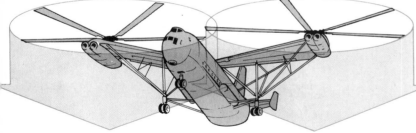

7 A tandem helicopter has twin rotors mounted one behind the other. The first tandem helicopter, the "Flying Banana", was built by American engineer Frank Piasecki in 1945. Such helicopters can be made large enough to serve as passenger vehicles or troop transports. Other twin-rotor machines have side-by-side rotors intermeshing like an eggbeater, or coaxial rotors one above the other.

8 A "flying crane" lifts a heavy field gun during army manoeuvres. Such operations are quick and dispense with the need for towing vehicles. Standard helicopters are useful for carrying freight and some interesting tasks have been proposed for the most powerful machines. They could rapidly unload containers from ships offshore and do away with the need for deep harbours. Another idea envisages the carrying of a Sky-lounge – a bus-like vehicle that would gather passengers in a city and then be lifted by helicopter straight to the door of an aircraft at the airport. Flying cranes are particularly useful in wartime for retrieving aircraft that have crashed but are not beyond repair.

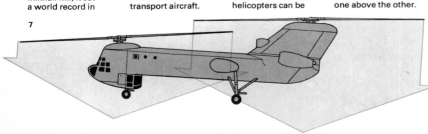

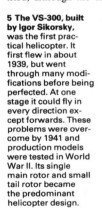

Space vehicles

Since the Soviet Sputnik 1 was launched on 4 October 1957 several nations have between them launched hundreds of artificial satellites into orbit round the Earth. The United States and the Soviet Union have sent exploratory "probes" to orbit or soft-land on the Moon, Mars and Venus. Other planets have been studied at close quarters using unmanned space vehicles. The greatest achievement was probably the landing of men on the Moon during the American Apollo programme and there is good reason to suppose that by the end of the twentieth century the whole Solar System will have been explored – but by unmanned probes.

Getting into space

The use of vehicles to explore space dates from the development of rockets powerful enough to launch the vehicles and enable them to "escape" from the Earth's gravity [Key]. This requires a velocity of 11.2km per second (approximately 40,000km/h or 25,000mph), which is technically known as the Earth's escape velocity.

To reach such speeds, multi-stage rockets are employed. These make use of the piggy-back principle [1] – the rocket entering orbit is fired at the edge of the atmosphere, having been carried there on top of another rocket that, in turn, may also have been lifted on an even more powerful first-stage rocket. This technique of overcoming gravity was first proposed by the Russian pioneer of rocketry Konstantin Tsiolkovsky (1857–1935). In 1949 an American multi-stage rocket sent a vehicle up to a height of more than 390km (242 miles) above the surface of the Earth.

Rockets and satellites

All rockets are reaction motors. They work using the principle of Newton's third law of motion which, describing the behaviour of any moving object, states that action and reaction are equal and opposite.

In a rocket the "action" is the escape of hot gases roaring out of the tail; the "reaction" to this action forces the body of the rocket in the other direction. The principle can be demonstrated by blowing up a balloon and releasing it; the action of the jet of air escaping from the neck of the balloon is balanced by an equal and opposite reaction that pushes the balloon through the air. For this reason a rocket will work in the airless near vacuum of outer space; it does not, like a jet engine, require a supply of air for the burning of fuel. The presence of air is actually a handicap because it sets up a resistance to the rocket's motion.

The fuel in a firework rocket is a solid propellant explosive such as gunpowder. But solid fuels are too weak and uncontrollable to be used alone in space rockets. Instead two liquids are used – a fuel and an oxidant. When mixed in a combustion chamber they react together to produce hot gases that are expelled from the exhaust and create thrust. The first successful liquid-fuelled rockets were made in the United States in 1926 by Robert Goddard (1882–1945). By the time of Goddard's death German scientists, led by Wernher von Braun (1912–77), had developed the V2. This was a liquid-fuelled rocket that carried a one-tonne explosive warhead and was the direct ancestor of modern space rockets. After World War II, von Braun and his colleagues went to the

---

1 Multi-stage rockets consist of a number of smaller rockets combined to make one big one. At the start of the flight the large, lower stage is used; here it accounts for 83.3 per cent of the prop-ellant but acceler-ates the rocket to only 33 per cent of its final velocity. When it has used up its fuel, it drops away and the second stage takes over. Only the third stage goes into orbit.

2,542m
127,868m
922
118,420kg
4,489m/sec
481,441kg
71,526m
2,972m/sec
2,283,034kg

3rd stage
2nd stage
1st stage

2 The American Van-guard rocket was launched in 1958 in the early days of space research. Rockets were not reliable but this craft was a major American success, with a minute payload.

3 The Soviet "Moon crawler" Lunokhod 1 [A] was taken to the Moon by a Luna rock-et probe; after landing it was sent down a ramp [B] on to the surface. Lunokhod 1 landed upon the grey plain of the Mare Imbrium and crawled along for months, controlled from the USSR, sending back invaluable data. A second Lunokhod operated in the Mare Serenitatis near the landing site of the Apollo 17 module.

4 Since 1957 hundreds of space probes have been launched. The Soviet Cos-mos vehicles [A] are artificial satellites, brought back to Earth after limited flight times. Mariner 9 [B] went into Mars orbit in late 1971. Continuing well into 1972 it sent back detailed photo-graphs of the Martian landscape. The first probe launched by the Soviet Union to Venus [C] was not a success.

United States to continue with their work.

Sputnik 1 was the size of a football and carried little apart from a radio transmitter. Some of today's satellites are the size of a large truck. They have been used in many ways: for mapping [7], communications and scientific research into phenomena impossible to study properly from the ground because of the Earth's atmosphere. Communications satellites have evolved from the early passive type, which consisted of a "silvered" balloon that acted like a mirror to reflect radio signals beamed up to it back down to Earth, to the modern active satellites that amplify received radio signals before re-transmitting them.

Manned satellites have now become relatively common and in 1973 Skylab was placed into orbit as the first true space station. Docking procedures have also been carried out between two spacecraft; in 1975 an American vehicle docked with a Soviet one, the first such meeting between traditional rivals in space. All such manoeuvres require precise information about orbits and velocities. This is provided by radar sets on the craft and on Earth and the necessary complex calculations are carried out using computers suitably programmed for their task.

Probes to the Moon and planets

The first target for unmanned space probes was the Moon. In 1959 the Soviet Luna 3 made a circumlunar voyage and subsequently the whole of the Moon's surface was mapped by automatic probes. Soft landings on the surface were also made [3] and mechanical fingers used to collect dust and rock.

The lunar probes were followed by the first attempts to explore the planets. In 1962 the American Mariner 2 made a fly-by pass of Venus and vehicles have since been sent to Mars, Mercury and Jupiter. By 1975 a Soviet probe had soft-landed on Venus and in the same year a vehicle was on its way to Saturn. The American Vikings made soft landings on Mars in 1976.

Vast amounts of invaluable information have been collected. Telescopes and spectrometers in space vehicles aid Earth-bound astronomers. And infra-red photographs of Earth can reveal new resources.

All space vehicles are put into orbit or sent on their journeys to the Moon, other planets and beyond by powerful rockets.

This rocket launched the American Mars probe Mariner 9 in 1971, carried in the top part of the launcher. It was the first probe to be put into a close path round Mars and transmitted back to Earth thousands of high-quality pictures.

5 Various paths for space probes can be drawn assuming that the vehicles are fired horizontally from the top of a tall tower reaching above the Earth's atmosphere. At low velocity [1] the vehicle soon falls back to the ground. With greater velocity [2] the vehicle travels farther before landing. But with orbital velocity [3] it does not land at all and enters a closed and stable orbit.

6 Satellites may travel in orbits of various kinds [A]. Some move in the plane of the Equator [1], others have inclined orbits [2] and some use polar orbits [3]. For a "stationary" satellite of the Syncom communications type [B] the period is exactly one day. Its distance from Earth is 35,900km (22,300 miles); it appears stationary and is ideal for television relays.

7 An orbiting satellite is better for photographing the Earth than is an aircraft. One exposure from a space vehicle [A] can cover an area that would need hundreds of photographs from an aircraft [B].

The whole area can be shown with greater accuracy and detail. Also, a vertical space photograph does not have the distortion inherent in aerial mosaics of a wide area. Aerial photographs require lengthy and specialized processing to make them into a mosaic map, whereas this task is greatly reduced using space photographs. Any necessary revisions can therefore be made more easily.

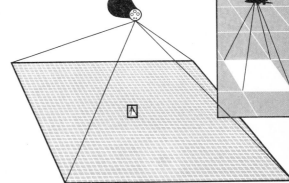

8 A comparison of space and aerial photography clearly shows the far superior structural definition of the former. The Richat craters in Mauritania, West Africa [A], probably of volcanic origin, are well defined in the photograph from the orbiting Apollo 9 vehicle. A mosaic of aerial photographs of the same area is shown in [B]. The Apollo photograph clearly reveals previously unrecorded features including depressions up to 1,500m (nearly 1 mile) across.

Man in space

Yuri Gagarin (1934–68) of the Soviet air force was the first man in space. In April 1961 – less than four years after the launch of the first artificial satellite, Sputnik 1 – he made a complete circuit of the Earth in Vostok 1, above the bulk of the atmosphere. before landing safely in a prearranged area.

Gagarin and zero gravity
Gagarin's flight was a truly pioneering venture. Nobody at that time had any real idea of how the human body would react to a prolonged period of weightlessness. Yet during his flight Gagarin experienced conditions of zero gravity – something that cannot be simulated on Earth for more than a brief period.

Zero gravity [1] does not mean that the orbiting astronaut has completely escaped the pull of the Earth's gravity. The best way to picture it is to think of a book placed on a piece of card: the book presses on the card and with reference to it the book is "heavy". If both are then dropped the pressure of book on card ceases; the two objects move in the same direction at the same rate.

The same situation occurs when an astronaut is inside his vehicle; the two move at the same rate so that the passenger does not press down upon his craft and "weight" vanishes. (His mass – the quantity of matter in his body – does not change.)

Gagarin found that zero gravity was neither inconvenient nor unpleasant. This has been confirmed by all later space travellers although "walking" in space [4, 5] is extremely exhausting. The first man to venture outside an orbiting vehicle was the Russian cosmonaut Alexei Leonov, and this has since been repeated many times by both Americans and Russians.

Americans in space
The first American in space was Alan Shepard, who made a sub-orbital flight lasting for about 15 minutes in May 1961. In the 1960s manned satellites carrying two or three astronauts were sent up and there were elaborate docking operations in which two independent spacecraft were skilfully manoeuvred together and joined.

One initial difficulty facing international docking was that American and Soviet designs differed because their space programmes had been developed independently of each other. But following the success of the US Skylab space station plans were made for a joint exercise and this was accomplished with the Apollo-Soyuz mission in 1975. Both vehicles had been suitably modified – the Soviet cosmonauts generally breathe ordinary air at normal pressure, for example, whereas the Americans prefer pure oxygen at reduced pressure. For the joint mission a special "adaptation chamber" had to be set up between the two control cabins.

During manned flights many experiments are carried out. The Earth can be closely studied and there have been vast improvements in man's knowledge of the circulation of the atmosphere, which should bring better weather forecasting; plant and mineral resources can be assessed; and nearly all other sciences can benefit.

Predicted space-flight dangers from meteoroids (solid particles moving in space), cosmic radiation and weightlessness have failed to materialize. On the other hand mechanical mishap both on Earth and in

1 Free fall is the condition of weightlessness or zero gravity. [A] shows an astronaut training in a flying aircraft. In [1] he is experiencing normal gravity; in [2] the plane is put into a curving dive that simulates the free-fall state for a very brief period; in [3] he takes to a pressure couch to counter the extra g force as the aircraft levels off. [B] shows how, in an orbiting capsule, gravitational pull (mg) is balanced by centrifugal force (mv^2/r) to produce zero gravity (m = mass; r = radius of orbit; v = velocity and g = acceleration due to gravity).

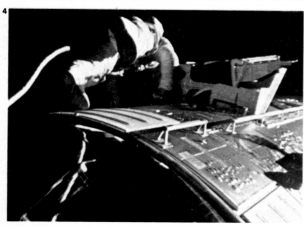

2 **The Gemini programme** followed the first US manned programme (Mercury). Gemini 7, shown here, was able like her sisters to carry two men, could conduct docking procedures and allowed for "spacewalking".

3 **Apollo 15's command and service modules** were photographed by lunar module pilot David Scott. At this time the probe was orbiting the Moon above the Sea of Fertility (Mare Fecundatis).

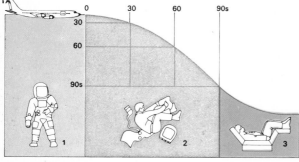

4 **Astronaut Alfred M. Worden** spacewalked outside Apollo 15 on the return trip; he recovered film equipment that had been used earlier. At the Moon he did not go to the surface with Jim Irwin and David Scott but remained in orbit in the Apollo command module.

5 **Astronaut Edward White** carried out the first US spacewalk in 1965 during the Gemini programme. (The first spacewalk ever was made by the Russian Leonov earlier in 1965.) Astronauts outside a craft do not drift away but remain in the self-same orbit. White was later killed in the fire at Cape Kennedy that destroyed a capsule under test.

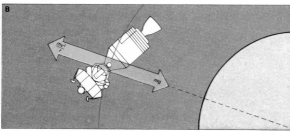

space is a danger and there have been deaths of both Americans and Russians. Manned flights to the Moon have so far been the preserve of the Americans; Russians have concentrated on automatic exploration.

The Apollo programme [6–9], initiated in the early 1960s, reached its climax with the Apollo vehicles of 1968 and 1969. During the Christmas period of 1968 Frank Borman, James Lovell and William Anders orbited the Moon in Apollo 8. In the following year the lunar module was tested close to the Moon's surface. Finally in July 1969 Neil Armstrong and Edwin Aldrin landed on the waterless Sea of Tranquillity. The gap between Earth and Moon had finally been bridged by man.

Inherent problems of Moon missions

The fuel problem is such that it is not yet possible to send a single-stage vehicle to the Moon and back. The initial launching is by step-vehicle; the command and service modules combine then travel to the neighbourhood of the Moon and enter closed orbit. Next, two of the astronauts make the final descent in the lunar module, the only func-

tion of which is to shuttle its crew from the main spacecraft to the Moon's surface and back. Nevertheless, the procedure has its dangers. The explorers depend entirely on the ascent engine of their lunar module; if this fails there can be no chance of rescue for the men on the surface.

All the landings made so far have fortunately been successful. The only in-flight failure came when an explosion aboard Apollo 13 on the outward journey put the main propulsion unit out of action. The astronauts were forced to use the motors of the lunar module to pass round the Moon and return safely to Earth.

Apollos 11 and 12, and 14 to 17 have made great progress in lunar study. ALSEPs (Apollo Lunar Surface Experimental Packages) have been set up and are still operating. During the last three journeys the astronauts were able to drive across the surface in lunar rovers or Moon cars. Yet the Apollo system was limited in scope: before men can go to the Moon in large numbers there must be provision for rescue, and this may not be possible for another 15 years at the earliest.

An astronaut's eye-view of Earth taken by an Apollo crewman *en route* for the Moon shows both North Africa and Arabia. There is considerable cloudcover – but a great part of the Earth was still visible to the astronauts.

6 Command and service modules of Apollo 16 orbited the Moon in 1972. Below lay the inhospitable lunar surface with several well-defined craters. The photograph was taken from the lunar module which carried astronauts Charles Duke and John Young to the Moon's surface.

7 Lunar rover vehicles (LRVs) considerably extend the area of exploration for astronauts on the Moon. Charles Duke is seen here with the LRV of Apollo 16, near the peak that was soon unofficially named Stone Mountain. In the background the bright rays are from South Ray Crater.

8 The first Moon landing was made from Apollo 11 in July 1969. Edwin Aldrin stands on the lunar surface filmed by Neil Armstrong who was first to descend the ladder from the lunar module. The entire mission – and the "Moon walk" – was shown on TV.

9 Hadley Delta, one of the peaks of the lunar Apennines, forms the background for David Scott and the Apollo 15 LRV. It is farther from Scott than it looks – the distance is more than 30km (19 miles). On the Moon there is no atmospheric scattering so distances can be deceptive and the sky is always black. The US flag does not flutter on its pole since the Moon has no wind – the fabric has to be wired to make it stand out.

10 The ascent motor of the lunar module worked perfectly on each occasion that an Apollo craft left the Moon – this is the view from Apollo 15. Yet this was the weakest link in the entire programme. If for any reason the ascent engine failed there could be no hope of rescue; it is not likely that men will return to the Moon until rescue provision is made. The ALSEPs left on the lunar surface are powered by solar cells and are still functioning.

Earth-moving machines

Building Iron Age forts, digging canals, making railways and constructing modern motorways have all required the shifting of hundreds of tonnes of soil. As a result, from the Iron Age to the present day men have devised various machines for moving earth.

One of the earliest earth-moving machines was the wheelbarrow, developed in China before 118 AD. The Chinese version had a large wheel 1m (39in) or more across with the load carried above and at the sides of the wheel. The early European wheelbarrow, similar in style to that used today, had a fairly small wheel and the load was carried between it and the handles. Using only wheelbarrows, picks and shovels to assist them, the navvies (short for "navigators") built the whole system of European canals and many of the early railways [Key].

Modern earth-moving machines

Wheelbarrows are still used on small-scale building projects, but today's civil engineers can choose from many specialized earth-moving machines. The digger or excavator was one of the first of these and a mechanical

digger was an early nineteenth-century application of the steam engine.

Today there is a wide range of excavator designs, each suited to a particular task. The dragline excavator, for example, has crawler tracks for moving over uneven or soft ground [3]. The digging bucket is suspended from a jib and after scooping up its load is winched back to be dumped. The size of the "bite" taken by the bucket has to suit the material being excavated. So for soft earth and for moving existing stockpiles of earthy minerals, such as crushed ore, a light bucket is used. A medium-weight bucket is employed for general digging duties, but for deep digging, or in rocky terrain, heavy buckets are essential to give enough penetration and prevent undue wear. In all these operations, the digging action occurs as the bucket is dragged back along the ground after being dropped from the end of the jib.

For size and capacity the largest bucket-wheel excavators [2] are among the world's greatest engineering achievements. They belong to the largest of self-propelled land machines and can be used for rapid

excavating or for shifting vast quantities of loose material such as crushed ores or coal. They can move up to 10,000 cubic metres (354,000 cubic feet) of material in an hour.

Dredgers are merely floating excavators used for keeping docks, harbours and river channels free from mud and silt. They can also be used for "mining" underwater, to scoop up sand and gravel and other minerals. They have boat-like hulls, which may be passive and thus have to be towed to the site of operation, or fully powered and equipped with the necessary machinery to travel in the open sea. They have diesel engines that drive the machinery directly or power a generator to supply electric motors.

There are three main types of dredgers: bucket dredgers [6], grab and dipper dredgers and suction dredgers [7]. Bucket dredgers have an endless chain of buckets, on the conveyor belt system, that scoop up material from the bottom. A grab and dipper dredger has either a mechanical shovel (the dipper) pivoted at the end of a boom or a "clamshell" (the grab) for excavating materials in bulk. Most grab and dipper dredgers have a

1 A hydraulic shovel has rams hinged at the base of the bucket. By skilfully controlling these rams, the driver is able to excavate material without having to move the machine forwards. For speed of operation a machine may have a crawler hull so that it can swing round to dump into a truck parked behind it in a maximum of 15 seconds.

2 A digging-wheel excavator, with a scoop-tipped wheel up to 20m (66ft) across, can shift many cubic metres of soft material on to its internal conveyor belt. It is particularly useful for shifting dumps of powdered minerals such as china clay or coal-dust.

3 A dragline excavator, which is a kind of revolving shovel with a long boom, is ideal for stripping the topsoil, called over-burden, from near-surface deposits of coal and other minerals. With very long booms, the bucket must be light or the machine must have a counterweight.

4 A shovel dozer, designed for digging and loading, can also be used for moving "spoil" over short distances. The crawler-mounted type can have a bucket holding up to 4 cu metres (140 cu ft) of soil. Special attachments allow the machine to lift and remove rocks and tree stumps.

pair of metal legs, called "spuds", which are lowered to the bottom to stabilize the craft. Suction dredgers work like giant vacuum cleaners and use powerful pumps to suck sludge up from the bottom.

Shovels and dozers

The workhorse of land-based earth-moving equipment is the mechanical shovel, often known today as a hydraulic loader [1]. It may have crawler tracks or wheels (with two-wheel or four-wheel drive). The crawler version can turn in very confined spaces – even in its own length – but the wheeled loaders travel much more quickly. In both the usual cycle of operation consists of loading the excavator bucket, travelling to a heap of "spoil" or to a dumper truck, dumping and travelling back to the excavation position.

The dumper trucks, also essential machines in a modern operation, have a capacity of 20 tonnes or more. Even so, several may have to be used to keep pace with a giant excavator.

If the soil or other material does not have to be moved too far it can be pushed to its new site by a bulldozer or carried there by the hybrid machine known as a shovel dozer. An angledozer merely pushes the material to one side. A shovel dozer [4] can use tracks or wheels, depending on the site. It can dig, load and transport "spoil".

Scrapers and graders

For building level, modern roads the specialized earth-movers employed are scrapers and graders. A scraper may be self-propelled or pulled by a tractor [5]. It has a knife-like cutter that planes off a layer of soil into an internal reservoir called a bowl; this can hold up to 40 cubic metres (1,413 cubic feet) of soil. The depth of cut is controlled by hydraulic rams and the machine can transport its load to a nearby site for dumping. The "spoil" is dumped – gradually or in one lot – by moving the rear tailgate.

For precise finishing of the earth road foundation before concreting, a machine called a grader is used. It has an angled blade 2–4m (7–13ft) wide hydraulically controlled and slung between its wheels. Most of these finishing machines are self-propelled.

In the early days of railways, cuttings were largely excavated by hand; picks and shovels were used to dig out the soil and wheelbarrows to cart it away. The 3km (2 mile) Tring Cutting between London and Birmingham was dug in 1838. Horses pulled the loaded barrows up planks laid up the sloping sides of the cutting, but navvies had the dangerous job of guiding the barrows. Inevitably, accidents were frequent.

5 A scraper is one of the key machines in modern road-building projects. Self-powered or hauled by a tractor, large ones can carry 100 cu metres (3,500 cu ft) of soil. For extra power, a second diesel engine may be mounted at the rear. It is this massive power that enables the scraper blade under the machine to skim off layers of earth and force them back into the body or "bowl" of the machine. The heights of the scraper and of the tailgate, which is lifted or slid aside to release the load, are controlled by hydraulic rams, also powered by the main engines. All scrapers have huge tyred wheels to cross uneven ground.

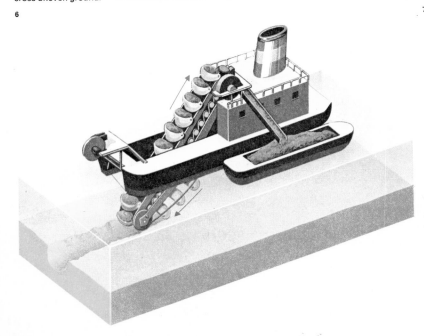

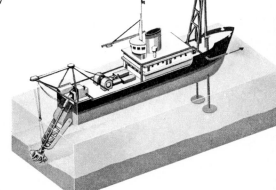

6 A bucket dredger has an endless chain of buckets that scoop up sludgy material from the bottom of the sea or river. The "spoil" is automatically tipped into a discharge chute and into a barge moored alongside or, when working in a dock, directly into a dumper truck. Most bucket dredgers have no engines and therefore have to be towed into position by tugs, although self-propelled ones are sometimes used for excavating canal banks or other confined areas.

7 A suction dredger has powerful pumps that suck up the "spoil" in the form of a watery mud called slurry. Any hard material is broken up by high-pressure water jets or cutters. Most suction dredgers are self-propelled and can move to dump.

Moving heavy loads

Ordinary cranes, used in the construction industry or for loading ships, can lift weights of up to 200 tonnes. But consider the following problems: a prefabricated 1,500-tonne section of a ship (such as the whole superstructure or the front part of the bow) has to be placed in its final position [2]; a 6,000-tonne rocket has to be moved 5km (3 miles) to its launching site [3]; a 7,000-tonne section of a stadium has to be placed in a new position [4]. Each of these involves moving a heavy load, and each has been solved.

What are heavy loads?

The ability to move heavy loads is increasingly important to the engineering industries because the cost-saving of building assemblies on a specific site before moving them to their final places is now accepted. But prefabricated structures are becoming larger and heavier. As new load-moving techniques have been developed, other industries have assessed their usefulness and have had to adopt them.

The word "heavy" is arbitrary, but for these purposes it includes loads ranging from hundreds of tonnes to tens of thousands of tonnes. Moving heavy loads has presented engineers with problems for thousands of years. Many suggestions have been put forward as to how stone was moved in the building of the pyramids and Stonehenge. Certainly a method using tree trunks as rollers would have been known at that period of history and animal or human power could have provided the motive force.

Man started with the lever and soon discovered the arrangements of the moving force, the load and the fulcrum (pivot) that would be most useful in particular applications. Archimedes [Key] is reputed to have claimed, "Give me a firm place on which to stand and I will move the earth". He realized that to use a long lever to gain a mechanical advantage would mean that a small movement of the load could be obtained with a large movement of the applied force.

The problems involved

Moving heavy loads has always involved two different problems: how to reduce the friction underneath the load and how to provide sufficient force to overcome the friction remaining once the load is moving. To reduce friction, rolling logs were used and later wheels of various types. Grease was also applied to ease the movement of the load, particularly in the shipbuilding industry. More recently various "slippery" plastic coatings, such as polytetrafluorethylene (PTFE), have been used, as well as air and water cushions that operate like hovercraft.

There are two kinds of friction involved in moving anything. Static or stationary friction has to be overcome to start something moving and dynamic or moving friction opposes its continued movement. The coefficient of friction between two materials is defined as the ratio of the force required to move the load to the weight of the load. Static and dynamic coefficients have wide ranges. These maximum values drop between the traditional slippery slope of steel on greased steel (used for ship launching) from 0.25 and 0.17, down to 0.10 and 0.05 for steel on PTFE plastic. (They have already been halved.) The values fall to 0.01 for air-bearing systems.

1 The idea of reducing friction below a heavy load was known to prehistoric man. Examples include the large stones that were used in the building of Stonehenge [A] on Salisbury Plain in England, probably moved with logs underneath the stones acting as rollers [B]. As the load moved forwards, the logs would be removed from the back and brought round to the front. Large diameter logs would not fall into small ruts and long logs would reduce the ground loading. The motive force could be direct man or animal power, but levers could have been used to roll the logs. Very large loads can be moved in this way.

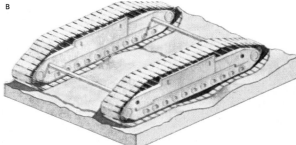

2 The principles of multiple pulley blocks and their use for gaining mechanical advantage has been known for centuries. If the blocks are threaded with a single rope, then a count of the number of lines effectively supporting the load gives the gain. In [A] a gain of six is shown. Nearly every crane system uses this technique. A disadvantage of the technique is that a great length of hauling rope must be winched in to achieve only a small movement of the load. Extremely large portal cranes [B] can lift 1,500 tonnes and are now used in shipyards throughout the world.

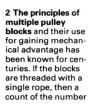

3 The caterpillar crawler mechanically transfers linked plates from the back to the front for the load to roll over them [B]. By increasing link width, ground loading is reduced. The motive force is also supplied through the wheels and track. This technique was chosen to transport the 6,000-tonne US Saturn rocket and launcher [A].

The use of friction-reducing systems can introduce further difficulties. Loads of thousands of tonnes, once they have started moving, also have to be stopped. For this reason, when coefficients of friction are low, suitable braking systems must be incorporated. After a ship is launched, strong chains and cables are needed to stop it.

Any conventional system can be used for motive power, providing that it can overcome the frictional forces that remain. When large cranes such as portal cranes [2] are used to move a load from one point to another, they are merely lifting the load to reduce the coefficient of friction between it and the ground. This means that stresses are then put into the ground at chosen points, which have previously been strengthened.

Strengthening the surface
A third difficulty concerns the amount of preparation required for the surface on which the load is to be moved. This involves a calculation of the maximum permissible ground loading. For many materials this quantity is known – for example, compacted gravel will withstand a ground loading of 33 tonnes per square metre and wet sand 5.5 tonnes per square metre. At greater loadings than these the gravel or sand "collapses" and the load sinks in. The loading is a pressure – a weight on a given area – and for a given load increasing the area of contact obviously lowers the pressure. This is why snow-shoes support a man on loose snow whereas in ordinary boots he would sink.

In most heavy load-moving techniques there must be a way of spreading point loads. But even this is not a complete answer to ground-loading limitations. A hovercraft or air-cushion system that can carry loads over water has been known slowly to bury itself in dry sand as the sand is blown out from underneath the load.

It rapidly becomes clear that there is no universal way of moving a variety of loads over various surfaces for different applications. The answers to the problems illustrated here are merely a few modern solutions – a portal crane to lift a ship structure, caterpillar crawlers to move the Saturn rocket and air-cushion units to move the stadium stands.

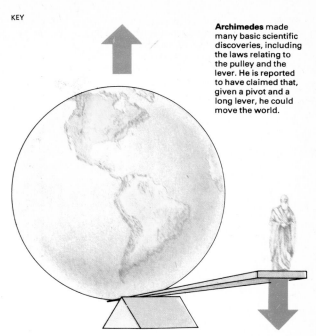

Archimedes made many basic scientific discoveries, including the laws relating to the pulley and the lever. He is reported to have claimed that, given a pivot and a long lever, he could move the world.

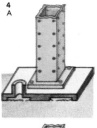
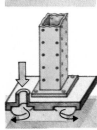

4 **The air-cushion technique** uses high air pressure underneath a load to lift the load slightly so that air can escape [A]. This continually escaping air acts as a bearing for the load and very low coefficients of friction can be obtained. The loading is spread over the area of the cushion. The Ohau Stadium in Hawaii was designed so that the stands could be moved from a rectangular shape [B] for football to a diamond shape [C] for baseball. The air-cushion system was chosen because it reduces friction. Problems on the smooth surface have arisen because of wind loadings and slopes that could cause the loads to run away. Movable friction grippers are used for braking.

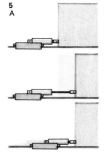

5 **Hydraulic jacks** can move extremely large loads, such as this 4,000-tonne ship section [B], if they have reaction points. Hydranautic gripper jacks provide these by using hydraulic forces to give grip as well as push [A]. The sequence shows the grippers being pulled up behind the load and repeatedly locked into position.

6 **The walking beam** uses two "footprints" which take the load alternately [A]. The area of the footprint can be designed to suit any ground loading. By choosing appropriate geometry, the walking beam can be made to move in any direction and also to rotate. Four walking beams carry and rotate this oil platform module [B].

Road building

The first roads used by man were probably beaten out by the hoofs of animals as they made their way between feeding- and watering-places. Routes that began as mere cattle tracks or hunting and supply trails developed after the invention of the wheel into harder-wearing roads criss-crossing the ancient world and linking great trade markets. The Romans built a more permanent and extensive road network [Key] so that the empire could back up the authority of remote administrators by rapid troop movements.

Stone paving

Few authenticated records exist of pre-Roman road paving. But given the known skill of the ancient stonemason, we may assume that heavily used roads of the earliest civilizations were surfaced with slabs of cut stone. A drained earthen track becomes compacted by foot and hoof but cannot stand up to the wheel, which gradually cuts and breaks the surface.

The engineering of Roman roads [3] is well documented. Descriptions are detailed and some roads lasted so well that the orig-inal formation has been discovered, almost intact in places, by archaeologists. The Appian Way, started in 312 BC, which linked Rome with Brindisi, was typical. About 4.5m (14.75ft) wide across its two-way central lane, it was built in five layers and had three features to ensure drainage: it was constructed above ground level with a cambered surface and flanking ditches. The wearing surface was of crushed lava (plentiful in south Italy) on a gravel core. The larger stones of the base course of many Roman roads were mixed with lime mortar as a binder or with *pozzuloana* (natural volcanic cement), forming what was virtually a concrete footing. The surface of Roman roads varied with local materials and their availability.

The Romans employed cheap, expendable slave labour under military supervision for road building. After them, no administration could afford to repair their highways, let alone build new roads, until the introduction of tolls in the late Middle Ages.

Modern road technology evolved in eighteenth-century France. The Corps des Ingénieurs des Ponts et Chaussées was set up in 1720 within the French army. Twenty-seven years later the Ecole des Ponts et Chaussées was established as a state college at which civilians could study. It was Pierre Tresaguet (1716–96) who designed and built the first roads that combined good engineering practice with sound economics. He taught that there were two essentials for a lasting road – a firm foundation protected by a water-resistant surface [6].

Influence of McAdam

The French lead was soon followed elsewhere in Europe and the names of two British engineers became closely associated with improved road design. Thomas Telford (1757–1834), originally a stonemason, built roads similar in section to those of Tresaguet. But Telford's pavement was costly and it was a Scotsman, John McAdam (1756–1836), who found a way to cut costs without impairing efficiency. McAdam eliminated the deep foundation, recognizing that it is the soil that ultimately supports the weight of traffic, and that compacted soil, kept dry, will support any load. McAdam's road [4] was

1 Road construction methods grew from simple compaction of early routes by foot and horse-drawn traffic. The Romans [A] made their routes more permanent by removing obstacles, laying foundations of gravel, surfacing with crushed stones or paving slabs and leaving drainage ditches at both sides. In the eight-eenth century [B], major roads were built of tamped gravel on top of a foundation of large blocks. Roads in the nineteenth century [C] were similar but were sometimes raised and had an upper surface of rolled gravel. With the vast increase of traffic in the twentieth century and the introduction of heavy vehicles [D], roads had to be made more durable. Most modern roads have a lean concrete base with a surface composed either of reinforced concrete or of rolled asphalt.

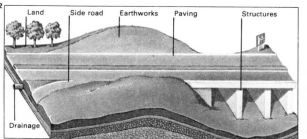

2 A cost breakdown for a modern motorway shows that earthworks are the most expensive item.

Earthworks	25%
Paving	18%
Structures	18%
Drainage	7%
Land	4%
Side roads	4%
Engineers' fees and miscellaneous	24%

cambered for drainage and was surfaced with stone chips which were crushed and rolled by the steel-clad wheels of his time into a smooth water-resistant surface.

The McAdam pavement served its purpose well until the invention of the rubber tyre. The tyre no longer compacted the crushed stone surface, but seemed to suck the finer material from between the larger stones until the surface broke up. A binder was needed and the answer was found in natural tar. The new surface was called tarmac.

Concrete paving

The final stage in the development of the modern road followed the steady increase in the weight of heavy road vehicles. Lean concrete (which has a lower cement content) began to be used for the footing and fine concrete for the surface of the "rigid" pavement which spreads heavy axle loads over a greater area. The modern "flexible" or "black-top" pavement has a tar surface up to 10cm (4in) thick over a 25cm (10in) base layer, such as lean concrete, laid on a sub-base course of any locally available granular materials such

as stone or clinker. In the modern reinforced concrete road, a granular base course is topped by a concrete slab up to 30cm (12in) thick, with a mat of steel reinforcement 5cm (2in) below the surface.

The rapidly expanding need for more and more roads has led to the development of sophisticated road-making machinery. Giant scrapers, graders and other heavy earth-moving machines are used to prepare the roadbed and lay the footing. Machines for automatic laying of an asphalt surface to a predetermined thickness are commonplace; advanced models can lay and consolidate a 20cm (8in) asphalt layer in one pass, providing a black-top pavement that needs no further treatment.

The modern automatic concrete paver [7] spreads and tamps a continuous slab of concrete up to 30cm (12in) thick and 5m (16ft) wide, handling about 300 tonnes of material an hour, its hopper fed by tip-trucks. Reinforcement, in the form of mats of welded steel rods, is either sandwiched between two layers of wet concrete or pushed down into the body of a single slab.

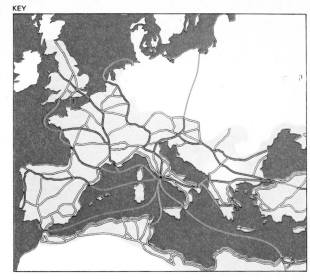

KEY

The Romans built 85,000km (53,000 miles) of roads to link Rome

to its overseas centres of supply. Major land and water routes

are marked on this map in orange; other routes shown are secondary.

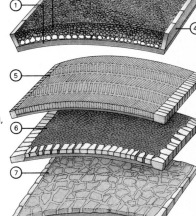

3 The Roman road pavement was based on a compacted earth footing [1] with a layer of small stones in mortar [2] and above this hard filling [3] and a slab surface [4]. At the sides were retaining stones [5] and ditches for drainage [6].

4 McAdam's pavement had a compacted, cambered earth footing [1], a 10cm (4in) base course of stones [2], a 10cm middle course of stones [3] and a wearing surface of small stones [4] which the steel wheels of the time crushed and rolled to a smooth surface.

5 A typical modern pavement has a granular sub-base [1], a 25cm base layer of lean concrete [2], a 6.5cm layer of tar or rolled asphalt [3], a 3.5cm wearing course of rolled asphalt [4], a concrete haunch [5] and a hard shoulder of asphalt on a concrete base [6].

6 Tresaguet's road in the latter half of the eighteenth century had a foundation of heavy stones rammed into an earth base slightly below ground level [1]. Above this was a 16cm (6in) layer of medium-sized stones [2] and an 8cm (3in) wearing

surface of tamped small stones about the size of walnuts [3]. Retaining stones [4] were placed at the sides. The construction ensured good drainage. Different surfaces included herringbone [5], *opus testaceum* (brick and tile) [6] and cobbles [7].

7 Road making is automated in the modern concrete "train". Ready-mixed concrete is fed into a paver which extrudes an even layer as it creeps along. This layer is compacted with poker vibrators. After a mat of steel reinforcing has been laid over the wet concrete a second paver places another layer of concrete over the steel. A vibrating beam is used to compact this thin layer without dis-

turbing the steel. Surface irregularities are then eliminated with an automatic screeding machine carrying two transverse vibrating metal strips which spread a slight wave of excess mix over the surface. After final levelling by means of straight edges manipulated by hand from a travelling bridge, mechanical brushing is used to produce a non-skid surface. The concrete is protected with waterproof tenting.

Traffic engineering

Modern road systems evolved over many hundreds of years out of the network of routes that linked villages and townships across the length and breadth of every country. In early times, the farmer's cart threaded its way between fields, skirting woods, avoiding water and seeking the most convenient routes across hilly ground. In mountainous country, the principle of siting roads in the general direction of contours was developed to maintain reasonable gradients.

The Romans attempted to reduce the wastefulness of meandering roads by driving theirs, wherever possible, in simple, straight lines, using civil engineering techniques to carry the roadway over soft ground, natural depressions and rivers.

Development of road construction
By 1826, the British engineer Thomas Telford (1757–1834) had reconstructed the road from Shrewsbury to Holyhead to specifications which minimized curvature and gradient and provided perfect drainage. Now a part of Britain's A5 highway, his road was a model of its time, providing what is still a top-gear highway for the whole of its length.

Special highways for fast motor traffic appeared in America and Europe in the 1920s, notably around Milan where a system of single-carriageway *autostradas* was developed by private enterprise. In Germany, Adolf Hitler was impressed by the military potential of these roads and a vigorous programme of highway building began with the Frankfurt-Darmstadt *autobahn* in 1933–5. With subsequent design improvements, the modern high-speed freeway or motorway emerged. High speeds do not necessarily imply danger. Research has shown that a segregated freeway can handle much more traffic at faster speeds and much more safely than a typical arterial road with cross junctions, kerbside parking and other hazards.

The essentials of freeway design are relatively simple – no frontage development, separate up and down carriageways, no turns across the path of oncoming traffic, no sharp curves, and marked lanes of 3.7m (12ft) standard width. Simple though these principles are, old roads can rarely be upgraded to freeway specifications. Freeways are therefore built as new roads. A typical modern freeway with a design speed of 110km/h (70mph) meets the following specifications: three-lane carriageway width 11m (36ft); central reserve width 5m (16.4ft); crossfall grade for drainage 1 in 40; minimum curve radius 900m (2,950ft); super-elevation for 900m curve 1 in 22; uninterrupted visibility at 1.1m (3.6ft) above road surface 250m (820ft).

Urban freeways are designed for lower speeds with more frequent access for local traffic. Because it is impractical to drive urban freeways through existing cities at ground level, they are often built as elevated structures or in tunnels. Though tunnelled roads are more costly they may justify their expense by avoiding the damage elevated roads do to the environment.

Traffic controls
Some of the earliest attempts to control traffic were made in Rome with the banning of daytime cart traffic in the city during the first century AD.

With the expansion of trade and commerce during the Renaissance, several cities

1 Freeway interchanges are designed to minimize traffic conflict. Different needs are met by a number of designs. [A] The Almondsbury interchange between Britain's M4 and M5 motorways allows traffic to flow safely towards any destination without much loss of speed. [B] The trumpet interchange provides a freeway T-junction with three-way access and minimum conflict. [C] Where a freeway is crossed by a major road, the major road is divided to form a roundabout either over or under the freeway itself. [D] Purpose-built junctions are designed to connect a country road network with a freeway. [E] The classic "cloverleaf" freeway interchange achieves safe access to and from all directions with little traffic conflict. Traffic that is changing direction must reduce speed in compact interchanges of this form.

2 Electronic signs on British motorways are operated by police at central control stations. They are normally blank but can be activated to show a variety of illuminated symbols. Surrounding these signs, coloured lamps flash to draw motorists' attention.

3 Language problems have been overcome in recent years by the introduction of a standardized system of road signs which can be recognized by motorists internationally.

Speed

Lane closed

Road clear

Change lane

Leave motorway at next exit

Stop and wait until signal changes

Information

Instructions

30

Warnings

Prohibitions

introduced rudimentary traffic regulations, including the use of one-way streets and parking restrictions. Leonardo da Vinci even envisaged separation of traffic on two levels.

The arrival of the motor age at the turn of the century saw the tentative beginning of scientific traffic engineering with the adoption of a traffic code for New York in 1903. Customary rules such as keeping to the left in Britain and giving way to the right on the Continent, began to be enforced by law. The introduction of safety road signs, automatic traffic lights at busy urban junctions and roundabout systems followed. Traffic engineering is a distinctively twentieth-century science, born out of the hazards brought to human societies by a torrent of motor vehicles. Its object is to provide safe, convenient and economic movement of vehicles and pedestrians.

More recently, traffic engineering has been defined as the science of fitting roads to traffic by planning and design, and traffic to roads by regulation and control, in order to achieve maximum capacity with safety. This depends on analysis of traffic flows, conges-

tion and accidents. On motorways, increased capacity at high speeds with safety is sought by minimizing the chance of traffic conflict. The road designer must achieve these aims with the least harm to the environment.

City traffic
The complexity of traffic engineering increases off the freeway as vehicles seek facilities to stop or park throughout the city. Expedients to reduce congestion include parking restrictions, designation of clearways where no stopping is permitted, bans on U-turns, extensive one-way systems and tidal flow systems of traffic lights to allow an unimpeded path along busy routes. In many cities, the policy is to reduce private traffic by both the improvement of public transport and the control and restriction of car parking. Already in some cities, traffic surveillance by remote-controlled TV cameras enables experienced traffic officers to operate electronic signs to reroute or restrict traffic.

Semi-automatic road systems now under study could conceivably lead to an electronically controlled flow of cars on major roads.

KEY

Today's road-user is served – or perhaps confused – by a proliferation of warnings, prohibitions and instructions applied in his own interests by the modern science of traffic engineering.

4 Urban freeways have to be designed within the confines of existing cities. Access points must fit local traffic needs, both in their location and their capacity. As freeways cannot be accommodated in existing cities at ground level (except

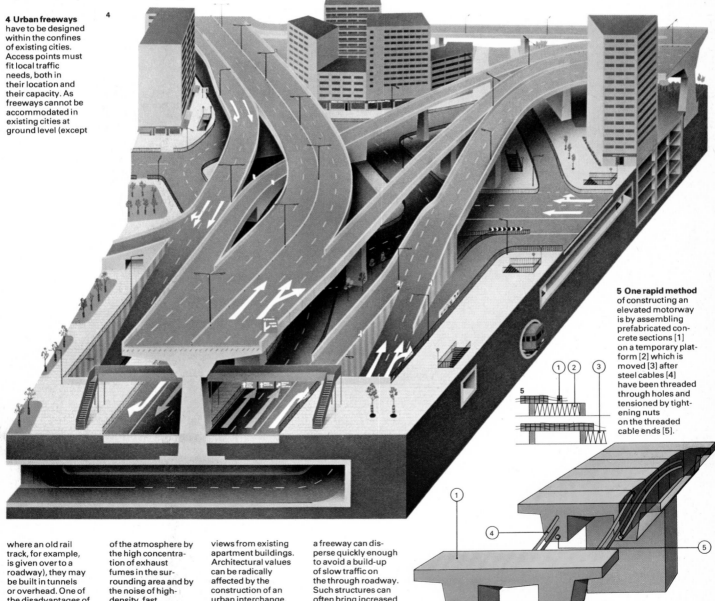

5 One rapid method of constructing an elevated motorway is by assembling prefabricated concrete sections [1] on a temporary platform [2] which is moved [3] after steel cables [4] have been threaded through holes and tensioned by tightening nuts on the threaded cable ends [5].

where an old rail track, for example, is given over to a roadway), they may be built in tunnels or overhead. One of the disadvantages of surface routes and elevated city freeways is pollution

of the atmosphere by the high concentration of exhaust fumes in the surrounding area and by the noise of high-density, fast traffic. Overhead roads may also look unattractive or spoil

views from existing apartment buildings. Architectural values can be radically affected by the construction of an urban interchange. Complex structures are needed to ensure that traffic leaving

a freeway can disperse quickly enough to avoid a build-up of slow traffic on the through roadway. Such structures can often bring increased congestion to the old roads near the freeway exit.

Airports and air traffic

When Orville Wright (1871–1948) and his brother Wilbur (1867–1912) made man's first powered flight on 17 December 1903 at Kitty Hawk, North Carolina, USA, they revolutionized transportation. In theory the new aircraft made possible the movement of men and goods from any point on earth to any other without the need for massive engineering projects on roads, bridges, tunnels and seaports. Landing facilities were necessary but before the 1920s any large, dry, level space sufficed for the purpose.

Runway size and strength

From the early 1920s the establishment of public air passenger services, and the increase in size, weight and speed of aircraft, resulted in the need for complex installations including suitable runways and facilities for passengers and cargo. The rapid growth in the size of aircraft since their invention is illustrated by the fact that during the 1930s an aircraft carried on average 20 passengers, weighed about 12,000kg (26,450lb) and needed 600m (1,950ft) of runway while in the 1970s Jumbo jets weighing 372,250kg

(818,950lb) were carrying up to 500 passengers and needed more than 3,500m (11,480ft) of runway to take off. These lengths are for sea-level airports and at higher altitudes runways must be even longer. Typical commercial air speeds also increased from approximately 280km/h (173mph) to 1,000km/h (620mph).

Runway width varies today between 50m and 70m (160–230ft) with taxiways 25m (80ft) wide connecting the runways with the loading and unloading areas. The heavier airliners have a cluster of landing wheels to spread their weight; thus modern design practice specifies a runway strength sufficient to bear 100 tonnes per single wheel or 125 tonnes for a pair of dual wheels.

Most busy airports have at least two runways lined up in different directions [Key]. This enables the aircraft to take off and land into the prevailing wind . A good layout (neglecting noise considerations) is a six-pointed star providing a pair of runways in each of three directions separated by 120 degrees. But such a layout requires a clear area of 10 square kilometres (3.9 square miles), so it is

usual to economize on space by building all airport facilities and control, passenger, cargo and car parking in the centre and served by approach tunnels. An example of this design is London's Heathrow airport.

Airport location

Airports must be located as near as possible to major population centres if air transport is to retain its advantage of speed, especially on short-haul routes. London Heathrow to Amsterdam Schiphol [2], for example, takes about 45 minutes flying time. But the road journeys from the West London Air Terminal to Heathrow (24km [14 miles]) and from Schiphol to Amsterdam city centre (12km [7 miles]) can take up to 90 minutes and passengers can spend much time at the airports waiting for customs clearance and their flights to be called. Buenos Aires international airport is 50km (30 miles) from the city centre while Hong Kong airport is only 7km (4 miles) from the main centre.

Airports must be serviced by good road and rail facilities to enable the efficient inflow and outflow of passenger and freight traffic at

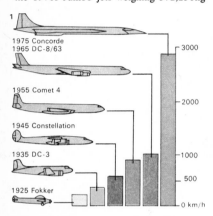

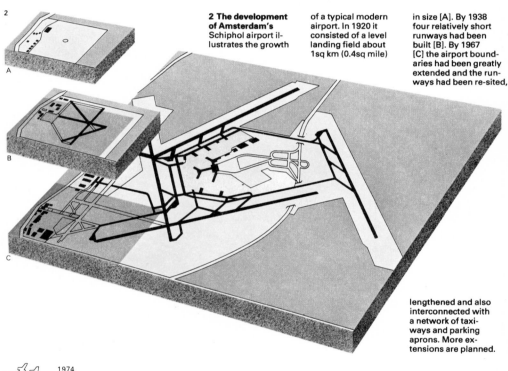

1 The technology of aviation has advanced much more rapidly than that of most other means of transport. Fifty years have seen aircraft speeds increase to as much as 2,335km/h (1,450 mph) in the case of Concorde. When the total area available limits runway length the only solution consistent with safety is to construct a new airport at a new location. It is doubtful, however, that aircraft speeds will increase in the near future due to the controversy over noise levels. Typical passenger transport aircraft and their maximum speeds are shown on the chart.

1975 Concorde
1965 DC-8/63
1955 Comet 4
1945 Constellation
1935 DC-3
1925 Fokker

3000
2000
1000
500
0 km/h

2 The development of Amsterdam's Schiphol airport illustrates the growth of a typical modern airport. In 1920 it consisted of a level landing field about 1sq km (0.4sq mile) in size [A]. By 1938 four relatively short runways had been built [B]. By 1967 [C] the airport boundaries had been greatly extended and the runways had been re-sited, lengthened and also interconnected with a network of taxiways and parking aprons. More extensions are planned.

3 The problem of aircraft noise near airports must be faced by all airport management authorities. In the enforcement of noise abatement programmes a balance must be struck between the demands of efficiency and the minimization of disturbance. Heathrow airport, London, is the busiest airport in Europe; because of its situation close to a number of suburban localities strict rules have been made to control noise. In 1958 noise limits were set at 110 PNdB (a measure of perceived noise) during the day and 102 PNdB at night, and there has been no relaxation since the advent of the larger more powerful and potentially noisier jet-engined aircraft of today. Noise abatement procedures include keeping within a defined flight path, making the approach for landing at a fixed angle of 3° from a height of 300m (1,000ft) and reducing power and the rate of climb as soon as the aircraft has reached 300m after take-off. The environmental battle over Concorde has been based as much on the question of exceeding accepted maximum take-off and landing noise as on the vexed question of sonic boom.

1974 flight path
pre 1971 flight path
Urban land at 90 + PNdB
Urban land at 50 + PNdB
M'way at 80 PNdB
Rural land
Airport runway
Pre-1971 noise footprint
Flight path shadow
1974 noise footprint

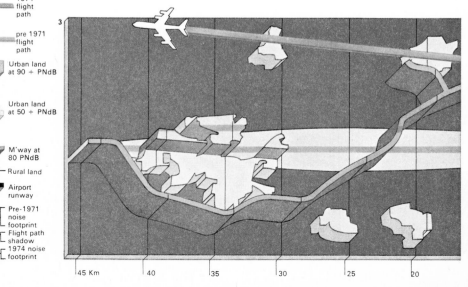

45 Km   40   35   30   25   20

densities equivalent to the airport's capacity. Some airports such as Kennedy airport, New York, can be reached by means of helicopter shuttle services.

Modern jet aircraft are noisy and airports must therefore be sited so that the take-off air lanes avoid populated areas as far as possible. Current legislation in most countries limits take-off noise [3] to between 110 and 120 PNdB (perceived noise decibels) at ground level in the flight path.

Passenger and cargo handling

Passenger facilities [6] at a modern airport have to be designed to deal with a wide variety of services: airline booking and checking in, baggage handling, open and duty-free shopping, departure and transit waiting and restaurant service, passport control, customs and short- and long-term car parking. These must be adequate to service the full loads that arrive with each giant airliner every few minutes. Cargo facilities include vehicle access, booking offices, warehousing, handling gear and customs. There must also be provision for airport police, and fire and ambulance services in case of an emergency.

The air traffic control facilities required at a modern airport are considerable. The control tower must be sited so that control staff can see all runways in fair weather and airport lighting must allow for comparable visibility during the night as well as providing pilots with adequate airport recognition and runway lighting for landing and take-off. There must be equipment to provide VHF radio-telephone contact between the control tower and pilots of all aircraft on the ground and in the air.

Landing aids [4], essential in low-visibility conditions, include radio beacons to provide control signals for blind landing. Full radar scanning is also necessary to enable staff to "see" all aircraft at night or in fog.

Airports must also be safe places. One of the new safety measures on the ground is the extensive search necessary to thwart potential hijackers. Airport personnel, aided by electronic devices, carry out these searches. The airport lighting system acts as a direction guide for a pilot, to make landing and take-off safe at night as well as in bad weather.

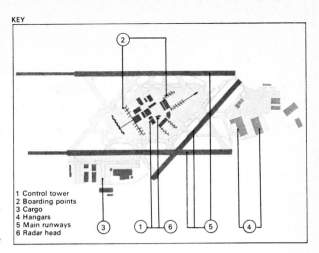

KEY

1 Control tower
2 Boarding points
3 Cargo
4 Hangars
5 Main runways
6 Radar head

The ideal airport provides landing and take-off directions into, or nearly into, the prevailing wind. This layout is the basis of London's Heathrow airport.

As the heavy aircraft of today are less affected by cross-winds, the full star is no longer necessary and runway extension has been confined to where it is most needed. The runways have been lengthened from time to time to accommodate these new aircraft. The longest runway today is 3,900m (12,800ft).

4 Aircraft navigational aids include VOR beacons (very high frequency navigational facility) [1] at flight path intersections to give bearings and distance.

At airports traffic plotted by a primary radar [2] is called up by surveillance radar [3], individually identified and guided to a holding stack [4] in which in-bound aircraft fly in oval circuits at successively lower levels controlled by a radio beacon [5]. Stack control is essential at modern take-off and landing rates; those waiting their turn must remain in the stack. When the aircraft reaches the bottom the pilot locates the radio-defined glide path leading down to the runway, enabling a safe landing even in the worst visibility. Airport surveillance radar [6] "sees" all ground vehicles even in dense fog and the staff at the control centre [7] co-ordinate all movements by means of two-way radio. Near large airports there are additional stacks to hold extra aircraft if landings are temporarily stopped.

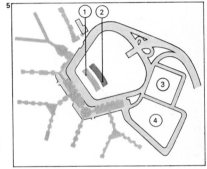

5 O'Hare International Airport, Chicago, is one of the busiest in the world. It has two domestic multi-berth terminals [1] in addition to an international one [2], and its other facilities include an hotel [3], car parks [4] and a restaurant as well as the usual passport controls, customs agencies and the means of handling air freight and other types of cargo.

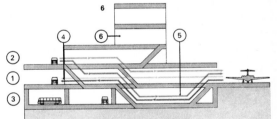

6 Passenger and baggage routes are kept separate in modern airport terminals to increase speed and efficiency. The diagram shows traffic flow to [2] and from [1] an aircraft; parking [3], customs and excise [4], baggage [5], and service [6] areas.

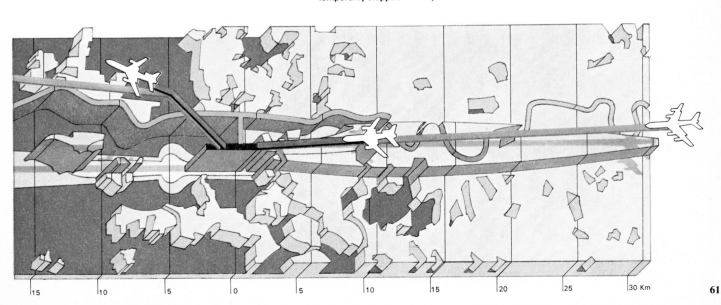

15   10   5   0   5   10   15   20   25   30 Km

Tunnel engineering

Tunnelling was probably one of man's earliest exercises in the field of civil engineering. The ancient Egyptians are known to have built tunnels for transporting water and for use as tombs. They also undertook mining operations, cutting deep tunnels to excavate copper ores. Today tunnels are used for road, rail and pedestrian transport, for carrying water – especially at dams – and in mining.

Some early tunnels

The first underwater tunnel was probably built in about 2160 BC by the engineers of Queen Semiramis of Babylon. The Euphrates had been diverted and the engineers dug a channel in the river bed. In this they built a brick-lined tunnel some 900m (3,000ft) long, waterproofed with bitumen plaster about 2m (6.5ft) thick. It connected the palace with a temple across the water.

Tunnels have often been used in warfare to penetrate enemy defences. Historians suggest that the walls of Jericho were almost certainly brought down by driving a tunnel beneath them and then lighting a fire to burn away the wooden props supporting the roof.

Tunnels, some cut through hard rock, were used extensively by the Romans in building their famous system of aqueducts. The Appian aqueduct, built in about 312 BC, ran as a tunnel for almost 25km (16 miles).

After the time of the Romans no large tunnels were built for more than a thousand years. It was the coming of the canal age in the seventeenth century that produced a new generation of tunnel builders.

Man's first great tunnel built for transportation was part of the Canal du Midi. It was completed in 1681 and ran across France from the Bay of Biscay to the Mediterranean. At Malpus, near Beziers, a 158m (515ft) tunnel was cut to carry the canal through a rocky ridge. It was the first tunnel built with the aid of explosives – gunpowder was placed in hand-drilled holes.

Rail and underwater tunnels

Throughout the eighteenth century canal tunnels were built both in Europe and America, but with the onset of the railway age in the early nineteenth century canals fell into disuse as a means of transport. The

construction of railways, however, itself produced a huge increase in tunnelling. One of the most remarkable and difficult tunnels was the Simplon tunnel under the Alps, completed in 1906. It runs for 20km (12 miles) and connects Switzerland and Italy, with a 2.1km (1.3 mile) stretch below Monte Leone through rock.

Between 1825 and 1841 the British domiciled French engineer Marc Brunel (1769–1849) built the first major underwater tunnel – still in constant use by the London Underground – beneath the Thames at Rotherhithe. Brunel constructed his tunnel by means of a tunnelling shield [1] – a device consisting basically of a vertical face of stout horizontal timber baulks that could be removed one at a time to enable clay to be dug out, each baulk then being replaced farther forwards. Brunel's shield preceded the modern circular tunnelling shield.

Soon after Brunel's triumph plans were prepared to build a tunnel under the English Channel. In 1882 an army engineer, Colonel Frederick Beaumont, designed and built a tunnelling machine suitable for cutting a hole

1 Brunel's tunnelling shield consisted of 12 vertical cast-iron sections. The men were protected by horizontal timbers held against the tunnel face. These could be removed for digging, one at a time. When the face had been excavated about 30cm (12in) the jacks holding the timbers were released and the shield moved forwards by means of large jacks that acted against the tunnel shields.

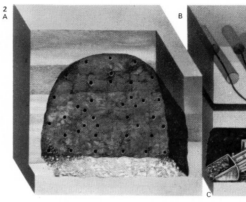

2 A typical drilling pattern for blasting through rock involves a centre group of holes that are packed with a high explosive such as dynamite. [A] shows the holes in a vertical cross-section. [B] is a horizontal section showing the explosive placed in the rock face. After the explosive charges have been detonated a heap of rock lumps and rubble block the tunnel face. Engineers drill the hole-pattern in such a way that the rock is smashed into manageable lumps. The machine for the removal of blasted rock [C] includes a rock shovel near the face, which loads material into a long shuttle car with a steel-slat conveyor for moving the rock rubble back to trucks. The whole machine is gradually moved towards the face.

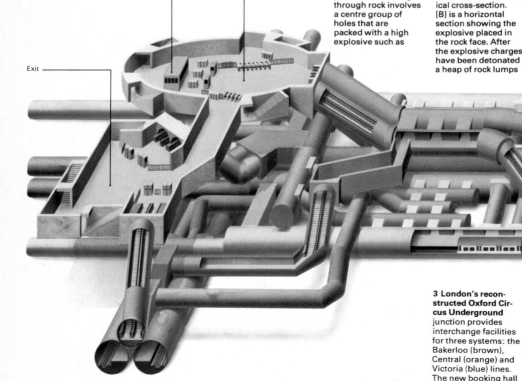

Ingoing passengers to all lines   Booking hall

Exit

3 London's reconstructed Oxford Circus Underground junction provides interchange facilities for three systems: the Bakerloo (brown), Central (orange) and Victoria (blue) lines. The new booking hall was built under a steel 'umbrella', temporarily above street level. The Victoria line was excavated mainly by automatic "drum-digger", which advanced up to 18m (59ft) a day. This machine consists of two steel drums, with the edge of the outer drum bevelled to cut through the London clay. At one Victoria line station water-bearing ground was frozen by pumping liquid nitrogen into tubes driven 1.6m (5.5ft) apart. Station tunnels on the Victoria line are 6.5m (21.5ft) in diameter.

2.3m (7.5ft) in diameter through chalk. Driven by compressed air, the machine advanced 12m (39ft) every 24 hours and had cut a hole 1.6km (1 mile) long eastwards from Dover when work was stopped for political reasons. A second tunnel, begun in 1973, was abandoned in 1975 because of the escalating construction costs.

Modern tunnelling methods

Tunnels through hard rock are usually built by drilling and blasting [2]. A pattern of holes is drilled into the rock face by using compressed air drills operated by men on a moving carriage or "jumbo" running on temporary rails. A drill tipped with a tungsten-carbide bit can penetrate 2 to 3m (6 to 10ft) in four to five minutes. When a round of holes is ready a high explosive such as dynamite is packed in and detonated. A mobile rock shovel lifts the shattered rock into dump cars which are hauled away by a locomotive.

Soft material such as sandstone, clay and chalk is cut through by automatic machines [Key]. One of the largest of these machines to be used cut five 9m (29ft) tunnels through

480m (1,600ft) of sandstone and limestone during the building of Pakistan's Mangla dam in 1963. Machines of this kind have a hydraulic cutting head that turns slowly and scrapes out the material at the face of the tunnel. This is lifted by a mechanical shovel on to a conveyor which carries it back to dump cars behind the machine. Mechanical arms lift and place in position huge prefabricated sections of concrete tunnel lining.

Shallow tunnels are sometimes built by the "cut and cover" method. A deep trench is excavated, the completely roofed tunnel lining is built at the bottom and this is then covered with excavated material.

In underwater tunnelling the working area may have to be pressurized so that the internal air pressure exceeds the pressure of water. After placing the tunnel lining engineers pump cement grout, a sealing mixture, round it to make it watertight. Another method sometimes used in water-bearing gravel is to sink tubes on each side of the path of the tunnel and pump in liquid nitrogen. The water in the gravel is frozen solid and the tunnel can then be cut.

The Mersey Mole, a new soft tunnelling machine, was used in 1967 to cut a 10.3m (34ft) hole through the soft rock under the River Mersey at Liverpool, England. The machine can cut away the tunnel face and convey the material back to skips running on rails. It also contains handling gear to position fabricated concrete lining sections.

4

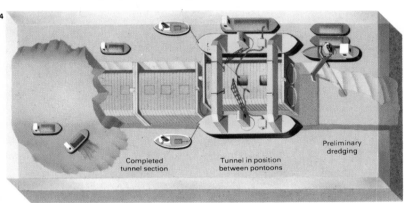

4 Underwater tunnels are increasingly being built by the immersed tube method. Prefabricated steel or concrete sections of tunnel are sealed at the ends and floated into position. There they are sunk into a trench dredged into the bed of the lake or river. The sections are then joined together end to end with watertight joints and covered with previously dredged material. It is economical to make all the tunnel sections close to the tunnel site and factories for this purpose may be built on the shore; the tunnel sections are floated to the site on barges. Alternatively, prefabricated concrete or steel tunnel sections can be made in a floating dry dock that is moored alongside the site at which they are to be sunk into the dredged trench.

Completed tunnel section — Tunnel in position between pontoons — Preliminary dredging

5

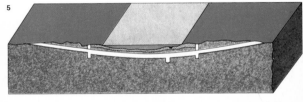

5 The first Mersey road tunnel at Liverpool is shown here in section. The tunnel falls steadily from its portals to a central point where pumps operate to remove any water that may seep in. This tunnel has a diameter of 13.5m (44ft), carries four traffic lanes (with space, never used, for two double-decker tramway lines below) and runs for 3.2km (2 miles), half of it under water. The tunnel was hand excavated in four stages. First two pilot tunnels were cut, one above the other, then the entire tunnel was opened out, top half first. The tunnel was completed in 1934.

7

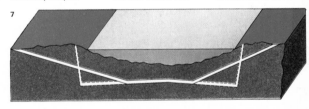

7 The Seikan tunnel, now due to be completed in 1981–2, links Japan's main island of Honshu with the north island, Hokkaido. At 36km (22 miles) it will be the world's longest tunnel. Although 100m (328 ft) of rock cover the tunnel under the deepest water, the danger of a leak at high pressure prompted the designers to extend the low section to a lower level at each end, providing a major drain-off facility to the high-power pumping plant. The tunnel runs for 22km (14 miles) through volcanic rock. The drilling and blasting method and rock tunneling machines are both being used.

8

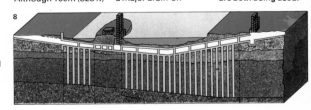

6

6 The Chesapeake Bay bridge-tunnel was one of the boldest prefabricated underwater tunnel projects. This 2km (1.25 mile) tunnel between two man-made islands passes under one of three shipping lanes along the remarkable 28km (17 mile) causeway that crosses Chesapeake Bay on the US east coast. There is a second, similar tunnel and at the east end of the structure, between two islands, there is a high-level bridge. The four man-made islands built of sand, stone and concrete are each 450m (1,480 ft) long and 70m (230ft) wide. The tunnels were built by sinking prefabricated double-skinned steel tubes into a dredged trench.

8 The four-lane road tunnel under the IJ river in Amsterdam, completed in 1967, was built mainly by the immersed tube method although one section, where the ventilation facilities are located, was constructed on site. The prefabricated reinforced concrete tunnel elements were from 70–90m (220–300ft) long and weighed up to 17,000 tonnes. They were designed as a flat box with two 7m (23ft) roadways side by side with service ducts between them and a fresh and foul air duct below each. As the river bed was very soft the tunnel sections were laid on sliding plastic bearings on a concrete raft supported by long piles. The tunnel sections were waterproofed with a bituminous membrane and a steel skin.

63

History of bridges

The earliest bridges were probably logs thrown across streams or the stone slab "clapper" bridges such as those still surviving in Devon, England. Another type of water crossing was provided by bridges formed of boats fixed together. The Greek historian Herodotus (*c.* 485–425 BC) provides the earliest record of a more permanent structure. This crossed the River Euphrates at Babylon about the eighth century BC.

Less durable perhaps, but certainly as remarkable technically, was the bridge of boats built for King Darius (548–486 BC) in 512 BC. It enabled the advancing Persian army to cross the Bosporus and invade south-eastern Europe. Darius's successor Xerxes (*c.* 519–465 BC) instructed his engineers to repeat the Bosporus exercise on the Helles-pont (now the Dardanelles) [2]. On this occa-sion two bridges using 674 boats were built side by side spanning 1.4km (0.87 mile).

Rivers in mountainous country pose different but equally difficult problems and provoke some equally impressive solutions. Fâ-Hsien, a Buddhist monk, writing in AD 412, came across a 92m (300ft) bridge of ropes traversing a deep ravine while he was travelling in India. This form of primitive suspension bridge is known to have been widely used in South America, Central Africa, South-East Asia and China as well as in India. Jungle creepers served as ropes for many of these bridges, woven split bamboo being used in the construction of others. The Incas of Peru were still building such bridges to carry mountain roads over ravines as late as the sixteenth century [3].

Roman bridge building
The Romans developed the art of bridge building, like most things they tackled, systematically. The Pons Sublicius built over the River Tiber in Rome in 621 BC was 150m (492ft) long and famous for being defended by Horatius in 508 BC. Built entirely of timber, it was founded on timber piles driven deep into the river bed. The most remarkable Roman timber bridge was the 420m (1,378 ft) structure built across the River Rhine in 50 BC. The last plank was placed in position just ten days after Julius Caesar had ordered the bridge to be built.

The Romans' legacy to bridge building was the heavy masonry arch bridge, hundreds of which were built throughout Europe [5]. In this, large stone blocks were wedged against each other to form an arch. The central stone at the top of the arch was known as the keystone. The finest surviving example of such a bridge is the Pons Fabricius in Rome. Completed in 62 BC the bridge (now called the Ponte Quattro Capi), has two fine semicircular arches each spanning 24m (78ft). A small "relief" arch in the central springing of the two main arches releases excess water in times of flood.

Priests and professionals take over
So prolific and efficient was Roman building that it was hundreds of years before Euro-peans took to bridge building anew. Then, surprisingly, it was the Christian Church which, recognizing the advantages of good road communications in a developing soc-iety, took the lead. In France a group of interested priests formed a new order, the Frères du Pont, to design and build lasting bridges. Most famous of this order's works

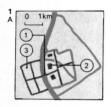

1 This drawing of the Euphrates bridge [B] at Babylon has been projected from an-cient records. [A] The bridge [1] connected the old city [2] with a newer residential suburb on the west bank [3] of the river.

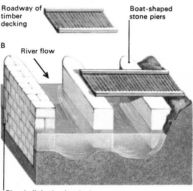

Roadway of timber decking

River flow

Boat-shaped stone piers

Piers built in dry river bed

2 A unit of King Xerxes' army of 480 BC crosses the Hellespont by a bridge of boats in this artist's im-pression. Alexander the Great crossed the Indus in India on a pontoon bridge.

3 Suspension bridges built from jungle creepers and stakes have been used for centuries by prim-itive societies in hilly regions. This Indian bridge in Peru is a typical modern example.

Heads of martyrs, traitors and criminals displayed over Great Stone Gate; collapsed and rebuilt 1437–40

Houses joined by gallery (hauptas) spanning street

Nonesuch House (1577) built on site of Newstone Gate

House and shop built over chapel remains

Remains of Peter of Colechurch's chapel

4 Old London Bridge was designed by a priest. Finished in 1209 after 30 years of toil, it had piers built on heaps of rubble dumped in the river and held in place by encircling rows of closely spaced wooden piles driven deep into the river bed. Over one of the piers stood a chapel dedicated to Thomas à Becket. The sixth span from the south was a timber draw span, which could be open-ed for tall ships to pass. Multi-storeyed houses and shops were built along the bridge with a wide enclosed corridor forming the roadway below. These build-ings were destroyed by fire on several occasions and rebuilt each time in the current architectural style. The bridge's 20 pointed arches varied in span from 4.5m (15ft) to 10.5m (34ft), the piers occupying half the total river width. For many years London's only dry crossing, old London Bridge stood for more than six centuries before being replaced in 1831.

was the Pont d'Avignon built in 1177 over the River Rhône. It had 21 arches in all, the longest being 35m (115ft) in span. Likewise in England it was Peter de Colechurch, a chantry priest, who conceived, designed and eventually built the first stone bridge over the Thames – the famous multi-span London Bridge [4].

Until the late seventeenth century bridges continued to be designed and built largely by priests or architects with a flair for engineering. In Florence the local chamber of commerce commissioned the architect Taddeo Gaddi (c. 1300–66) to replace the Ponte Vecchio, which had been destroyed by flood. Gaddi's chief design innovation, incorporated in his bridge over the River Arno, was arches that were only part of a semicircle. Gaddi's idea was adopted by the architect-priest Giovanni Giocondo (c. 1433–1515). He used the segmental arch in Paris's first masonry bridge, built in 1507.

Such complex and essential work could not rest in the hands of gifted amateurs for ever. In 1716, following the work of French army engineers, France stole a march on the rest of the world by forming the Corps des Ingénieurs des Ponts et Chaussées (Corps of Bridge and Road Engineers). Jean Rodolph Perronet, chief engineer of the corps, replaced the segmental arch with the even more daring and flatter eliptical shape [7].

Iron and steel bridges

In 1779 the first bridge to be made of iron was built across the River Severn, England, at Coalbrookdale. The iron ribs and plates were cast at the local works of the ironmaster Abraham Darby.

Wrought iron was the next major material for bridges and Thomas Telford (1757–1834) used it for the chains of his 178m (580ft) bridge of 1826, which spanned the Menai Strait to link Wales and Anglesey. Robert Stephenson's (1803–59) nearby tubular railway bridge (1850) also used wrought iron.

For long-span railway bridges carrying heavy loads, an arch or cantilever is the best design. An early bridge of this type was the steel arch over the River Mississippi at St Louis (1874) by James Eads (1820–87).

KEY

A

B

C

Bridges as a means of transporting people or goods have evolved to meet the needs of society.

In medieval times [A] road bridges were used in conjunction with ferries. In the 19th century [B] these

were supplemented by rail bridges and in modern times [C] by flyovers and multi-purpose bridges.

5 A most impressive Roman bridge was built over the River Tagus at Alcantara, Spain. Finished in AD 109, it was 204m (670ft) long with six stone arches and stood 52m (170ft) above the water.

The Romans built aqueducts in a similar way, to carry the water supply to Rome. Some of these also had a roadway. All Roman arches were semicircular, giving the name Romanesque to this type of arch.

6 This timber cantilever bridge is of a type that has stood for centuries in Srinagar, capital of Kashmir. Built on stone foundations these bridges have log piers spanned by Indian cedar.

7 The Pont de la Concorde, Paris, was completed in 1791 by Jean Perronet. He was the engineer who replaced the circular arch with the more graceful ellipse, later to be widely copied by others. The arch under construction is shown supported by timber falsework, and a coffer dam encloses the pier keeps out the water

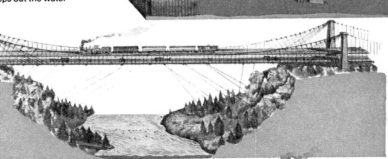

8 The stayed suspension bridge at Niagara Falls, completed in 1855 by John Roebling (1806–69), had a rail track above and a road below. Spanning 250m (820ft), the main supports for the rail and roadway were cables of wrought iron wire. The stays anchored the structure and reduced vibration in it in winds or when trains passed over it. The decks were hung on wires from the cables.

9 Eads' bridge over the Mississippi at St Louis was opened in 1874. It was the world's first major steel bridge and carried a roadway above a rail track. The centre arch is 156m (512ft) in span; the others 6m (20ft) less. Eads sank the foundations down to rock using pressurized caissons to exclude water from the working area on the river bed. The main arch had to give sufficient room above the water-level for boats to pass.

Modern bridges

Two nineteenth-century inventions led to a revolution in bridge building. These were Portland cement and mass-produced steel. Cement is the vital ingredient of concrete, and mass concrete can be used to build piers, abutments (bank supports) and arches of "artificial" stone to any required shape. Well-made concrete is extremely strong in compression (when squeezed) but it has very little strength in tension (when stretched). On the other hand, steel can withstand great tension as well as compression, and can be used for building girders of far greater strength than the wooden trusses of early days. High-tensile steel wire cables will support immense suspension bridges.

Reinforced concrete bridges
These new materials, concrete and steel, can also be used in combination with each other. For example, a concrete structure does not have to be designed so that the material is entirely in compression, because steel rods can be used to carry the tension.

The French engineer Eugene Freyssinet (1879–1962) overcame the remaining weakness of reinforced concrete (the fact that steel in tension stretches, allowing the concrete immediately around the steel to stretch and frequently to crack) by using high-strength tensioned steel wires as the reinforcement. This technique permitted Freyssinet to "pre-stress" concrete (pre-load it in compression), so that it would never be subjected to tension at all. The result was a material so versatile that it could be used to make stronger, lighter and more architecturally satisfactory bridges.

Types of bridge
There are four basic types of bridge: beam, arch, suspension and cantilever [1]. The beam bridge is, in effect, a pair of girders supporting a deck spanning the gap between two piers. Such a beam has to withstand both compression in its upper parts and tension in its lower parts. Where it passes over supports, other forces come into play. A beam may be a hollow box girder or an open frame or truss.

An arch bridge can be designed so that no part of it has to withstand tension. Concrete is therefore well suited to arched bridge design. When reinforced concrete is used, a more elegant and sometimes less costly arch can be designed and most concrete arch bridges are, in fact, reinforced.

A suspension bridge consists, basically, of a deck suspended from two or more cables slung between high towers. The cables, of high-tensile steel wire, can support an immense weight. The towers are in compression and the deck, often consisting of a long slender truss (used as a hollow beam), is supported at frequent intervals along its length.

A cantilever bridge is generally carried by two beams, each supported at one end. Unlike a simple beam supported at both ends, the cantilever must resist tension in its upper half and compression in its lower.

There are also many composite forms of bridges. The bridle-chord bridge is a combination of a long beam (usually a trussed girder) partially supported by steel wires from a tower at one end, or from towers at each end. Most cantilever bridges are designed so that a gap remains between two cantilevered arms that reach out from their abutments; the gap is bridged by a simple beam. "Movable" bridges, like London's

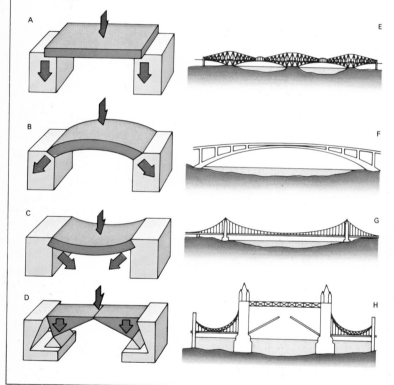

1 **Bridges are of four main types**: the beam bridge [A], the arch bridge [B], the suspension bridge [C] and the cantilever bridge [D]. The three main structures of the Forth railway bridge [E] are cantilevers and the two steel trusses that connect them are end-supported beams. In [F] it is the lower member that forms the arch. The suspension bridge [G] has its roadway hanging from enormous steel cables passing over tall towers. The two rising arms of Tower Bridge in London [D, H] are cantilevers, whereas the slender truss which connects the top of the towers is a long beam.

2 **The Howrah Bridge** at Calcutta is the world's fifth longest cantilever, spanning 453m (1,500ft). The two main piers of this bridge were built hollow with twenty-one vertical shafts. By digging out the sand at the bottom of these shafts, the piers were made to sink steadily down until they reached impervious clay. The bridge was opened in 1943.

3 **The Gladesville Bridge** over the Parramatta River at Sydney, Australia, is the world's longest concrete arch. Completed in 1964, it spans 305m (1,000ft) and carries an 8-lane roadway.

4 **The Medway Bridge** in southeast England is the longest pre-stressed concrete cantilever bridge. Its 150m (490ft) main span is made up of two 60m (196ft) cantilever arms linked by a 30m (98ft) suspended beam. It was opened in 1963.

famous Tower Bridge, have cantilevered arms or "bascules".

There is more to a bridge than the main span and without proper foundations for the piers or towers the whole structure would fail. Most modern bridges have reinforced concrete foundations, often keyed into bedrock. They may have to be designed to withstand the scouring action of tides, buffeting from pack ice and even mild earthquake tremors. If solid bedrock is too deep to be reached by excavating, foundations can be built on piles driven into the subsoil.

Theoretical limits of bridge spans

A bridge carries two loads. The useful load is the live load of crossing traffic. In addition it must carry its own weight, the dead load. The longer the span of a bridge, the greater its dead load: consequently there is a theoretical span limit for any given material and method of construction. Theoretical limits can be compared with current achievements using modern materials. The longest steel arches in existence are the 496m (1,652ft) Bayonne Bridge in New York City and the 503m (1,650ft) Sydney Harbour Bridge in Australia [7]. The theoretical span limit for steel bridges of this type is about 1,000m (3,280ft). In theory engineers have considerable scope here. But the limiting factor is cost, and a long steel arch is not usually the most economical way of bridging a wide gap.

The longest steel cantilever is the 540m (1,771ft) Quebec Bridge in Canada. This was a great achievement considering it was completed in 1918. The theoretical cantilever span limit is about 750m (2,460ft).

The longest reinforced concrete arch yet built is the 305m (990ft) span Gladesville Bridge at Sydney, Australia [3].

The modern suspension bridge has the greatest span potential. The longest yet built is the 1,298m (4,240ft) Verrazano-Narrows Bridge at the mouth of New York harbour. The new Humber Bridge, under construction in Britain, will extend this record span to 1,410m (4,610ft). Suspension bridges already hold the span record, and their potential is even greater. Experienced designers consider a span of 3,000m (9,840ft) to be possible with present-day materials.

The Bosporus Bridge at Istanbul, opened in 1973, has a main span of 1,074m (3,520ft). An example of the modern trend in suspension bridge design, this bridge is far lighter and therefore more economical than many earlier suspension bridges. A similar bridge, now being built across the Humber at Hull, will break the world's long span record.

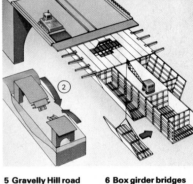

5 Gravelly Hill road junction near the city of Birmingham, England, seen here under construction is a complex of box girders with simple beams that carry the various links of the free-flow junction over each other. A large number of concrete columns support the many spans. Known popularly as "Spaghetti Junction", the complete work is a fine example of the combined skills of the civil and the traffic engineer.

6 Box girder bridges are increasingly used today because of their high strength-to-weight ratio. Building a bridge of this type often involves construction outwards from a support [1] in the form of long cantilevers. The method imposes stresses [2] on the structure which will not occur when it is complete, and it is vital for these to be adequately allowed for. Once complete, the bridge assumes its designed strength.

7 The Sydney Harbour Bridge is the longest steel arch bridge. Four urban rail lines and 6 motor lanes are carried by it over a clear 503m (1,650ft) span, 52m (170ft) above water. It was opened in 1932.

8 This complex of slip roads leads to an urban motorway junction at Copeley Hill, Birmingham, England. The elevated Aston expressway in the foreground is a good example of a reinforced concrete beam bridge.

Harbours and docks

A harbour is any place that provides sea-going ships or boats of any kind with a measure of protection from the wind and waves. To fulfil this role, a harbour must be deep enough to accommodate the largest ships that may use it, and have a bottom that will hold them at anchor. A port is a harbour with facilities for transferring passengers and cargo from shore to ship and vice versa.

Natural harbours

A harbour is often a natural product of geography [Key], whereas a port is a man-made communications facility and usually has piers, wharves, quays and docks. There may be cranes and other cargo-handling equipment, warehouses, customs and excise facilities and passenger facilities, including immigration control. Large ports have repair facilities for ships – perhaps including a dry dock [4] – and facilities for supplying water, food, oil and sometimes coal.

The Phoenicians used the natural eastern Mediterranean harbours of Tyre and Sidon from the thirteenth century BC until the Romans ended their power with the sack of Carthage (146 BC). The port of Alexandria (founded 332 BC) was an early example of a well-developed port. The natural harbour had land on all sides but the east where the deep-water pier was built within the protection of a line of reefs.

To guide ships safely into the harbour, Ptolemy II of Egypt built the 135m (443ft) Pharos lighthouse, one of the Seven Wonders of the ancient world, in about 280 BC.

The growing prosperity of Europe in the Middle Ages led to the establishment of extensive trade through the ports of Venice and Genoa, where docking and repair facilities were provided. Genoa was the terminal for sea communication with western Europe via the Straits of Gibraltar, whereas Venice was the link with Constantinople, which had direct overland trading contact with the countries of the Far East.

Among early British harbours known to have been developed by primitive civil engineering techniques were those built at Hartlepool (AD 1250) and Arbroath (1394), where the works consisted basically of protective breakwaters. Dover, formerly an exposed seaside town, was provided with an artificial harbour in the reign of Henry VIII by the construction of an enclosing breakwater of stone and timber.

Until the eighteenth century most harbours were natural. It was the Industrial Revolution in England that saw the founding of the science of harbour engineering by John Smeaton (1724-92), Thomas Telford (1757–1834) and John Rennie (1761–1821). One of the most famous harbour conceptions in recent times were the Mulberry Harbours, built by the Allies and used during World War II for the invasion of Normandy (1944). They were constructed of prefabricated concrete sections and floated to the French coast. There they provided instant harbour facilities for the landing of troops, vehicles, ammunition and supplies.

Harbour types

There are four main types of natural harbours. These are harbours in a coastal bay [1], river estuary harbours [3], inland harbours and the open roadstead harbour where a stretch of coast is relatively sheltered from

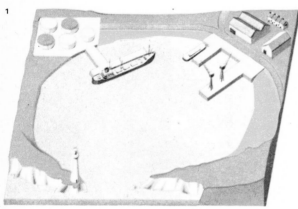

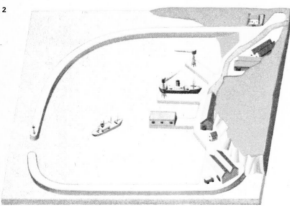

1

2

3

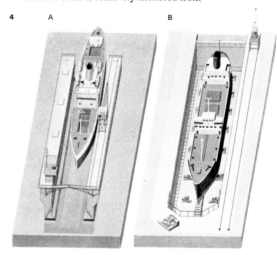

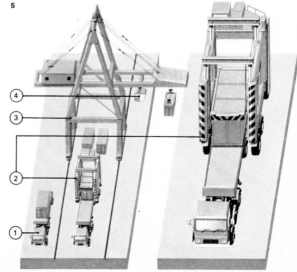

4   A   B

1 Natural harbours can be used without necessarily introducing improvements by engineering works. They are usually located in sheltered areas, such as enclosed bays or river estuaries. Those at Kingston, Jamaica, Southampton and San Francisco are examples. New York Harbour is one of the finest natural havens in the world with deep water, shelter, accessibility, small tidal variation and moderate current.

2 An artificial harbour, or shelter, can be formed in an exposed bay by the construction of a breakwater projecting from each shore. A single entrance is left open where the deepest water is found. The harbour at Colombo, situated in an exposed location in an embayment on the Sri Lanka coast, is typical. Others are the ferry port at Dover in the English Channel and the port of Monaco on the Mediterranean.

3 Estuaries often have wide entrances and then the river gradually narrows. Tides, therefore, are accentuated. The great tidal variation necessitates various devices to keep a relatively constant level between vessels and the shoreside facilities. At ports such as London, Liverpool, Le Havre and Antwerp large artificial basins are provided, separated from the tidal estuary by locks (wet docks), through which sea-going ships can enter.

4 A floating dock, or a dry dock, is where underwater ship repairs are carried out. A floating dock [A] is partly submerged and the ship is brought in. A dry dock [B] is a solid, permanent structure.

5 The container dock is equipped with special devices for handling pre-packed cargo. A lorry [1] brings containers to the dock. The "Spider" or travelling crane [2] carries the containers from the lorry and places them in a suitable position for the crane [3], which loads the containers on to the ship. The crane's central cabin [4] follows the container as it is loaded.

storms (moorings may be protected by breakwaters). Ports, too, are of four main types: commercial ports, naval ports, fishing ports and (a modern development) leisure ports, often called marinas, for yachts and power craft.

Commercial ports are vital to today's economy based on industry and trade, and they play a variety of specialized roles. There are highly mechanized cargo ports, including container ports [6]; passenger ports for ocean liners; short-haul passenger and drive-on ferry ports; and the new hoverports.

There are many natural harbours in the world, and among the finest in constant use are New York, San Francisco, Liverpool, Buenos Aires, Montevideo, Le Havre, Brisbane and Sydney. Of these New York has the advantage of enormous capacity providing about 720km (450 miles) of potential natural berthing along with 240km (150 miles) of man-made piers. The inner harbour is a perfect land-locked haven with adequate depth, a tidal range of less than 1.7m (5.6ft) and moderate tidal currents. The outer harbour, beyond the Verazzano Narrows, is protected

from rough weather by extensive sandbanks.

Inland ports are typified by Chicago, situated on Lake Michigan. It is 3,000km (1,900 miles) from the Gulf of St Lawrence, but connected to it. The channel runs via Lake Huron, Detroit, Lake Erie, and the 9m (30ft) deep Welland Ship Canal, which carries ocean-going ships 44km (27 miles) from Lake Erie to Lake Ontario (bypassing the Niagara Falls). From there it runs along the St Lawrence Seaway, via Montreal and Quebec, to the Atlantic Ocean.

Port maintenance

Most important of the maintenance operations of most river ports (and the majority of the world's ports are river ports) is dredging out the silt that accumulates in estuaries. Most modern ocean-going ships have a draught (depth below the waterline) of between 10 and 15m (33 and 49ft), and trailing suction dredges are kept constantly at work maintaining the depths of the channels. The new breed of supertankers need up to 25m (82ft) of water, so modern oil ports require unusually deep channels.

Falmouth's natural harbour on the south coast of Cornwall, England, has had a place in history for hundreds of years as a haven for ships seeking shelter from Atlantic storms, as a coastal port and as a mail-packet station. Today it is the headquarters of the Royal Cornwall Yacht Club.

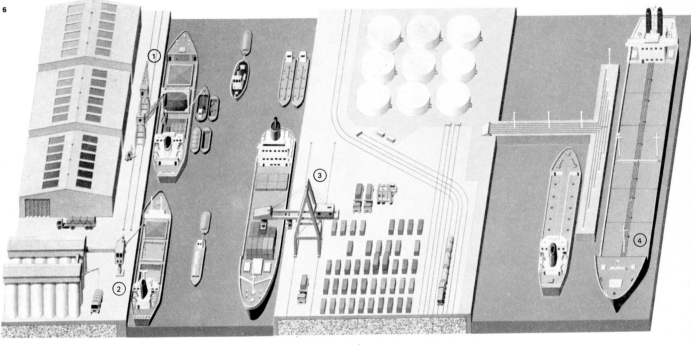

6 A multi-purpose port handles various types of cargo from different types of ships. When a normal cargo ship unloads at a typical dockside [1], the cargo is removed from the open hold by cranes and stored in warehouses. The cranes are generally mounted on rails so that they can be moved along the quayside. Some cargo may be unloaded by the ship's own derricks into barges or lighters moored alongside. A bulk grain ship [2] is loaded or unloaded by means of pumps connected with dockside silos. A container ship [3] provides maximum speed and efficiency for mixed cargo, as described in illustration 5. Today's large oil tankers [4] and supertankers have too great a draught to be able to dock normally in a port. They may moor offshore, unloading their crude oil by hose to land or into smaller tankers moored alongside.

7 The cargo-handling capacity of a modern port is in proportion to the capital invested in cranes and other heavy mechanical handling devices. Apart from the traditional luffing crane running on dockside rails, special grab cranes are used at industrial ports for the handling of coal and ore. Floating cranes operating from pontoons are used for unusually bulky and heavy lifts. Rotterdam currently handles more goods each year than any other port. Next in size are New York and Marseille. Each crate on this diagram represents 25 million tonnes of cargo in and out of the ports each year. The port of Rotterdam handles 268 million tonnes a year, New York 132 million, Marseille 83 million, Antwerp 67 million, London 66 million and the port of Tokyo 46 million. In the 20 years up to the mid-1970s the tonnages handled by some of these ports increased by seven times.

8 Harbour construction presents many problems. These necessitate building firm foundations and protecting against salt water corrosion. Quay construction varies. The solid type [A] has a paved apron [1] above the water level [2], supported by concrete blocks [3]. The bottom is dredged [4]. In one pile type [B] the timber apron [5] above the water level [6] rests on concrete piles [7]; it can be backed by sheet piling.

7

	Million tonnes
Rotterdam	
250	
225	
200	
175	
150	
New York	
125	
100	Marseille
75	Antwerp London
50	Tokyo
25	

8A

B

Canal construction

Modern canals provide important transport highways throughout Eurpe and, to a lesser extent, North America. The rivers Rhine and Moselle feed an extensive canal system in Germany that has connections to the Dutch, Belgian and French networks. A new major waterway is under construction to connect the Rhine with the Black Sea, via the rivers Main and Danube, and a great network has been developed around the rivers Volga, Ob, Yenisei and Lena across the USSR.

Canals ancient and modern

The four greatest achievements by canal engineers were undoubtedly the Suez Canal, opened in 1868 [8], the Panama Canal, completed in 1914 [6], the canals of the St Lawrence Seaway, opened in 1959 [2] and the 320km (200 miles) of canal linking the White Sea to the Baltic, opened in 1975.

One of the earliest reports of a man-made canal tells of one completed by Ptolemy II (died 247 BC) of Egypt to link the River Nile with the Red Sea. Natural inland waterways such as major rivers had been used as transport routes since earliest times and primitive single-gate locks are known to have been used in China from about 500 BC. These were openings in weirs through which water poured. Boats were carried downstream by the rushing waters or winched up against the current. A two-gate lock, built at Vreeswijk, Holland, in 1373, is believed to have been the first true pound-lock – a lock in which the flow of water is controlled by alternately lifting up or lowering the gates. The first to have swinging mitre gates of the kind used today was designed and built by Leonardo da Vinci (1452–1519) when he was engineer to the Duke of Milan. Mitre lock gates, when closed, form an angle pointing upstream so that water pressure holds them shut.

In 1681 French engineers made history when they completed the 250km (155 mile) long Canal du Midi linking the Atlantic Ocean with the Mediterranean Sea by a man-made waterway. It had many locks connecting the River Garonne, near Toulouse, with the River Etang de Thau, near Sète and included three aqueducts and a tunnel.

The greatest single obstacle to the industrial development of Europe and the United States in the eighteenth century was poor internal communication. Thus it was the needs of industry that brought about the dawn of the canal age on both sides of the Atlantic.

In the United States canals were built to link the Ohio and Mississippi basins [1] with the east coast ports, to provide routes from inland areas to the navigable rivers and to bypass natural obstacles on these rivers. The most spectacular early American achievement was the completion, in 1825, of the 580km (363 mile) Erie Canal linking New York City with Lake Erie. It took eight years to build. The lake was subsequently connected by canal to the Ohio River and so to the Mississippi and the port of New Orleans.

The British achievement

By 1850 England was traversed by more than 8,000km (5,000 miles) of navigable rivers and canals. Canals were also constructed throughout Europe, especially along the North Sea coasts of the Netherlands, Belgium and France.

During the nineteenth century British

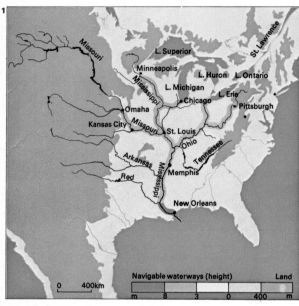

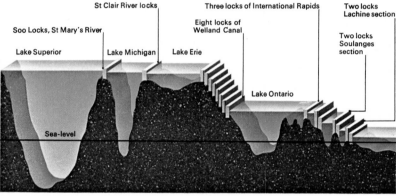

2 The St Lawrence Seaway provides a 3,830km (2,380 mile) inland route for ocean-going ships from the Atlantic to the heart of Canada and the USA. From Montreal it rises 51.5m (169ft) to Lake Ontario via two small lakes, three canals and seven locks. Between Lake Ontario and Lake Erie the waterway bypasses the Niagara Falls, rising 98m (322ft) in 45km (28 miles) through the eight locks of the Welland Ship Canal. From Lake Erie the route passes via Detroit and the St Clair River and lake into Lake Huron. This lake connects directly with Lake Michigan, via the Mackinac Strait, so linking the port of Chicago with the sea. The St Mary's Falls, between the northern point of Lake Huron and Lake Superior, are passed by a canal with five locks. This section is icebound in winter.

1 The river systems of the Mississippi and Ohio form one of the largest in the world. Their basins cover two-thirds of the USA. Many of the rivers are navigable and canals have been built to connect other waterways, extending the system to provide a continuous water route from New Orleans in the south to Chicago and the St Lawrence Seaway, and via the Ohio River direct to New York. Pittsburgh and Philadelphia were also in the 19th-century canal network, which connected with both the Columbia River and Chesapeake Bay. There is also a link from New York direct to the St Lawrence.

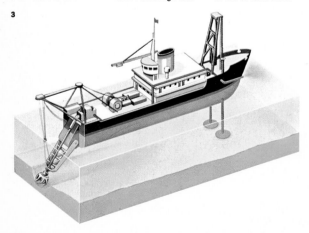

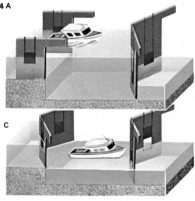

3 The depth of a shipping canal must be rigorously maintained to ensure that ships do not ground, causing delay not only to themselves but to all shipping along the length of the water channel. Dredgers of many types are used. This cutter dredge has a twin-leg bracing system to resist the action of the rotary cutter. A suction pipe close to the cutter draws off the debris and discharges it away from the vessel or into a barge moored alongside.

4 Passing down a lock, a vessel first enters it from the higher level [A] and the gates are shut behind it. Sluices in or around the lower gates are then opened [B], allowing water from the lock to pass to the lower level, lowering the water level and with it the floating vessel. When the lock level equals the lower canal level [C], the lower gates are opened [D]. Sluices in or around the upper gates are used to raise the lock level whenever a vessel passes up the canal.

civil engineers conceived and constructed a perennial irrigation system in northwestern India [5] in which huge masonry barrages were built across the rivers to divert part of the water into a great network of canals. By the time India and Pakistan gained independence in 1947 the subcontinent had more than 20 million hectares (50 million acres) of previously arid land under irrigation.

Technique of canal engineering

A canal, unlike a road, must be built in level sections and the canal engineer's first problem is the selection of a route along which a level can be maintained with the minimum of engineering work. This problem is approached by siting a canal to run as far as possible along the natural land contours. Where high ground must be crossed the cut can be correspondingly deeper or the canal can be built in a tunnel. Where there is an unavoidable depression in the ground the best solution is to construct the canal along a low embankment. There comes a point where the rise or fall of the land to be traversed requires so deep a cut, so long a tunnel or so high an embankment or aqueduct that it is more economic to build a lock and continue the canal at a new level.

Wherever canals are built obstacles, such as roads, streams and rivers, have to be crossed. If they are roads or railways, bridges must be built; if they are waterways, then either the canal or the waterway must be carried on an aqueduct [9]. Where locks are introduced there must be a sufficient supply of water at the highest level to replace the water that flows when any lock is used [4].

A canal must not lose excessive water by seepage into the ground. Where the ground is porous, and where a canal runs along a man-made embankment, the engineer must waterproof its bottom and sides. In early canals this was achieved by lining the canal with puddled clay. Today there are alternative materials including bituminous materials, sheet polythene and concrete. Machines have been developed to lay a continuous concrete lining at minimum cost [7] and these are increasingly used for irrigation canals in the Middle East and other arid areas to carry water long distances.

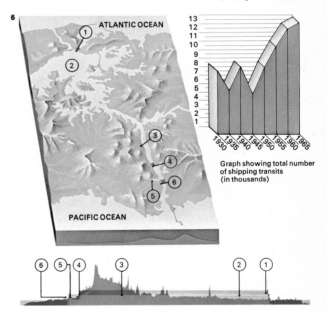

KEY

A massive excavation 5.6km (3.5 miles) long was made in 1893 across the isthmus at Corinth to link the Ionian and Aegean seas. The Corinth ship canal has no locks, the whole waterway being at sea level to allow the direct passage of vessels.

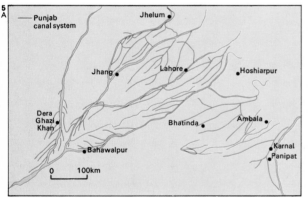

5
A

Punjab canal system

Jhelum

Jhang   Lahore   Hoshiarpur

Dera Ghazi Khan   Bhatinda   Ambala

Bahawalpur   Karnal
Panipat

0   100km

B

5 A system of irrigation canals in western Punjab [A], constructed by British engineers, was one of the major engineering achievements of the 19th century. These were running water canals fed from the River Indus and its tributaries by building great masonry barrages. They turned an arid area half the size of England into northern India's most fertile food-producing region [B].

6 The Panama Canal links the Atlantic and Pacific oceans, enabling ships that are less than 306m (1,000ft) long, 34m (112ft) in the beam and have a draught of less than 12m (40ft) to avoid the voyage around South America. From the Atlantic an 11km (7 mile) sea-level stretch ends at the Gatun Locks [1] leading to Lake Gatun [2], 26m (85ft) above sea-level. The route then runs 38km (24 miles) across Lake Gatun, along the Gaillard Cut [3] to the Pedro Miguel Lock [4] and Miraflores Lake [5], 16 m (53ft) above sea-level. Finally the Miraflores Locks [6] drop down to sea-level and lead to the Pacific Ocean.

ATLANTIC OCEAN

PACIFIC OCEAN

13
12
11
10
9
8
7
6
5
4
3
2
1

1930 1935 1940 1945 1950 1955 1960 1965

Graph showing total number of shipping transits (in thousands)

7 Construction techniques in canal engineering include the use of special lining machines, as in the Jordan Canal section of Israel's National Water Carrier. Wet concrete is fed on to a conveyor belt and, as the machine moves forwards on caterpillar tracks, an even layer 10cm (4in) thick is laid as a continuous strip. The Israeli system carries water 28km (17 miles) from Lake Tiberius southwards in an open canal to feed a pipeline extending much farther to the south.

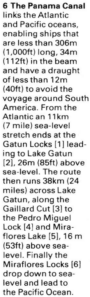

Port Said

MEDITERRANEAN SEA

Great Bitter Lake

Canal
Road   Suez
0   20km   RED SEA

8 The Suez Canal, opened after a decade of effort by French engineer Ferdinand de Lesseps (1805–94), was dug out of the desert by hand. It connects the Red Sea with the Mediterranean and covers a distance of 169km (105 miles). It has a minimum width of 150m (500ft) and a minimum depth of 10m (33ft). Britain bought a controlling share in the canal from the Khedive of Egypt in 1875 and retained control until Egypt's President Nasser nationalized it in 1956. The canal was blocked with sunken ships during the 1967 Arab-Israeli war and was cleared and reopened only in 1975.

9 An aqueduct built over a road is often necessary in canal engineering for economic reasons, as in this case in the Netherlands. Because the canal is full of water it has to be built to one level throughout, or in level reaches connected by locks. This is achieved by judicious choice of route, by cutting deeper into high ground and by building on a raised embankment over low-lying areas. Most roads cross canals by bridges.

71

Building dams

Control of his life-sustaining water supply has always been one of man's primary concerns. For 5,000 years, dams have been instrumental in this control, being used to avert floods, divert rivers, store water and irrigate land. Many of today's constructions fulfil these same age-old functions; dams are still used for agricultural irrigation and domestic water storage and supply, as well as for the more sophisticated purposes of hydroelectric power generation, land reclamation, control of erosion by floods and the prevention of build-up of silt.

The use of barriers to divert part of a river's flow into irrigation canals was developed by British engineers during the nineteenth century, and used widely in the Punjab of northern India. French engineers built a similar barrage across the River Nile, which allowed the summer flood to pass over it but formed a reservoir from which the water was led, during the spring and early summer, into irrigation canals. In this way, huge areas of previously parched land were made productive.

The development of modern engineering materials and techniques have since made it possible not only to divert part of a river's water, but also to hold and store water by the creation of huge lakes behind a solid dam wall. A typical early example is the Hoover Dam, built across the Colorado River in the United States. Completed in 1936, this dam has a reservoir capacity of 38,000 million cubic metres (49,000 million cubic yards) and a power output, from the water released through its turbines, of 1,340 megawatts.

Dam design

There are two main types of modern dams: embankment dams, built from earth and rockfill, and concrete dams (which may or may not be reinforced). Embankment dams came first and today are generally the cheapest to build because they need fewer workers. They include the world's tallest dams, such as the 310m (1,017ft) Nurek Dam in the USSR, and the 234m (770ft) Oroville Dam in the United States. They are built from the natural earth and rock found near the site, consisting essentially of a central earth core to hold back the water, faced and supported on each side with more earth or rock. "Filter curtains" between the various layers prevent fine grains from one being washed into the voids of the next.

Embankment dams are suitable for nearly all sites because they can withstand some settlement of the foundation and do not need strong valley sides. A deep trench filled with compacted clay or concrete forms a curtain to prevent water from seeping under the dam. A line of wells under the toe of the dam collects any seepage water and leads it back to the course of the river.

The greater strength of rockfill allows it to be used with steeper slopes. One of the cheapest types of dam has rockfill with a waterproof skin of bitumen concrete on the reservoir side.

There are a number of designs for concrete dams. The simplest, the gravity dam, works rather like a bookend, its own weight preventing it from being turned over by the force of the reservoir water. Volume of material is reduced by a buttress construction.

An arch dam, a more sophisticated construction, is like an arch bridge lying on its

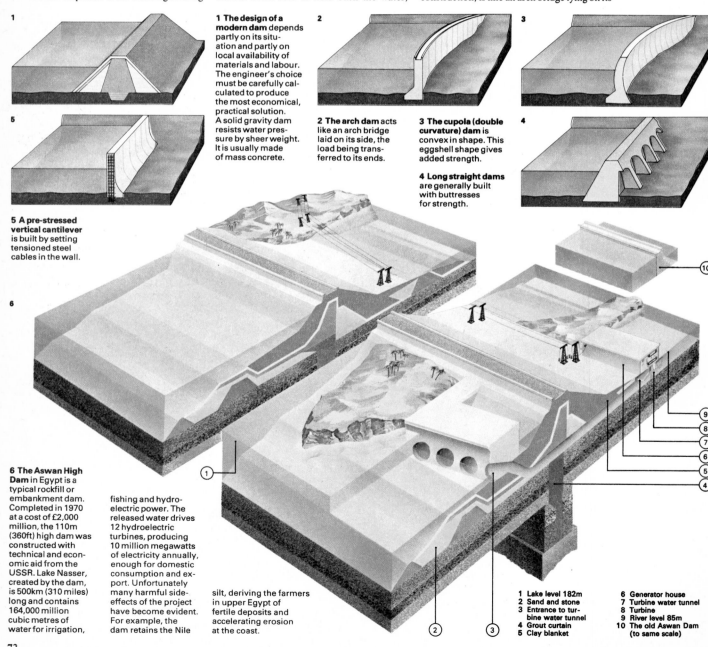

1 The design of a modern dam depends partly on its situation and partly on local availability of materials and labour. The engineer's choice must be carefully calculated to produce the most economical, practical solution. A solid gravity dam resists water pressure by sheer weight. It is usually made of mass concrete.

2 The arch dam acts like an arch bridge laid on its side, the load being transferred to its ends.

3 The cupola (double curvature) dam is convex in shape. This eggshell shape gives added strength.

4 Long straight dams are generally built with buttresses for strength.

5 A pre-stressed vertical cantilever is built by setting tensioned steel cables in the wall.

6 The Aswan High Dam in Egypt is a typical rockfill or embankment dam. Completed in 1970 at a cost of £2,000 million, the 110m (360ft) high dam was constructed with technical and economic aid from the USSR. Lake Nasser, created by the dam, is 500km (310 miles) long and contains 164,000 million cubic metres of water for irrigation, fishing and hydro-electric power. The released water drives 12 hydroelectric turbines, producing 10 million megawatts of electricity annually, enough for domestic consumption and export. Unfortunately many harmful side-effects of the project have become evident. For example, the dam retains the Nile silt, depriving the farmers in upper Egypt of fertile deposits and accelerating erosion at the coast.

1 Lake level 182m
2 Sand and stone
3 Entrance to turbine water tunnel
4 Grout curtain
5 Clay blanket
6 Generator house
7 Turbine water tunnel
8 Turbine
9 River level 85m
10 The old Aswan Dam (to same scale)

side. The curve of the arch is designed so that the concrete (weak in tension) is held permanently in compression. For success, this type of dam has to be firmly keyed into the rock of the valley sides at its ends.

The thinnest type of dam, also with its concrete kept in compression, is the double-curved cupola dam. It is shaped rather like half an egg, with the bulge facing into the pressure of the reservoir water.

Dam foundations
Engineers generally fill fissures in the rock foundation of a concrete dam with a curtain of grout. A drainage system leads away any seepage water, to prevent a build-up of pressure under the dam. There is often a row of drainage wells, drilled into the rock from a gallery running the length of the dam.

To construct the foundation of a dam while water is flowing, engineers generally drive a diversion tunnel through the rock of the valley wall around the dam site, before the construction work starts on the dam itself [7]. A temporary dam is then constructed to divert the water into the tunnel and the main

dam constructed on the dry downstream side of the temporary one.

Every dam construction must allow excess water to flow away in times of flood, without causing erosion in the process. The excess is usually dispersed in one of three ways: by a concrete-lined spillway at a level lower than the top of the dam; by an overflow shaft – usually funnel-mouthed – leading vertically down from a point well within the reservoir; or by an overflow channel or tunnel leading from a point at the side of the reservoir to below the dam.

Great modern dams
The world's greatest dams (in terms of reservoir capacity) are: Owen Falls, Uganda, built across the Victoria Nile in 1954 and holding a reservoir of 205,000 million cubic metres behind a gravity dam; Bratsk Dam, USSR, built across the River Angara in 1964 (169,000 million cubic metres), a concrete gravity dam; and Aswan High Dam [6], Egypt, built across the River Nile and completed in 1970 (164,000 million cubic metres), a rockfill embankment.

KEY

The Cubuk Dam, 10km (6 miles) north of modern Ankara, straddles the River Cubuk to form a reservoir with a capacity of 10 million cubic metres. This huge man-made lake provides Ankara with

most of its water supply and there is a hydroelectric station to exploit the energy of the water flowing out. Set in an attractive wooded valley, this important engineering achievement has

played a significant role in the industrial development of eastern Turkey. It has also been promoted as a recreation area and tourist centre, and has a fine casino and other forms of entertainment.

7

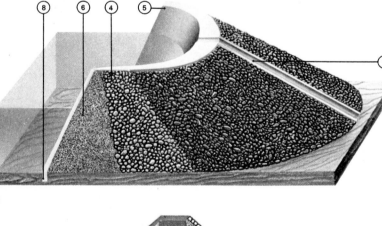

9

7 A river must be diverted before it can be dammed. A temporary coffer dam [1] is built and the water diverted via tunnels [2]. The permanent dam is then constructed behind the coffer dam. The rock core [3] of this gravity dam is first laid and compacted. Rubble [4] and an impervious facing [5] are added to the steep, concave upstream slope [6] and the spillway [7] to the downstream side. It is now vital that no subsequent settlement occurs. The impervious facing is grouted into the bedrock [8] to prevent seepage under the dam. The coffer dam is usually incorporated into the structure of the finished permanent dam.

8 Laboratory testing of hydraulic models often precedes the start of work on the actual dam. These models give advance data on patterns of erosion which the water flow may cause. By this means the

engineer who designs a river barrage or the outflow channels of a hydroelectric scheme can avoid the problems of water scour; he includes preventive measures in the design before construction begins.

9 An earthfill dam is begun by digging a trench until impervious rock is reached. This is excavated and the first layer of impervious core material (probably clay) is grouted into this trench [1]. Successive layers [2] of clay are added and rolled until

they are completely compact. Once this foundation is ready only the core is formed from impervious material [3]. The rest of the dam is constructed with layers of any soil [4]. The upstream slope [5] is covered with gravel [6]

and surfaced with rocks called rip-rap [7] to prevent water erosion. The downstream slope [8] is sown with vegetation [9] for stability. A spillway [10] is usually built into the slope to allow water to flow over the dam in times of flooding.

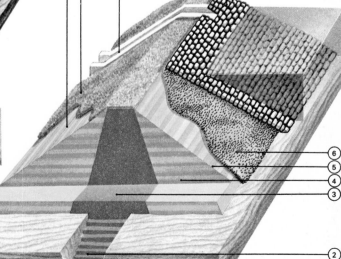

Water supply

The more sophisticated man becomes the thirstier he grows. In developing countries (the Third World), some communities manage with an average of 12 litres (2.5 gallons) of water per person per day. In most European cities the daily domestic consumption per head of population is nearer 150 litres (33 gallons). In the most prosperous urban areas of the United States the figure can be as high as 250 litres (55 gallons).

Demands and resources

Domestic consumption of water mounts steadily but even this is far outweighed by the demands of modern industry. The production of steel needs 300kg (660lb) of water for each kilogramme (2lb) of manufactured steel, although some of this is returned to its source. The total average daily water consumption in a Western city – domestic, commercial and industrial – may be as high as 2,000 litres (400 gallons) per head.

Agriculture's demands are even greater. To produce one kilogramme of wheat a farmer may "use" up to 1,500kg (3,300lb) of water from rain, irrigation or both.

Water is the world's most plentiful natural substance and is in constant circulation [Key]. But man's demand for water often exceeds the local natural supply. It is the engineer's job to transport water to where it is needed and to purify it as necessary.

Collection and storage

Water is normally collected from underground sources by drilling and pumping. The old farmhouse well and bucket provide an example of the extraction of flowing ground water by the simple expedient of digging until the natural water-table is reached. In the case of trapped "fossil" water, sometimes found under deserts, the water is not replaced by natural flow and the process of removing it is a form of mining – the extraction of a limited resource. Deep-lying water under pressure can be tapped by the bore-hole of an artesian well, in which the water is forced up the bore without the need for pumps.

There are three ways of exploiting surface water. The first is by pumping, from rivers [2] or lakes, the second is by building a barrage across a river and diverting its flow through

canals or pipelines and the third is by constructing a dam across a valley at the lower end of a natural catchment area.

Apart from short-term local storage, water is normally stored in large, open reservoirs into which it is pumped, or in the huge, man-made lakes which form, by means of gravity flow, behind the walls of valley dams.

Water purification

Natural water, other than the rain, is rarely pure. Rivers in peaty moorland pick up traces of organic acids. Ground water takes up mineral salts including common salt (up to 0.1 per cent is tolerable in drinking water), calcium bicarbonate (above 0.02 per cent makes water unacceptably "hard") and fluorides (amounts above 0.0001 per cent, but not exceeding 0.00015 per cent are said to reduce tooth decay).

The Industrial Revolution produced a new problem. The discharge of effluents – factory waste products – into rivers resulted in chemical pollution and the development of water-borne sewage systems caused bacteriological pollution. Today many coun-

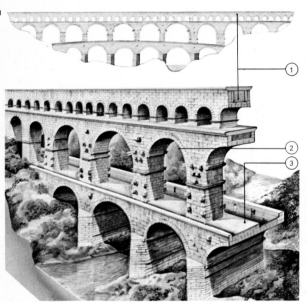

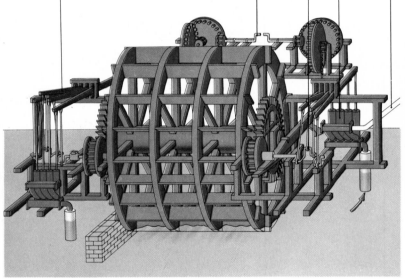

1 One of the first major water supply systems was built by the Romans. Their first nine aqueducts, constructed between 312 BC and AD 226, conveyed water by gravity feed from various sources to Rome. The longest, the Aqua Marcia, extended 90km (56 miles) and bridged low-lying land by a water channel of cut stone slabs raised on a succession of stone arches. The Roman aqueduct here is the 274m (900ft) long Pont du Gard in France. The top tier carries the water channel [1], the lower tier a footbridge [3]. So accurate were the Roman masons that the stones of the two lower tiers of arches, including the voussoirs [2], were laid dry without mortar.

2 As a city grows, so does its demand for water. The London Bridge Waterworks were opened in 1581 to serve the City of London. By the 19th century, the huge waterworks and pumps were capable of supplying almost four million gallons of river water daily. However the fall of water from the works was so great that it endangered navigation on the river and the works were completely removed in 1822. The river current turned the great wheel which rotated the crankshafts [3]. These operated the pumps [4] via levers [1], water being discharged through pipes [5]. The supply of water was controlled by turning the cranks [2] which raised and lowered the pumps.

3 The modern water treatment plant can be very complex as this diagram shows. Here raw river water is screened at the intake and drawn by pumps to an upward flow sedimentation tank. A flocculant (chlorinated ferrous sulphate) and softener (lime slurry) are added as the water enters, the lime also regulating the acidity. The sludge formed in the sedimentation tank is pumped to a sludge lagoon from which the clear water is recycled. Activated carbon is then added to absorb impurities of the kind that give an unacceptable taste, smell or colour to water. The water then flows into a rapid gravity filter in which any organic matter is decomposed by non-pathogenic bacteria to form unobjectionable inorganic products. One of two chlorinators supplies chlorine gas as a sterilizer and additional lime is added as the water enters the contact tank. (The second chlorinator feeds the flocculant supply.) A sulphonator feeds the contact tank with sulphur dioxide, which dechlorinates the sterilized water. Finally the treated water is pumped to the mains supply system where it is stored in water towers or reservoirs before distribution to domestic consumers and industry.

Diagram labels: Lime slurry; Chlorine; Chlorinated ferrous sulphate; Sulphur dioxide; Intake; Sedimentation tank; Activated carbon; Pump; Pump; Sludge lagoon; Rapid gravity filter; Contact tank

tries have laws to control chemical pollution, and bacteria are eliminated by treatment.

The principal processes of water treatment [3] are sedimentation, filtration, aeration and sterilization. Sedimentation is merely settling, carried out by allowing water to stand in large, shallow basins; solid particles sink slowly to the bottom. Sedimentation is aided by the addition of a flocculant, such as alum, which causes the smallest particles to clump together. Filtration is carried out by passing water through a sand bed – 100m × 40m (328ft × 131ft) is a typical size - in which harmless bacteria (in a layer up to 30cm (12in) deep) decomposes organic matter in the water passing through, forming unobjectionable inorganic substances. A rapid sand filter may be only 8m × 5m (26ft × 16.4ft) in size and 4m (13ft) deep. It is cheaper and filters 20 times faster, but the filtered water is never entirely bacteria free.

Aeration (usually effected by passing water over a cascade) increases the amount of dissolved oxygen in the water, reduces the carbon dioxide content by as much as 60 per cent and aids natural inorganic purification

by aerobic bacteria. Sterilization (killing harmful micro-organisms) is achieved, where bacteriological pollution has been high, by the addition of small quantities of chlorine or ozone. A dose of 0.0001 per cent of chlorine destroys all germs within four minutes.

Where exceptionally pure water is required, demineralization (softening) may be carried out. Here the exchange of the "salt" part of soluble mineral salts forms easily eliminated non-soluble compounds.

Where natural pure water is scarce and the sea near, the process of desalination (removing salt) is used today to produce water for both human and agricultural use. The main processes for eliminating the dissolved salts are called distillation, electrodialysis, reverse osmosis and freezing. Multi-stage flash distillation [5] is used in most modern desalination plants, using steam as the heat source.

Today most water is distributed by pumping it to a local storage facility (usually a water tower), which provides sufficient static "head", or pressure, to force the water through a network of pipes.

The hydrologic cycle, powered by the sun's heat, keeps the world's stock of water in constant circulation. Enormous quantities are moved by evaporation from the sea, lakes and rivers and by transpiration from trees, crops and other vegetation. It moves through the atmosphere, condensing as clouds, then returns to the land as rain or snow, forming streams and rivers leading back to lakes and seas. It sinks into the soil forming aquifers, reappearing as springs.

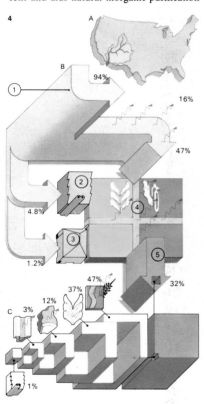

4 Growing salinity can pollute natural water. Man's "control" of the Colorado River in the United States has caused an excessively high salinity. The map [A] shows the location of the Colorado River. [B] shows how the water obtained from the river is used. The total capacity of the Colorado River [1] is approximately 60 thousand million litres per day; 94% is supplied to agriculture, although 16% of this is lost in evaporation before it reaches the farms.

Of total capacity 4.8% [2] is supplied to industry and 1.2% [3] for domestic use. Run-off from all uses is 32% [5]. 47% of total capacity [4] is actually used by agriculture. The run-off is highly saline when it returns to the river. Salinity [C] in the water is caused by evaporation from the river (47%), evaporation from land and transpiration of plants (37%), evaporation from reservoirs (12%), evaporation from canals (3%) and from industry (1%). In highly developed

industrial countries industry has been responsible for some other forms of river pollution. Industrial effluents can cause serious chemical pollution and the disposal of water-borne sewage can be responsible for serious biological pollution. Legislation has been passed in many countries to help keep river water clean.

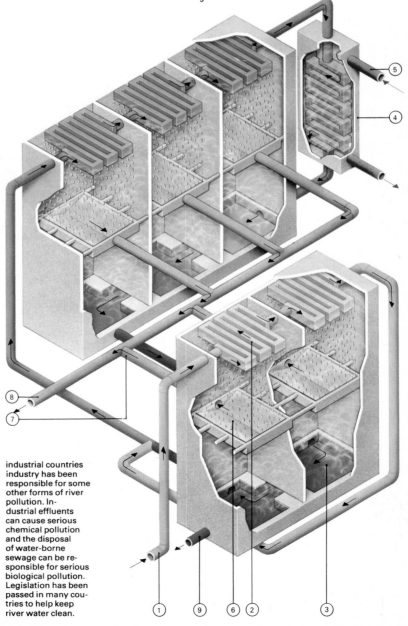

5 Desalination by flash-distillation is a widely used process. Raw seawater [1] is fed through the condensing coils [2] of the first two flash chambers. It is then mixed with strong brine from the brine pans [3] of these two chambers before passing on through the condensing coils of the third, fourth and fifth flash chambers. From there it passes through the heat exchanger [4] where it is heated by steam [5]. The seawater, then at 80°C (176°F), next flows through the brine pans of the five chambers in reverse order. Water vapour rises from the hot brine, condensing on the much cooler coils above. The condensate drips on to the fresh water catchment troughs [6] from which it is piped [7] into the main fresh water outlet [8]. Meanwhile the hot brine, on its way through the five chambers, grows progressively more concentrated and cooler. When it reaches the first chamber part of it is recycled by mixing with the sea water passing between the coils of the second and third chambers, the rest being discarded as waste [9]. Modern practice achieves economy in the desalination process by locating the plant, wherever possible, near a nuclear power station. The exhaust steam from the power plant can then be used as the main energy source for the distillation process.

Sewage treatment

As soon as early man established settlement he had the problem of getting rid of sewage – the organic wastes of man and, sometimes, domestic animals. Nature disposes of surplus organic material in four principal ways – by dilution, oxidation, putrefaction and filtration. Early man relied on these natural processes and generally dumped sewage in the fields. There its moisture seeped into the land, becoming filtered and purified. When rain fell on the solids they dissolved and were oxidized into natural nutrients for the soil.

The Roman system of aqueducts, built from 312 BC to AD 226, provided a water-borne sewage system that drained into the River Tiber. Today the large volumes of sewage from towns and cities need the resources of modern technology for efficient treatment and disposal. Also industrial wastes present additional problems for treatment plants if pollution is to be avoided.

Treatment by dilution
Sewage treatment by dilution works because water contains dissolved oxygen. When sewage contaminates a small volume of water, as in a lake or stream, aerobic bacteria (which oxidize the organic material) absorb the dissolved oxygen at a rate greater than it is naturally replaced from the air. As a result fish cannot live and the water is no longer self-purifying. But if the surface area of the water is large enough to dissolve oxygen faster than it is absorbed by the bacteria the water remains pure and unpolluted.

The River Thames in London provides an illuminating case history [Key]. In 1750 the city's population was 750,000 and the river was teeming with fish. It had long been used as a sewer but this had not seriously polluted the water. By 1840 the population was over two million and sewage, swollen in volume by industrial effluents, then exceeded the river's capacity for self-purification. Only eels had survived the advent of industrialization.

London's first sewage treatment works were commissioned in 1889. By 1900, with the population at over six million, six of the less sensitive species of fish had returned to its waters. Between the wars London's population grew to eight million people and industry increased. The sewage works could not handle the greater volumes of domestic and industrial effluent and by 1945 there were no fish in the river, which had become more polluted than ever. In the 1950s there was a drive to clean the river. New sewage works were built and by 1970 fish of many kinds had returned to the Thames.

The dangers of pollution
Health authorities today agree that the disposal of diluted sewage into lakes or rivers is satisfactory – if it contains not more than 30 parts per million of suspended solids and does not absorb more than 20 parts per million of dissolved oxygen in five days. The latter figure, called the "biochemical oxygen demand" (BOD), provides a means of measuring the degree of pollution.

Where there is sufficient water for effective sewage treatment by dilution, as on coasts, on the shores of major lakes, or near large rivers, sewage is sometimes discharged without prior treatment [4]. However, the growth of industry and high population densities usually require sewage treatment by processes designed to reduce its BOD to a

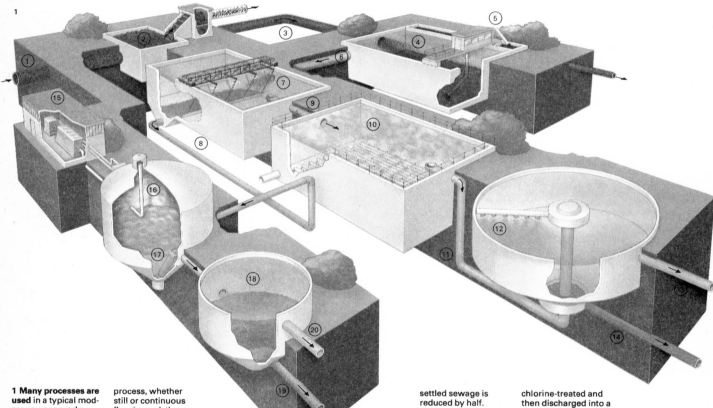

1 **Many processes are used** in a typical modern sewage works. The first stage consists of screening to remove solid material including heavy grit. Screenings are burnt to destroy microorganisms and render them inoffensive. Fine grit is next removed by gravity settlement. Screened, de-gritted sewage is then led to sedimentation tanks. The remaining suspended solids are eliminated. This reduces the liquid sewage strength by up to one half. As gravity precipitation is a slow process, whether still or continuous flow is used, the tanks provided for this purpose are usually duplicated and made large. The sludge and clear sewage are then treated separately. Clear sewage passes to aeration tanks where the organic content is destroyed by aerobic bacteria. The effluent from the aeration tanks is once again settled, the clear liquid chlorinated and discharged into a river or the sea. Sedimented sludge is fed to digestion tanks where it is warmed and allowed to putrify in the absence of air. This produces gas, to power the works itself and to heat the sludge tanks, and a nitrogen-rich "clean" sludge which is dried to form an excellent fertilizer. A typical process operates in the following way. Raw sewage [1] enters the works where coarse screens [2] remove solid trash (wood, rags and so on) from the sewage so that the machinery is not damaged or pipelines blocked. The screened sewage [3] is then pumped to grit-settling tanks [4] where grit and sand settle out and are dredged up, washed and then used as filling material such as aggregates for road-bed construction. The settled grit and sand [5] are removed to allow the grit-free sewage [6] to be pumped to the primary sedimentation tanks [7]. During this process 50 per cent of the suspended solids settle out to form sludge and the BOD of the settled sewage is reduced by half. The sludge [8] is then pumped to digestion tanks and settled sewage [9] pumped to the aerator [10], in which the sewage is mixed with bacteria-rich activated sludge. As the sewage is aerated the bacteria transform organic matter into harmless by-products. The aerated sewage [11] is pumped to a final settling tank or secondary sedimentation tank [12]. At this stage of the process activated sludge settles out, leaving a clear effluent. The upper liquid part [13] is filtered, chlorine-treated and then discharged into a lake or river. The activated sludge [14] is removed and re-used in the aerator with incoming settled sewage. In the power house [15], gas from the collector [16] – containing about 70 per cent methane – is burned to generate power for pumps and air compressors; some gas is used to heat the digestion tanks. The sludge that settles out is then pumped to the primary digestion tanks [17] which are kept at a temperature of 30°C (86°F). The temperature speeds the action of micro-organisms which, in the absence of oxygen, digest the sludge rapidly, producing gas and a relatively inoffensive sludge. The secondary digestion tanks [18] are where the digestion is completed (unheated) producing concentrated, nitrogen-rich sludge and relatively pure but bacteria-rich water. The sludge [19] is then removed and after going through a drying process is used as a fertilizer. Finally, water [20] is drawn off and discharged into a lake, river or the sea.

very low figure before discharge and sometimes to eliminate all bacteria.

Sewage treatment by putrefaction is a natural process in which anaerobic bacteria destroy organic matter by breaking it down into simpler substances. The products are nitrogen-rich humus and a mixture of gases in which methane predominates.

A modern sewage works [1] uses both the natural oxidation and putrefaction processes in treating sewage. It also uses several other processes that may include screening, sedimentation, flocculation, digestion, aeration, filtration and chlorination. Industrial effluents often require other special treatments to eliminate toxic substances before they are discharged into the disposal system.

Modern treatment processes

Screening is simply the removal of large, solid particles by passing the sewage through a wire screen or other form of mesh. Quiescent sedimentation is natural settlement of sediment by gravity in undisturbed tanks. Continuous-flow sedimentation achieves the same result by passing the fluid slowly,

without turbulence, through long, relatively shallow tanks and out over a weir. Flocculation, mechanical or chemical, makes non-settling material coagulate into particles of sufficient size to settle by gravity. Alum is an efficient flocculent but is too expensive for general use in sewage works. Mechanical flocculation is achieved by slow stirring.

Digestion uses natural aerobic putrefaction, producing gas and a sludge which, when dried, forms a useful fertilizer. Some sewage works use the gas to produce power and light, and often warm digestion tanks by passing gas-heated water through coils fixed inside them. Heating speeds the digestion process but it is generally too expensive because it consumes too much energy.

Aeration employs natural oxidation to reduce the BOD of clear sewage, following sedimentation. It is commonly achieved by pumping air bubbles through the lower part of the tank and redistributing the clear sewage over the surface in the form of a rotating spray. Filtration and chlorination remove the final effluent from the water, leaving it totally free from bacteria.

In 1858 the Thames was so polluted that *Punch*, England's weekly humour magazine, printed this savage caricature of Death rowing through its flotsam and jet-sam. The flow of sewage, a product of the Industrial Revolution, into the Thames created an enormous health hazard. *Punch* called its cartoon "The 'Silent Highway' – Man" and gave it the sub-title "Your MONEY or your LIFE!" In 1889, 31 years later, London commissioned its first sewage works.

2 A septic tank can process sewage from buildings not connected to the local authority's drainage system. It is a watertight, airtight underground tank that serves the triple purpose of sedimentation, digestion and sludge storage. Digestion is automatic, being effected by anaerobic bacteria. Effluent should be led to a deep soakaway and sludge pumped out every 3 – 6 months. The tank's walls are waterproof [2], usually of cement-rendered brick. Sewage enters through the inlet pipe [1] and is delivered low in the tank [3] without stirring the contents. Relatively pure water [4] separates above the sludge, anaerobic bacteria digest the sewage [5] and the sludge sinks [6]. Gas escapes up the vent pipe [7] and a gas trap [8] prevents it passing back into the inspection chamber.

3 The sludge from a septic tank must be pumped out once every three to six months. A custom-built tanker, the sludge gulper, is used by local authorities for this purpose. A sludge removal vehicle must have a tank large enough to empty the largest septic tanks in its area in one lift, for partial emptying results in the scum being left behind. The vehicles pump out liquid sludge through a long flexible hose.

4 Untreated sewage used to be discharged into rivers, estuaries or the sea [A], leading to pollution and the possible spread of disease. Today most industrialized countries process sewage in treatment plants [B]. One of the problems of modern sewage treatment is the presence in urban waste of ever-increasing quantities of detergents. Domestic detergents must by law be biodegradable, so that they are digested by bacteria, but most sewage treatment plants are unable to remove the phosphates usually found in detergents. These act as nutrients to green algae, which grow too quickly and upset the natural biochemical processes that keep water pure in lakes and rivers.

5 The digestion of sedimented sewage sludge in a modern sewage works results in the production of a relatively inoffensive nitrogen-rich sludge which, after drying, forms an excellent general fertilizer ready for immediate use on the land.

History of printing

Movable metal type was probably first produced in the Royal Type Foundry of Korea in 1403 and a book was printed from this type six years later. But not until 1439 is there evidence of printing, as we know it today, in Europe. It was a German, Johannes Gutenberg (1400–68), working in Strasbourg, who developed printing using movable type.

Early printing methods
In the year 1456 the first substantial printed book appeared. This was a Latin Bible printed in Mainz, almost certainly by Johannes Gutenberg and his associates [2]. How Gutenberg manufactured his type is not known and it was not until 1540, in Vanoccio Biringuccio's book *De la pirotechnia*, printed in Venice, that there was a description of typefounding. Type was made by pouring molten metal into a copper matrix or mould formed by punching an engraved steel character into a piece of copper.

From the days of Gutenberg there were, for many centuries, no significant changes in the basic methods used for printing. Metal type was set by hand into pages known as formes and these were inked and printed on to single sheets of paper in a hand press [Key]. The first change came in 1795 when Firmin Didot (1764–1836) tested ways of making duplicate printing plates (stereotypes) from set type.

Three years later lithography was invented by Aloys Senefelder (1771–1834) of Munich. While seeking a practical method of printing musical scores he tried drawing the music in reverse on a flat slab of stone, using an ink made of wax, soap and lampblack. His original idea was to etch the stone with acid but his experiments led to an entirely new printing process based on the mutual repulsion of oil-based ink and water.

From plates to printing machines
Didot's stereotype process was perfected in 1800 by Charles Stanhope, third Earl Stanhope (1753–1816), who used plaster of paris to make the moulds of the set type. Molten metal was then poured into the plaster moulds to produce solid printing plates, a whole page at a time. In 1806 Anthony Berte of London invented a mechanical device for typecasting, using a pump to force molten metal into the matrix.

In the meantime Friedrich König (1774–1833), a German printer who moved to England in 1806, built the first successful printing machine in which a series of leather-covered rollers, fed with ink from a container, automatically inked the type as it travelled to and from the printing platen. Except for the laying on and removing of the paper from the platen, this steam-powered press was automatic. In the following year König designed a cylinder printing machine in which the type forme was fixed to a bed which moved first under leather-covered inking rollers and then under a cylinder around which the paper was held. Soon after the first single-cylinder machine was successfully demonstrated in London two machines, each with twin cylinders, were manufactured.

Nineteenth-century progress
In 1816 an Englishman, Edward Cowper (1790–1852), secured a patent for a method of bending stereotype plates for rotary printing, the plate first being cast flat in a

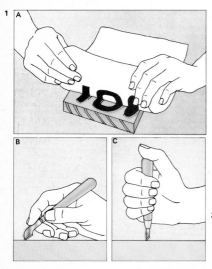

1 The woodcut was developed from the early 15th century onwards to produce devotional prints and playing cards. The artist cuts away the part of the design that is to appear white, so that only the parts to be inked appear in relief [A]. The block is cut along the grain using well-seasoned wood from apple, pear, cherry, sycamore or oak trees. Some early woodcuts were hand-coloured but prints can be produced by using a series of blocks. A variety of tools were used, such as the English knife [B] and the Japanese knife [C].

2 The first substantial book printed from movable type was the Latin Bible published in Mainz, Germany, in 1456. This remarkable book had 643 leaves, each page printed in two columns of 42 lines. Known after its celebrated printer, Johannes Gutenberg, as the Gutenberg Bible, it is not only the first major product of modern typography, but is still among the finest examples of the printer's art.

This illustration, taken from a page of the Bible, shows the typeface used by Gutenberg. This face was known as Textura and it was cut to resemble the manuscript hand used in the 15th century in Germany to prepare handwritten Bibles and church service books. The Gutenberg Bible was printed in ten sections on six presses at once, the edition running to 150 copies on heavy paper and 30 on fine vellum.

4 Typefounding is the process of making individual pieces of type by casting molten type metal into moulds. Type metal is an alloy of tin and lead, with added antimony for hardness. In this Victorian typefoundry dozens of workers operate individual machines belt-driven from a shaft running the length of the room. Single casting of individual type was superseded by the linotype machine, which casts a whole line at once.

3 The first self-inking treadle platen press was designed and built by an American, Stephen Ruggles, in 1839. This improved design built by him 12 years later became the model for the popular jobbing press. In this machine the forme of type is clamped in a near-vertical position. Above the forme is a rotating disc that serves to distribute the ink. Three composition rollers roll down over the disc, picking up ink and then down over the type forme. When the rollers have returned, the platen (on which the paper has been laid by hand) moves up against the type forme.

5 Letterpress printing includes the platen press [A] in which paper is pressed up against the inked image. The paper in the flat bed press [B] is laid on the image and pressed down by roller. The rotary press [C] has a curved image on one roller, the paper passing between this and a pressure roller. Metal type [D] has a face [1], a shoulder [2], a body [3], a foot [4] and a nick [5]. Zinc blocks [E] have unwanted metal [6] etched away from round the design [7].

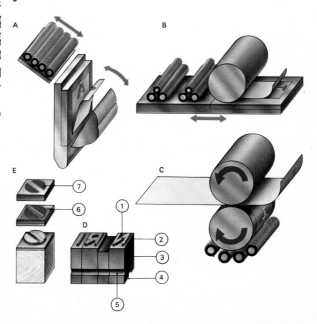

plaster mould of a type forme. In the same year Friedrich König and Andreas Bauer (1783–1860) built the first perfecting machine – which could print on both sides of the paper.

A traditional printing press uses mirror image type. In 1817 an Englishman, called Augustus Applegath (1788–1871), designed a machine to print bank-notes with the same design on each side of the paper and with each colour in perfect register with the others. In this machine a curved stereotype first printed on to a leather pad fitted around the printing cylinder. When one revolution was complete the paper was fed between the stereo and the leather pad so that the metal printed on one side of the paper and the inked leather pad on the other. The idea was to produce bank-notes that could be forged only with difficulty, and Applegath's machine in fact printed the lower side of the notes by what is now called the offset method. The leather pad was printed with a mirror image of the original type matter which it then transferred to the paper. As a result the printed image on the lower side of the paper was identical to the original stereo. This principle was later made use of in offset printing, in which the type matter is identical to the finished print.

The next 70 years saw numerous advances in the art of printing. Stereotype preparation from papier mâché moulds [9] was originated by Claud Genoux of Lyons. These moulds or "flongs" were strengthened with clay and glue. In 1845 the French printing firm of Worms and Phillipe patented the idea of casting curved stereos direct from a curved flong. This is the method still used in most newspaper printing today.

In 1838 the American David Bruce, Jr (1802–92) built the first commercially successful mechanical typecasting machine, which made 100 characters an hour.

In 1852 the first printing by photolithography was carried out experimentally by Alfred Lemercier, a Frenchman. Lemercier coated his printing stone with a light-sensitive substance which was exposed through a paper negative. After washing with turpentine the design on the stone could then be inked for normal lithographic printing.

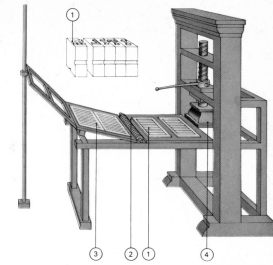

Early printing presses resembled 15th-century linen presses. The type matter [1] was wedged in a sliding tray [2] and then inked by hand. The paper was placed on a parchment covered "tympan" [3] which hinged into position over the type tray. This slid under the screw-down press [4].

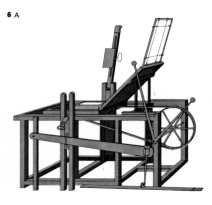

6 Lithography is based on the mutual repulsion of greasy ink and water. The image to be printed is drawn, in reverse, on stone using a greasy pencil or ink. The stone is then soaked in water and inked. The ink adheres to the image but not to the wet stone. The machine [A] presses paper from the holder on to the stone, thus making the print. The process was used originally for printing hand-drawn music [B].

8 When an etched plate has been inked and wiped, ink remains only in the grooves made by the acid and can thus be printed. This is the principle of intaglio, in which the image is below the surface of the printing plate and so retains the ink when the polished surface is wiped clean. James Whistler (1834–1903), who used etching as an art form, made this etching of Black Lion Wharf, Wapping, London.

7 In an etched printing plate the ink fills the grooves made by acid in a polished metal plate (copper, zinc, aluminium or steel). The plate is coated with acid-resisting wax. The image is drawn in the wax with an etching needle [A] exposing the metal. The scribed plate is then put in acid [B] which eats into the metal where the wax has been removed. After cleaning off the wax the plate is inked, then wiped.

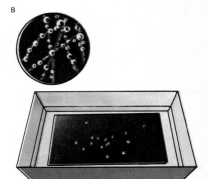

9 The principle of printing on paper fed from a roll with the sheets being cut after printing was invented by Rowland Hill (1795–1879), who later introduced the penny post in England. Rotary machines were developed for newspaper printing from 1846, using curved stereotypes cast from curved papier mâché moulds (flongs) of the original flat type formes. This early Victory press printed at speed from a paper roll (web) and folded the cut sheets.

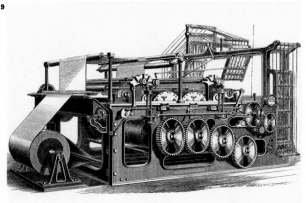

10 The linotype composing machine, invented by Ottmar Mergenthaler (1854–99), an American of German parentage, was probably the greatest single printing innovation of all time. The machine was first used to typeset the *New York Tribune* in 1886. The operator "types" the copy on a keyboard and the machine sets letter moulds (matrices) in the correct order. At the end of each line a complete line of type (slug) is cast in one piece.

Modern printing

There are three main kinds of modern printing processes: relief, intaglio and planographic. In relief printing the ink-bearing surface of the type or engravings (for illustrations) stands out above the surrounding non-printing area. Letterpress printing is an example of relief printing and includes printing from one-piece stereotype plates and from formes made up of both type matter and illustrations, which may be metal line blocks, halftone engravings (which have tonal shades formed from minute dots), woodcuts or linocuts.

In letterpress printing the platen (flat plate) press and various kinds of cylinder presses are widely used. Paper is fed into the machine (by hand or automatically). The mechanism picks up single sheets from a stack (usually by means of suction pads) and feeds them into the machine.

Intaglio printing is relief printing "in reverse". In this case the ink is trapped in cavities in the printing plate surface, the polished non-printing area being "wiped" clean of ink before printing. Photogravure is the principal intaglio process of today; formerly it was used for printing artists' engravings made on steel and copper and for aquatints and etchings (in which lines were etched in the metal by acid).

In planographic printing the printing and non-printing surfaces are completely flat. The printing plates are treated in such a way that the mutual repulsion of oil and water keeps the ink from the non-printing area. Lithography is the principal planographic process of printing.

Rotary printing

Modern high-speed printing is carried out on a rotary press [1] using continuous paper from a roll. The printing formes are prepared flat, using type (text) and blocks (illustrations). A papier-mâché "flong" mould is made, again flat. The mould is placed in a casting box which has been bent to a half circle, so that when molten metal is pumped between the flong and the circular backing of the mould a semicircular stereotype plate (stereo for short) is produced. The edges are cleaned up, the white (non-print) areas routed out, the inner side shaved to form a perfect semicircle and two stereos are fitted around each printing cylinder in the press. This forms a circular printing surface.

Modern photogravure, developed from hand etching, uses photographic techniques to produce copper printing cylinders or plates. Positive prints of the type matter and illustrations are printed photographically on to a gelatin-coated carbon tissue. When developed and laid on a copper sheet this forms an etch-resistant pattern (called a resist), which allows acid or other etchant through the image area, leaving the copper surface untouched in the non-image areas. The etched copper cylinders are then fitted to a high-speed rotary gravure press, which operates in much the same way as a letterpress rotary. Rotary photogravure is widely used for the production of high-quality large-circulation magazines.

Web-offset lithography

Lithography, originally carried out by forming the image to be printed on a porous stone slab, was soon developed so that the printing surface could be prepared

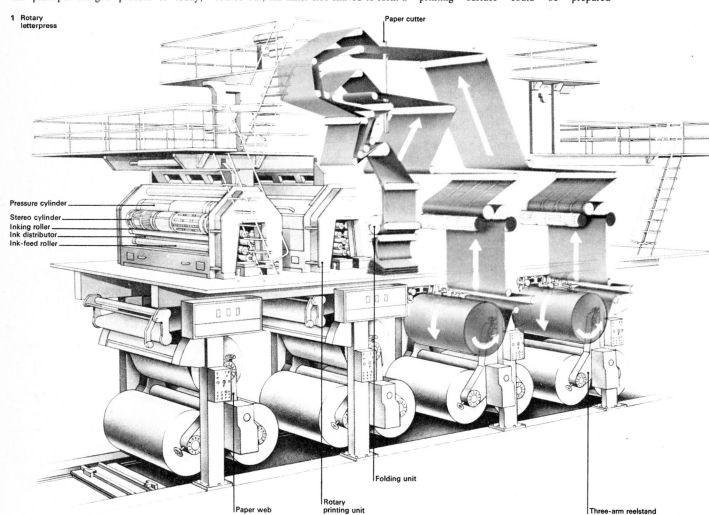

1 Rotary letterpress

Paper cutter

Pressure cylinder
Stereo cylinder
Inking roller
Ink distributor
Ink-feed roller

Paper web

Rotary printing unit

Folding unit

Three-arm reelstand

1 The newspaper industry has improved and developed its methods of printing over the last 100 years. A modern machine prints both sides of a paper web four pages wide, cutting and folding to make up a finished eight-page newspaper section. Shown here is a typical installation with four presses that can produce a complete 32-page newspaper at once. The three-arm reelstands allow the machine to run without interruption by pasting the paper from the following reel on to the tail of an exhausted web. Colour printing can be achieved by re-routing the paper web so that it runs through two machines in sequence, one using black, the other a coloured ink, or by adding multi-colour press units in the paper path following one of the single-colour presses. They then colour-print in the white space left by the normal press. Presses of this type are designed to deliver at least 50,000 copies per hour. Presses working at such high speeds are fitted with automatic devices to maintain correct paper tension and flow through the mechanism and to apply brakes if there is some failure such as a break in the paper web. Newspapers and magazines are printed increasingly frequently by photolithography, but many large-circulation magazines, printed in black and one other colour, are produced on automatic high-speed letterpress machines similar to newspaper presses. In Britain telephone directories and similar publications are printed on rotary letterpress machines at a rate of 15,000 copies per hour. Rotary presses sacrifice quality for speed; in eight hours several presses can print 2.5 million copies of a paper.

photographically on a sheet of metal such as zinc or aluminium. The methods used for offset platemaking vary widely, but the result is the same – a flexible metal plate that can be fitted around the printing cylinder of a high-speed rotary press [2]. Web-offset presses, printing on a continuous paper roll (the web), have been developed in recent years. As a result many small-circulation newspapers and magazines use this system of printing.

Modern printing techniques

In letterpress printing and lithography, the reproduction of continuous-tone illustrations such as photographs is achieved by photographing the picture through a "halftone screen", which is a fine grid of crossed parallel lines. This breaks the picture into tiny elements which are printed separately as dots of varying size [3].

Linotype machines (which cast a whole line of type at a time) continue to be used widely for newspaper production and the Monotype machine [4] (which casts one letter at a time), with its ability to set, say, symbols and complex mathematical equa-

tions, is still used extensively for book production. But photosetting, introduced in a practical form in 1955, is superseding the metal type processes in many fields.

Photosetting is an entirely new process in which the alphabet and other characters of each type style are stored on film or as tape-recorded instructions. The photosetting machine [5] produces positive or negative copy suitable for photographic platemaking processes and has the advantage that the size of any typeface can easily be reduced or enlarged photographically.

A modern photosetting machine, with appropriate lens systems, also produces condensed and expanded faces, and italics, from the same master negatives. It operates at high speed – computers control spacing and produce proofs as fast as the operator can use his keyboard. In gravure printing and lithography printing plates are made directly from the positive image produced by the photosetter. In letterpress work a negative image is made photographically into a metal printing plate in a similar manner to that used in the production of halftone blocks.

The essence of modern printing is speed. Millions of copies of daily newspapers appear every morning filled with news stories that were written the previous night.

2 Offset lithography

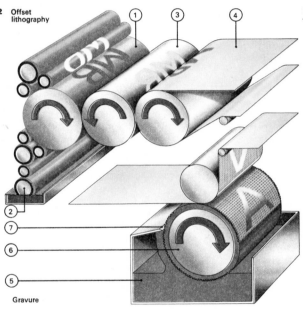

Gravure

2 Image areas of offset lithographic printing plates [1] accept a grease-based ink and non-image areas, damped by rollers [2], reject the ink. The inked image is offset on to a rubber roller [3] and then on to the paper [4]. The copper gravure printing cylinder [6] has the image etched as "cells" (small depressions beneath the surface), the volume of cell determining the quantity of ink and hence the tonal value. The cylinder is covered with ink [5] and the surface is then cleaned by a "doctor" blade [7], leaving ink only in the etched depressions. When the cylinder contacts the paper the ink in the cells is transferred to it. The gravure process is used principally for high-quality pictorial work.

3

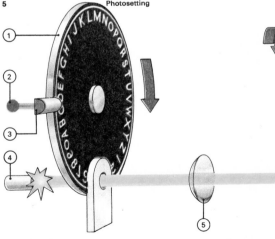

3 Yellow, red and blue are used in various combinations to print a wide variety of shades. Where all three overlap the result is almost black. In colour reproduction a greatly improved result is achieved by a fourth, black printing. More accurate colours are obtained by using magenta and cyan in place of red and blue. An image is printed in each colour [A-D] to give the combined effect, seen here magnified [E].

4 The Monotype machine, invented in 1887 by Tolbert Lanston (1844–1913), produces three characters of set type each second, using matrices (moulds) and molten metal. It is widely used for books. The operator types the copy on a keyboard, producing a punched paper tape. The tape is later fed into a second machine which casts individual letters, setting the type in lines of equal length ready for printing.

5 Photosetting

5 A typical photo-composing machine has a continually rotating disc [1] which bears negative images of all the letters, numerals and punctuation marks in a given type face. An exciter lamp [2] and photo-electric cell [3] sense the exact orientation of the rotating disc. When the chosen character is in line (instructions come from a computer tape by "typing" copy on a keyboard) a micro-flash unit [4] fires. The lens system [5] focuses an image on film or paper [7]. The transport system [6], also computer controlled, sets the images in lines with justification and hyphenation where necessary.

Copying and duplicating

Reproduction of the written word and of drawings and photographs is not exclusively the art of the printer. An increasingly large volume and variety of reproduced material is prepared quickly and relatively cheaply in offices found in most parts of the world by duplicating and copying processes developed for this purpose [1].

The hectograph and rotary duplicator

The oldest of office copying processes is the once familiar spirit duplicator [2]. The original material – the master – was drawn by hand using synthetic, aniline inks (purple, red and green were the most usual colours, although black, blue, yellow and brown inks are also available today) or by typing with special aniline dye ribbons. The master was then rolled face down on to a gelatin bed, which absorbed a proportion of the ink, to form a mirror image on its surface. Plain paper moistened with spirit was then pressed on to the gelatin and peeled off to leave a positive image on each sheet. This convenient process, which can print up to 50 or even 100 copies from a good master, has

been modernized and is the basis of the rotary duplicator. A "transfer" sheet surfaced with a wax film containing aniline dye is placed behind the master sheet and material is drawn or typed on to both sheets. In this way a mirror image in aniline ink is formed on the back of the paper, just as though a sheet of carbon paper had been placed below it, black side up. The master so made is fitted on to a cylindrical drum which presses against sheets of paper, moistened with spirit, to provide copies quickly and cleanly. A master can be made using a number of different coloured transfer sheets, the process printing the different colours simultaneously.

Modern copying processes

The ink duplicating machine, or mimeograph, has the advantage of being able to produce a thousand or more good copies from the master. This master, once made of wax on porous paper, is now generally made of a pressure-sensitive plastic composition. The image is either hand-drawn with a sharp stylus or typed on any machine with a fine typeface. The lines or letters cut into the sur-

face and break the skin so that ink can penetrate. The master so formed is a negative stencil. The modern mimeograph is a high-speed electrically powered machine and produces good quality copies at speed.

The blueprint [Key] is no more than a negative prepared photographically by contact with a translucent original. The modern process, which has superseded the blueprint, uses special paper sensitized with diazo compounds. This is placed in contact with the original and exposed to what is known as actinic radiation (mainly blue and violet light, together with ultra-violet rays). The radiation passes through the clear paper of the original and chemically alters the diazo compound. But where it is masked by the lines of the image, the diazo compound remains unchanged. "Dry" development by ammonia gas can produce a black or blue image; wet development can produce prints in red, sepia and some other colours. Variations of this process are used in the many dry, "semi-wet" and heat development azo copiers available today. The process has the advantage of producing copies of large drawings more cheaply

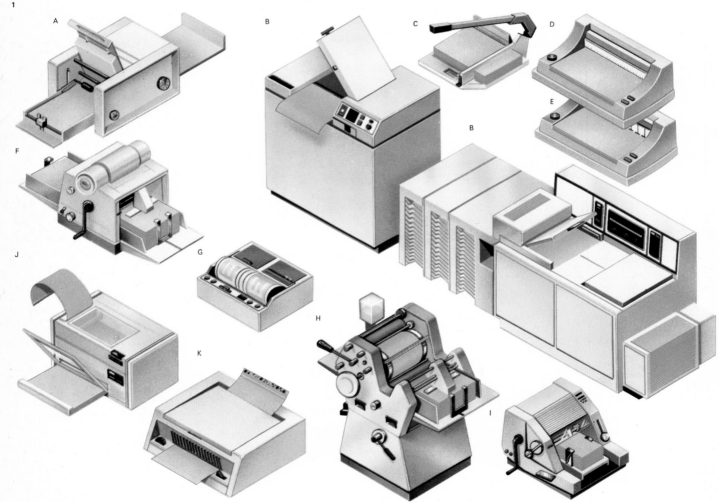

1 The in-house print room of a modern commercial office, research establishment or other organization where reproduction of printed matter and illustrations is required quickly and often, contains a variety of machines, each

serving a specific purpose. Among typical machines shown here there is a spirit duplicator [A] for short runs, a mimeograph [I] for medium runs of non-illustrated material and an offset-litho press [H] for high-quality printing

that may include colour work as well as drawings and photographs. For rapid copying and high quality, a type of photostatic copier [B] is generally used. Large drawings can be quickly reproduced on a diazo copier; "semi-wet" and dry

working types are available. Stencils for a mimeograph can be typed by hand on an ordinary typewriter or produced on a thermal stencil maker [K]. A high-speed stencil duplicator [F] can reproduce these much faster than can a mimeo-

graph. Litho plates can also be made on a typewriter, and an electrostatic litho-plate maker [J] can produce them from drawings and photographs. Also shown here are an electronic machine for making mimeograph masters [G], a guillo-

tine [C], paper punch [D] and binder [E]. A well equipped print room can copy any documents, drawings, pages from books or any other originals, and it can print circulars, memoranda, publicity material, invitations, house journals, technical

reports and even good quality letter headings. Among other methods of graphic reproduction (not shown) are microfilm systems. There are also titling systems such as adhesive transfer lettering and machines for printing serial numbers.

than any of the other copying processes.

The introduction of photostatic copying machines in the mid 1960s [4] has resulted in a minor revolution in the copying field. The term xerography, which was based originally on a proprietary name, has come into general use for processes marketed by many companies. Photostatic copying depends on the phenomenon of photo-conductivity [5].

Offset lithography is another process widely used in modern offices. The office offset machine uses the principle employed in commercial lithography – the fact that water and an oil-based ink will not mix. The offset-litho masters can be prepared in several ways: photographically, as in commercial printing; by the use of a suitable toning powder in a photostatic copier; or simply by typing or drawing with a special ribbon or ink direct on to plastic or thin metal plates.

Preparation of copy

The first step in the traditional printing process is the setting of movable type – a complicated procedure ill-suited to the office print room. It was the possibility of preparing

printing masters on standard typewriters that made the hectograph and the mimeograph, and later the offset-litho press, practical alternatives to commercial printing.

The standard typewriter, however, has three drawbacks. The quality of the typed copy is variable in intensity and clarity, the typeface cannot be altered and the letter spacing is constant, unlike that of movable type where "m"s and "w"s, for example, occupy much more space than "i"s or "l"s.

All three weaknesses have been overcome with the invention of more sophisticated typewriters. The modern electric machine, with a carbon or plasticized ribbon used only once, produces uniformly clean and clear jet-black letters. Machines with interchangeable typefaces have also been introduced. Finally machines with "proportional" spacing were invented, so that narrow, medium and wide letters do not have to occupy the same space. The most advanced machines incorporate the alternative type facility as well as proportional spacing and have special spacing facilities for the typing of fixed-width columns.

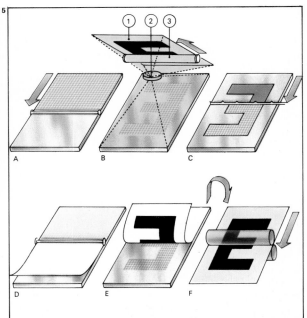

The original blueprint used by architects and engineers for the reproduction of plans and drawings is a photographic negative, white on blue, made on paper sensitized with a ferric (iron) salt and potassium ferrocyanide.

3 Adhesive transfer lettering, which is available in a wide range of typefaces and sizes, has made possible the preparation of titles quickly and cheaply, complementing the modern electric typewriter's function of producing near-perfect printed material. Line borders, human figures in various attitudes and sizes for use in simple artwork, electronic symbols, mathematical signs and a wide variety of other symbols and colours are produced in the form of adhesive transfers. Transfer lettering is produced on a transparent sheet; letters are placed in the position required and rubbed on to the paper below where they remain fixed after the sheet above is removed. "Instant" lettering is ideal for small-scale print operations at a relatively low cost.

2

2 The original spirit duplicator used a gelatin or clay bed which absorbed some of the aniline ink with which the master copy [1] had been prepared. Some of the ink mirror image in the surface of the "jelly" bed [2] was then transferred back to sheets of paper that had been moistened with spirit and pressed on to it by means of a rubber roller [3]. As aniline inks of various colours could be used on the master the flat bed hectograph could reproduce several colours simultaneously. Its disadvantage lay in the fact that only short runs – fewer than 100 copies – could be printed.

3

4

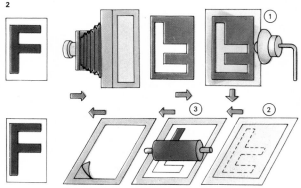

4 Modern photostatic copying machines are produced in a wide range of sizes and types. Table-top machines, designed specifically for use in offices where noise must be kept to a minimum, require no expertise on the part of the operator. A dial is set to specify the number of copies and the original is then fed in through the slot. The sheet trips a micro-switch which sets the process in motion. The copies emerge singly, followed by the original. Floor-standing copiers usually have a flat bed for the original, making reproduction from open books possible without the removal of separate sheets. Enlargement or reduction of the image is possible on the most comprehensive copiers.

5

5 The photostatic copying process uses a metal plate (which is often wrapped around a cylinder) coated with a material that conducts electricity only when exposed to light. In this process: the plate is first given an overall charge [A]. Then an image [B] of the original [1] is focused on to the plate using a lens system [2] and a light source [3]. Where the light falls the charge is conducted away. [C] Toning powder is now dusted over the plate. This adheres to the charged image area but not elsewhere. [D] Resin-coated paper is pressed in contact with the plate. [E] The powder adheres to the paper. [F] The image is fixed by heat.

Newspapers and magazines

Newspapers that can be properly so called – because they contained topical information with an attempt at regular appearance – date from the early 1600's. Perhaps the first was the *Nieuwe Tijdingen*, published in Antwerp from 1605.

Early English newspapers suffered heavily from censorship. A government-issued licence to print, which could be revoked if a newspaper offended the government of the day, acted as an effective curb until the Licensing Act was allowed to lapse in 1694. The relaxation led to a host of papers and journals and Britain's first daily newspaper appeared on 11 March 1702, priced at one penny. Papers were printed by hand and circulations were small: in 1711 total daily sales were only 7,500 papers. Not until *The Times* of London introduced a steam printing press in 1814 could the modern newspaper be said to have arrived.

Birth of popular papers

Stamp tax, introduced in 1712, also severely restricted newspaper circulations. In 1836 it was reduced from 4 to 1 old pence (d) a copy and new Sunday papers, carrying accounts of crime, sex and sport, and appealing to a new type of reader, began to make their appearance. The *News of the World*, the largest selling Sunday newspaper in the Western World today, dates from this period. In 1855 the tax was abolished and several more "middle-class" dailies were established.

The 1870 Elementary Education Act, which increased literacy among the British working and lower-middle classes, stimulated further growth. Alfred Harmsworth, later Lord Northcliffe (1865–1922), launched the *Daily Mail* in 1896, priced at ¹/₂d. The first issue sold 390,000 copies, more than any other paper had ever sold in one day. The "popular" paper had arrived.

Editorial content

Modern newspapers should not be regarded merely as a public utility. Many are manufactured "goods", produced to make a profit. They get their income from selling the paper itself [Key] and by selling space in it to people who wish to advertise goods or services. Some, however, are produced at a financial loss as a public service, supported by other activities or by the proprietor.

The editorial content of all newspapers can be divided into two major sections: news and features. Most news is predictable: it comes from events that are known about in advance – the so-called "diary" events such as sessions of Parliament, court cases, athletic meetings and so on. But the news that the reader often finds most fascinating, and that may lead him to buy a newspaper because he catches sight of a headline, is "spot" news – the event, such as a presidential assassination, that cannot be predicted. Leading articles ("leaders" or "editorials") are generally based on a principal news item.

Features include articles giving the background of news; gossip columns; articles on specialist subjects such as gardening, fashion and cooking; strip cartoons and horoscopes.

All newspapers report "spot" news, but the quality newspapers carry much greater coverage of serious diary news – especially politics – than popular papers and supplement it with articles by specialist writers on science, medicine, education and current

1 Birth of a story in a newspaper.
7 pm: News of a fire at a politician's home comes over the teleprinter from the Press Association, an agency with a nationwide network of reporters. The story, or "copy", is assessed or "tasted" by the "copytaster" [1] who informs the news editor [2] and night editor [3]. They send a reporter [4] to the scene and the picture editor [5] sends a photographer [6]. 7.15: A reporter telephones that the man has died. Two reporters and a photographer are sent to assist in covering events. The "back bench" – the night editor and assistants [7] – decide that the story is the main front page news, the "splash". A staff writer [8] is briefed to compile the man's obituary, using reference books, contacting his friends and studying newspaper cuttings from the paper's own library. Pictures of the man are obtained from the picture library and an artist [9] draws a map of the house and grounds. 8.00: A reporter returns to write his story. It is a "running story" – as he writes, his colleagues telephone further information. A photographer rushes to the darkroom to develop his film. 8.15: With the designer [10] the back bench choose a picture and draw, or "lay out", a page, showing sizes of illustrations and headlines, and lengths of stories. 8.40: The reporter's copy is scrutinized by news and night editors. 8.50: Copy and scheme go to the chief sub-editor [11] who briefs a sub-editor [12]. He shortens the reporter's copy to the number of lines allocated, adds in late news, rechecks facts and writes a headline of the prescribed number of letters. His work is vetted by the revise sub [13] before it goes to the printer.

affairs. They also carry several pages of financial and industrial news. Popular newspapers report only the most arresting diary news, such as Parliamentary disagreements.

The task of a newspaper editor is to direct his journalists to produce stories and pictures that together strike a suitable balance between information and entertainment for his particular readers. On a mass-circulation newspaper he has assistant editors in charge of the various sub-sections – news, foreign news, sport, women's pages, leisure, business and general features. Each assistant has his own team of journalists.

The total number of pages in each issue of a paper is determined by the amount of advertising matter. Each morning the editor studies a "mock-up" of the paper that indicates the pages and positions of the advertisements. Knowing the space available, he then holds a news conference to deal with stories that are expected to develop during the day. Information comes from staff, independent or "freelance" journalists, or, by way of national and international teleprinter networks, from news agencies. At a later confer-ence the editor receives progress reports and finally decides which items deserve prominence and which can be put on one side.

The editor holds features conferences to discuss immediate ideas arising out of the news and those for future issues. At a leader conference (particularly on quality papers) he discusses with senior staff the attitudes to be taken to current affairs.

The magazine world

Periodicals focusing on narrow fields – such as gardening, homes, stamp collecting, motoring and chemical engineering – are prospering, as are low-priced women's magazines. But general magazines have suffered from competition from television and from magazines given away with newspapers. In particular, magazines of photo-journalism – features or news stories told in pictures – have all but vanished in all Western countries. Successful and comparatively new fields are glossy magazines for the newly rich teenagers and prestige journals distributed free to professional people such as doctors in order to attract lucrative advertisements.

Most sales of British newspapers and magazines are through newsagents. Between 50 and 80 per cent of newspaper sales are home deliveries – the rest are counter sales. A newsagent's profit is up to 28 per cent of the selling or "cover" price. Some local newspapers deliver direct to newsagents but national papers go first to area wholesalers who take about 10% of the cover price. Newsagents operating on "sale-or-return" send back unsold copies to the wholesaler. To lessen this possible loss, some newspapers ask agents to place firm orders and bear any loss themselves – but this can lead to under-ordering, a shortage of papers and sales for rivals.

2 Linotype machines convert stories into lines of metal type. The operator sits at a keyboard like a typewriter and re-types the edited copy. The keys release tiny moulds – matrices – of the letters, which form into a line. Finished lines move to a slot into which molten metal is pumped. A strip of metal – a "slug" – is formed with raised letters on its surface. Lines gather in a tray until the copy ends.

3 Pages are assembled on a metal workbench called a "stone". Following the editorial scheme, a compositor arranges the columns of type with the pictures (etched into metal blocks). The whole page is then locked into a "chase" and a proof copy taken. A journalist – the "stone sub" – reads proofs of each page and indicates which lines can be omitted if the metal does not fit. He also "passes" the final page.

4 A typical tabloid newspaper contains 30 to 45% advertising and 55 to 70% editorial matter. Half the editorial is text (nearly a quarter headlines) and the rest pictures. Most pages carry an advertisement, except for information pages such as television or racing; without them pages look dull. Pictures and headlines are placed to counterbalance advertisements and some pages contain nothing but advertising.

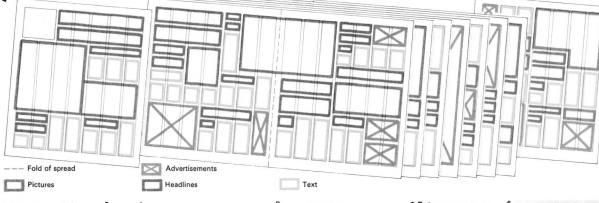

--- Fold of spread   ☒ Advertisements

▭ Pictures   ▭ Headlines   ▭ Text

5 A newspaper's income [A, B] is derived from advertisements and selling the paper. This chart assumes no profit. It shows [C] paper (called newsprint) and ink as the main costs and demonstrates how popular papers selling millions of copies depend more on sales, whereas quality papers selling perhaps 400,000 copies a day rely on advertisements (particularly classified). In local "giveaway" (free) news-sheets, profit is derived solely from advertising content.

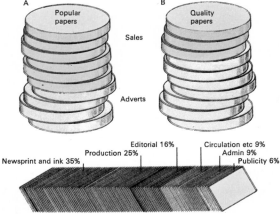

A Popular papers   Sales
B Quality papers   Adverts

C Newsprint and ink 35%   Production 25%   Editorial 16%   Circulation etc 9%   Admin 9%   Publicity 6%

6 Future newspaper production will be by computer, with typesetting machines phased out. Writers sit at visual display units (VDUs) which are keyboards with cathode-ray tubes linked to a computer. By tapping a key a letter shows on the screen. The finished stories are kept in the computer under code numbers until an editor calls one on to his own screen for amendments. The computer can then instantly produce a tape that works a typesetting machine.

Books and publishing

"Another damned thick, square, book! Always scribble, scribble, scribble, eh, Mr Gibbon!" So observed the Duke of Gloucester to the greatest of the 18th century historians, Edward Gibbon (1737–94). A hundred years later the greatest 19th century historian, Thomas Carlyle (1795–1881) refuted the implication: "A good book is the purest essence of a human soul."

The United Nations Educational, Scientific and Cultural Organization (UNESCO) defines a book as "a non-periodical printed publication of at least 49 pages, exclusive of the cover pages". In 1976 Britain alone published more than 30,000 books. They included everything from cheap, read-and-throw-away paperback novels to finely produced, limited editions of the classics. In the total were more than 1,000 works on religion, 2,000 on politics, 2,500 on natural sciences and 7,000 on literature. School textbooks and children's books accounted for more than 4,000 titles.

In spite of television, books are still the greatest medium for education, influence and entertainment that the world has ever known: probably as many square miles have been conquered by books such as Karl Marx's *Das Kapital* as by guns and tanks. And when the vision of an ideal state of society called communism contained in that book became perverted and distorted, one of the greatest instruments in the fight against it was another book, *Animal Farm* by George Orwell [2].

The business of publishing

Books like Gibbon's histories and Orwell's satires are grouped by publishers under the general term "trade books", that is books sold to the general public. They are a product of which the publisher is the manufacturer and the bookseller the retailer [Key]. To a businessman, they are exactly the same as mousetraps or motor cars and their sales are promoted in similar ways: just as the car industry has its annual trade shows, so the book business has its books fairs [6] at which both publishers and public can inspect the latest product.

Samuel Johnson (1709–84) said that nobody except a blockhead ever wrote except for money and with some modification the same could be said of publishers. But most established publishers are prepared to publish unknown authors – and make a financial loss – if they feel that the authors will one day become well known and therefore profitable. The initial losses are offset by profits from other books they publish. Publishers are in a way schizophrenic: Raymond Chandler (1888–1959) said of the publisher that "the minute you try to talk business with him he takes the attitude that he is a gentleman and a scholar, and the moment you try to approach him on the level of his moral integrity he starts to talk business".

The cost of producing a trade book is generally multiplied by about four to get the retail price. This "mark-up" allows for the publisher's profit, the author's royalty, and the bookseller's margin (which is normally 35 per cent of the retail price). Authors' royalties normally begin at 7.5 or 10 per cent and may increase on a sliding scale against the number of sales to a maximum of 15 per cent. Most of a publisher's outlay – about 80 per cent – is spent on typesetting, paper, printing

1 *The Godfather* by Mario Puzo was written originally in English and has been translated into most major languages. It has become one of the most successful fiction books of recent years.

2 **George Orwell** (1903–50), whose real name was Eric Blair, was a prolific and successful British author of more than ten bestsellers, including *Animal Farm* and *Nineteen Eighty-four*, as well as many essays.

3 Among the most successful books in terms of numbers printed and sold are textbooks and other books used in schools and colleges. An elementary book on mathematics, for example, may have several successive editions and reprints and can sell in large numbers for many years. In the past, books for classrooms were "hardback" with a stiff cloth-covered binding. But today the rising cost of books has forced publishers increasingly to produce paperback books for schools. Many advanced textbooks are available in both hardback editions (favoured by libraries) and as paperbacks (generally bought by students). Some never appear in hard covers.

4 High-quality books are produced by hand one at a time. Here the British craftsman Grahame Clarke is seen inking an etched metal plate [A] for an illustration, then [B] inking the type matter using a roller before [C] arranging the plate and type on a forme prior to printing. Sheets of paper for the book's pages are printed [D] in a flat-bed press and then any hand lettering carefully drawn in position [E]. Finally the book is bound; the pages are stitched together [F], the boards forming the covers are added and the cover bound in cloth or leather. Few people have all the skills needed to make books in this way and their products command very high prices.

and binding. The publisher takes a risk: if his estimate of sales proves wrong, he makes a loss. The author of this type of book is also at risk; if the book does not sell, many months or even years of work yield no income.

Compared with the production of illustrated books, publishing "text only" books is relatively straightforward. The author's manuscript is first edited for house style (the way in which the publisher chooses to present, say, numbers – that is, to print them as figures or to spell them out). It is then cast off – the process of estimating how many pages it will occupy when printed in the chosen typeface. The typeset "galley proofs" are checked for errors and marked up to indicate for the printer how the pagination of the text should be arranged. The printer "imposes" the pages in such a way that when a large printed sheet is folded [5] the pages fall into the correct sequence. These folded sheets (called "signatures" and usually 16, 32 or 48 pages long) are gathered together, sewn and bound. Most paperback books are not sewn but instead "perfect bound" – the folds are trimmed off and the back of the book held together, in its cover, with a special glue.

A successful textbook [3] can be highly profitable to both author and publisher. Britain's bestselling textbook author, Ronald Ridout (1916–), sold 50 million copies of his works in 25 years. Some novelists do even better: the Belgian writer Georges Simenon (1903–) has sold 300 million copies of his books. Story books for children also command large markets, generally about 8 per cent of all titles. Other main categories are fiction (25%), natural sciences (8%), history (7.9%), the arts (7.6%) and politics (7.4%). But the Bible is the best seller of all time: since 1800 about 1,500 million copies have been printed in various languages.

Home-made books

At the other extreme of the publishing business are those "cottage industry" publishers [4] who put as much art into production as the author puts into his text, making their own paper, cutting their own type and printing on small hand presses. Their books may make a reasonable profit, but they are not "economic" in the trade publisher's sense.

KEY

A large general bookshop, such as Foyles in London, may occupy several floors and have up to 750,000 volumes on display. Smaller shops may specialize in books on only one subject.

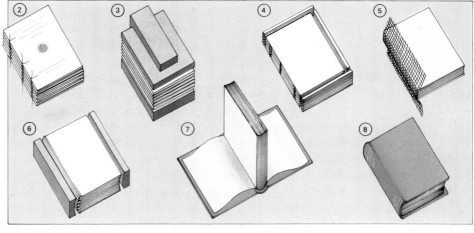

5 **Modern bookbinding** is carried out almost entirely by machines. The pages of a book are printed on flat sheets of paper, often eight pages at a time on each side of the sheet. Each sheet is folded [1] to give a "signature" (in this example, of 16 pages). All the signatures for a complete book are collated (put in page order) and sewn [2]. A heavy clamp [3] expels air from the sewn book, which is then trimmed to the finished size [4]. Net fabric called mull is glued to the spine [5] and the back of the book is rounded [6]. Colour is added to the edges of the pages at this stage. Endpapers are attached and the book fixed into its covers or "case" [7]. The title may be blocked – impressed into the cover [8] – and often a printed dust jacket is added to the finished book. Books are packed into boxes for distribution.

6 **The Frankfurt Book Fair** is held annually in the autumn. It is the principal market place at which publishers display existing and planned products and try to sell them to the book trade. International co-operation between publishers at the planning stage enables one book to be produced at the same time in several co-editions that differ only in the language in which the text is printed. And the same book that is printed as a single volume for one country may be produced in several volumes for another and as a weekly partwork for yet another; or a hardback book in one country may be a paperback in another, depending on the particular requirements of each market.

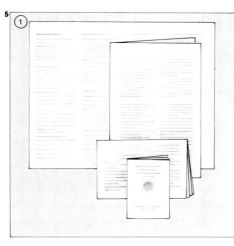

7

- Europe
- Soviet Union
- North America
- Oceania
- South America
- Asia
- Africa
- World average

7 **The world market** for books can be stated in terms of the number of new titles published each year. This diagram shows the number of titles per million inhabitants in each of the major continents in 1972. More books were produced in Europe than in any other continent, with the Soviet Union and North America the second and third largest producers. The Russian total (325 per million), however, changed little over a period of ten years while those of Europe and North America increased steadily. The figure for Asia, about 48 new titles per million inhabitants, has remained virtually unchanged for a period of 20 years.

Reference books and encyclopaedias

One effect of the explosion of human knowledge during the twentieth century has been to make a good reference library a necessary part of civilized life. The essential job of encyclopaedias, dictionaries and other reference books is to summarize knowledge in an easily accessible and comprehensive form. Encyclopaedias are about facts; dictionaries about definitions. Some encyclopaedias – and *The Joy of Knowledge* is one – also try to explain the more complex words they use, thus entering the intermediate category of the encyclopaedic dictionary.

Early encyclopaedias

The desire to summarize all human knowledge has a long history; the earliest surviving encyclopaedia in the West was compiled in Rome by Varro in the first century BC and in China encyclopaedias were in existence a thousand years before that. Varro's work was followed a century later by the *Historia Naturalis* of Pliny the Elder (AD 23–79). Like all early encyclopaedias, Pliny's work is arranged by subjects, as is the *Etymologiae* [1] of Isidore of Seville (560–636).

Pierre Bayle's *Dictionnaire Historique et Critique* (1695–97) attempted to give a comprehensive summary of human knowledge and appeared in many editions and translations. In 1704–10 John Harris (*c.* 1667–1719) brought out his *Lexicon Technicum*. The first true encyclopaedia in English, it was compiled at the request of the Royal Society and has a noticeable scientific bias. It was followed in 1728 by the *Cyclopaedia* of Ephraim Chambers (died 1740). This fully cross-referenced work was the model for all subsequent alphabetical encyclopaedias, including the largest European encyclopaedia ever published – the *Universal Lexicon* [2] of Johann Heinrich Zedler (1706–70).

The most famous foreign successor to Chambers' work was the *Encyclopédie* [3] (1751–65) of Denis Diderot (1713–84) and Jean le Rond d'Alembert (1717–83). Their approach was unashamedly radical and their enthusiastic humanism contributed to the undermining of the *ancien régime* in France. The original three-volume *Encyclopaedia Britannica* (1768–71), was conceived in part

as a more objective answer to the *Encyclopédie*. Always a monumental work, *Britannica* has grown through 15 editions to the completely reorganized 1974 edition.

Alphabetical order of subjects did not become standard practice until the late Middle Ages; even today some valuable encyclopaedias, such as the *Encyclopédie Française* (1937–   ) and the *Oxford Junior Encyclopaedia*, arrange their material in a logical sequence from subject to subject.

Advent of dictionaries

Without alphabetical order, dictionaries would be impossible to use. They are comparatively recent innovations. John Florio's *World of Words* (1598) was the first Italian-English dictionary, and Robert Cawdrey's *Table Alphabeticall* (1604) explained some of the learned "inkhorn" terms that had come into English from Latin.

In the eighteenth century the first modern dictionaries saw the light of day. In 1721 Nathan Bailey (died 1742) issued his *Universal Etymological English Dictionary*, which remained a bestseller for more than a

1 Isidore's *Etymologiae* was a compilation of seventh-century knowledge. This "Tree of Knowledge" is taken from an illustrated manuscript copy. The book was arranged thematically and included liberal arts, medicine, law, a time- chart, the Bible, the Church, people, language, state-craft, a Latin dictionary, man, zoology, heaven, air, seas and oceans, geography, cities and towns, building, geology, weights and measures, agriculture, ships, houses, dress and costume, food and drink, tools, and furniture. Isidore remained a standard work of reference for 1,000 years. Today it provides us with the best view available of the life and thinking that prevailed during the Middle Ages.

2 Zedler's *Lexicon* or *Great Complete Universal Dictionary of all the Sciences and Arts* was particularly strong on biography, genealogy and topography. Zedler a Leipzig bookseller, claimed that his work was more comprehensive and complete than any previous encyclopaedia. His work prompted rival ones that later put him out of business.

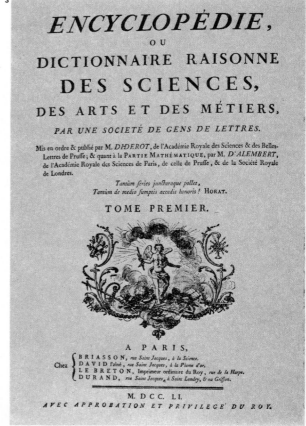

3 The *Encyclopédie* was first planned as a French edition of Chambers' *Cyclopaedia*. Following disagreements over rights, the publisher hired Denis Diderot, who had just edited the *Dictionnaire de médecine* to compile a new work. Diderot enlisted the aid of his friend Jean le Rond d'Alembert, a brilliant and famous mathematician who wrote the "preliminary discourse" in 1751. They recruited the best scholars and the most distinguished *philosophes* and gained support from the leading *salons*. Each volume as it appeared caused a sensation throughout Europe. The Establishment was outraged and the number of subscribers rose from 1,000 to 4,000. In 1759, a year after d'Alembert withdrew, the work was banned by the French attorney-general, but the publisher, Le Breton, continued it as an "underground" publication. There were numerous pirate editions.

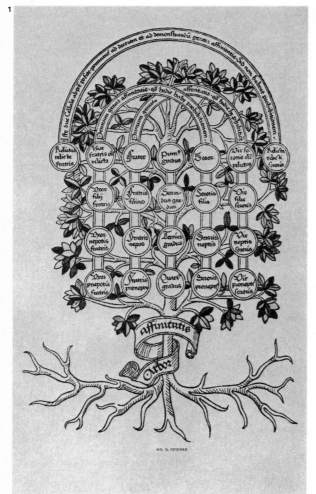

ENCYCLOPÉDIE,
ou
DICTIONNAIRE RAISONNÉ
DES SCIENCES,
DES ARTS ET DES MÉTIERS,
PAR UNE SOCIETÉ DE GENS DE LETTRES.

Mis en ordre & publié par M. DIDEROT, de l'Académie Royale des Sciences & des Belles-Lettres de Prusse; & quant à la PARTIE MATHÉMATIQUE, par M. D'ALEMBERT, de l'Académie Royale des Sciences de Paris, de celle de Prusse, & de la Société Royale de Londres.

Tantùm series juncturaque pollet,
Tantùm de medio sumptis accedit honoris! HORAT.

TOME PREMIER.

A PARIS,

Chez { BRIASSON, rue Saint Jacques, à la Science.
      DAVID l'aîné, rue Saint Jacques, à la Plume d'or.
      LE BRETON, Imprimeur ordinaire du Roy, rue de la Harpe.
      DURAND, rue Saint Jacques, à Saint Landry, & au Griffon.

M. DCC. LI.

AVEC APPROBATION ET PRIVILÉGE DU ROY.

century. It was the first attempt to collect and define *all* English words, as opposed to just "difficult" words, and it was the foundation on which Samuel Johnson (1709–84) based his more famous English dictionary. Johnson's chief innovations were the introduction of illustrative quotations to demonstrate shades of meaning and styles of usage, a willingness to make judgments about levels of usage ("clever, a low word . . ."), and some famous jokes among the definitions ("lexicographer, a harmless drudge").

Among Johnson's successors was the cantankerous American patriot Noah Webster (1748–1843). His *American Dictionary of the English Language* (1828) first listed most of the spelling differences between British and American English.

The best modern encyclopaedias expend great efforts to keep abreast of developments in all fields of knowledge and to present information in a format that will be most useful to the reader. Major dictionaries now adopt one of two approaches to language. The first, exemplified by the great *Oxford English Dictionary* (1884–1933), is the historical approach: through a systematic reading of the literature of a language, the history of each word is given – the *OED* also gives dates and examples of uses. In the other approach – the "synchronic" method – the lexicographer sets out to observe and record the language in its contemporary form. The most extreme example of this method – *Webster's Third New International Dictionary* (1961) – upset many people by its including such words as "ain't".

New works of reference
In the future, printed reference books will undoubtedly be supplemented by more technologically advanced ways of storing and retrieving information. Computer data banks can hold an enormous amount of information in a way that enables it to be instantly available and readily updated. Audio-visual techniques are now so far advanced that *The Joy of Knowledge Library* was itself carefully planned so that its printed pages could be related to general and educational films and audio-visual discs that could be shown on domestic and school television screens.

KEY

A general encyclo-paedia is the ideal reference work for helping young people with school work.

4
A

B

C

D

E

F

G

H

I

4 *The Joy of Knowledge Library* was produced in an unusual way, and text and pictures were assembled in various stages. After an author had been asked to write about a topic, he attended a briefing [A] at the publisher's office, together with the section editor and art editor. The artist drew a rough layout indicating the size, position and content of all the pictures. The author then researched and wrote the text [B] while an artist prepared a page layout [C]. A picture researcher obtained photographs [D] from agencies and photographers, or photographs were taken specially for the book. Artwork – paintings and drawings – was produced by a team of artists [E]. An editor [F] prepared the article for publication and ensured that it was consistent with other articles. Each author's edited manuscript was then submitted to a leading authority in the field, to make absolutely sure of the accuracy of all the facts. Printed proofs were checked [G] and assembled into a "paste-up" of the page [H]. The text was "married" with the colour pictures and a final full-colour proof was checked for accuracy and quality [I]. This process was repeated for every one of the major topics in the *Library*. Finally, cross-references were added to link various topics in related articles.

Information retrieval

In the Middle Ages, man's knowledge was restricted mainly to philosophy, history, medicine, astronomy and, to a very limited extent, geography. The boundaries of scientific and technical information were limited. Disregarding guesswork and unproven theories, it would have been possible at the time of Magna Carta to record all knowledge in a few hundred books.

The early recording systems

The volume of recorded knowledge grew slowly at first but, after the second half of the eighteenth century, men began to conduct systematic scientific research in many fields. Soon no one person could hope to read, understand and remember all recorded knowledge and instead people began to specialize in particular fields of study. The expansion of scientific and technical knowledge into new areas, each producing its own "literature", led to a rapid explosion of scientific information. Even modest libraries found it impossible to cope with the flood of new information.

The new problem led to the evolution of a

new expertise called information science – the science of storing, organizing, retrieving and disseminating information in such a way that anyone who knows the system is able to identify and retrieve all available information on any specific subject as and when it is needed. There are now many aspects of information retrieval including market research, mail-order selling and population censuses. Its principles can best be illustrated by considering the problems involved in a large library of books.

The first successful system of information classification was the decimal system invented by an American, Melvil Dewery (1851–1913), and first published in 1876.

The Dewey classification system

Dewey divided "knowledge" into ten main numbered classes: 100 Philosophy; 200 Religion; 300 Social Sciences (including Economics); 400 Language; 500 Natural Science; 600 Useful Arts (now Technology); 700 Fine Arts; 800 Literature; 900 History (including Travel and Biography); and 000 General Works (covering subjects not fitting

into the other nine categories). Each main class was subdivided into ten sub-classes (indicated by the second digit of classification number), and each of these into ten further sub-classes (third digit). Dewey made provision for even greater flexibility by adding a decimal point after the first three figures. The virtue of the system lies in the ease with which books can be given a numerical order on library shelves, so that related information is grouped together.

The Dewey system was widely accepted, but had one major drawback. Many books can be classified in more than one way and the Dewey system made little provision for this. To make it possible for a book or document to be given a classification number that indicates its subject-matter more precisely, the Universal Decimal System (UDC) was developed. This used the Dewey system as its basis and was first published by the International Institute of Bibliography, in French, in 1905. The Institute (which later became the International Federation of Documentation) has developed and widened the scope of the UDC progressively ever since.

1 This carpet loom is controlled by punched cards. It is based on a silk loom invented in 1801 by the French engineer Joseph Jacquard (1752–1834). Compressed air passes through the holes in the cards, joined to form an endless loop, as they pass over a perforated roller. Depending on the positions of the holes, the air operates mechanisms that lift the lengthwise warp threads of different colours. In the modern machine, push rods are used instead of compressed air to "read" the positions of the holes. Single punched cards, "read" by a lamp and photocell arrangement, are part of many modern data processing and information retrieval systems.

2 The punched card is the basis of most electro-mechanical data processing systems. Information is stored on the card by punching holes in specific locations according to a predetermined code [A]. In a population census, for example, there would be one card punched for each completed census form. The card sorter [B] uses electrical contacts to sense the holes and thereby sort cards into predetermined groups at high speed. For example, the sorter could sort cards into ten different age groups by sensing the "age" hole on each card, this being carried out in a fraction of the time possible by hand.

3

A STORES	B METAL	C METAL ROD	D METAL ROD, CIRCULAR
1 Metal	1 Sheet	1 Hexagonal	
2 Plastic	2 Bar	2 Circular	1 Brass
3 Fixings	3 Rod		2 Aluminium
4 Electrical	4 Angle		3 Steel
5 Tools	5 Tube		4 Copper
①②③④⑤	①②③④⑤	①②③④⑤	①②③④⑤

E METAL ROD, CIRCULAR STEEL	F METAL ROD, CIRCULAR STEEL, 10mm	G METAL ROD, CIRCULAR STEEL, 10mm	H METAL ROD, CIRCULAR STEEL, 10mm
1 5mm	1 Update	1 Update	1 Update
2 10mm	2 File	2 File	2 File
3 25mm	3 Read	3 Read	3 Read
4 50mm	9 × 2m	20 × 2m	29 × 2m
①②③④⑤	①②③④⑤	①②③④⑤	①②③④⑤

3 A computer display screen can be used to provide information about the stores of an engineering works. Suppose the store-keeper takes delivery of twenty 2m lengths of steel rod and wants to correct the records. The computer gives the "Stores" display [A], from which he selects "Metal" by pushing button number 1. On the "Metal" display [B] he selects "Rod"; from "Metal rod" [C] he chooses "Circular" and from the available types of circular metal rod [D] selects "Steel" by pushing button number 3. From the next display [E] he selects the 10mm size, and the following one [F] informs him that the present stock is 9 2m lengths. He feeds in the new stock [G] and checks the total stock situation [H].

When the US Library of Congress moved to new premises in 1897 it was already 97 years old and held about 1.5 million volumes and documents. The directors considered using the Dewey system but finally developed its own. In this, the LC system, subject-matter is first divided into 21 classes bearing the letters of the alphabet from A–Z, excluding I, O, W, X and Y. Each main class is then subdivided, each sub-class again bearing a letter. In this way the classification of every book or document begins with two letters and these give a fairly clear indication of the nature of the contents. The two letters are followed by figures, usually three or four, which are so devised to give the maximum detailed information on the contents of the book. Numerical sub-classes, where appropriate, are further subdivided by topics. Many advantages are claimed for the LC system; for example, it is easy to use.

Other classification systems

Other forms of information classification have particular advantages and are used in modern retrieval systems. Faceted classification recognizes that most subjects are compounds of several elements and seeks to enumerate the principal elements in every classification label. This system has not only been shown to be flexible but also to provide, if well conceived, a precise indication of, say, the contents of every book or document. Faceted classification is also easily adapted to use in punched-card information retrieval systems [2]. By defining all the "facets" of a subject on which information is required, a punched-card sorting machine can quickly identify all information cards bearing those facets in its classification label.

Information retrieval is an area in which computers are increasingly being used. As long as the "information" can be coded in a form that can be stored in a computer's memory banks, it can quickly be retrieved merely by calling it up using an appropriate code addressed to the computer. In addition, computer information can be continually updated, cancelling outdated material and replacing it with fresh data. The updating process in books and most other publications has to await complete new editions.

KEY

A record storage corridor in a US Patents Office, photographed here, gives a vivid impression of the steadily growing problem of information storage and retrieval. When an application for a patent is made, the authority must be sure that the idea is genuinely new. A century ago the descriptions of all existing patents could easily be filed in a single room and classified in such a way that the validity of new applications for patents could be quickly established. Today the number of current patents is so large that the problem of validating these applications in the old way has now become excessively time consuming.

4 Libraries of rare books must guard against losses and theft. The Victoria and Albert Museum Library in London [A] uses a system under which all books are guarded [B]. A user enters his request (author and title) on a form in duplicate, and hands this to an attendant. The latter files one copy, takes the book from the shelf (where the other copy is lodged in its place) and gives the book to the reader.

B

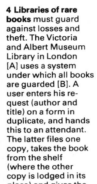

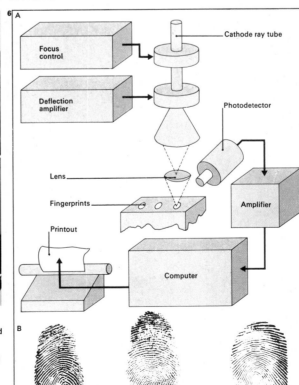

5 Large airlines operate 50 or more airliners flying daily on routes all over the world, and passengers may join or leave flights at 20 or 30 different major cities. The airline's information problem is to know instantly, at all booking offices, how many seats are available on each plane along each section of the route. This is overcome by having a computer at the head office with terminals at every booking office. The computer memory has a separate sub-store for every section of every flight and keeps a running total of the number of passengers booked for each section. If a proposed booking will exceed seat capacity on any section the computer informs the booking clerk instantly.

6 In the early days of police science the criminal investigation departments of even the largest countries held only a few thousand sets of fingerprints. Today the number filed at London's Scotland Yard is counted in millions. When a crime has been committed and fingerprints found at the scene, it may take days of searching to establish whether the prints belong to a known criminal. To solve the problem, scanning devices [A] are being developed that will provide information that can be read by a computer. When this new technique has been perfected, all fingerprint sets held by a national CID will be filed in a single computer store and it will be possible for the computer, if "shown" a print found at the scene of a crime [B], to compare it with every print in its store within a minute or two and come up with references to any matching fingerprints.

Focus control

Deflection amplifier

Cathode ray tube

Photodetector

Lens

Fingerprints

Amplifier

Printout

Computer

Photography

In just 150 years photographs, and allied processes such as photocopying, have become almost indispensable. Where words struggled to convey reality, and paintings could not capture the fleeting moment, the photograph came to achieve both, presenting in one dramatic image instant history, technical detail, or profoundly moving emotion. "Photography" comes from Greek words meaning "writing with light".

Development of photographic processes
The first photograph was taken by Nicéphore Niepce (1765–1833) in 1826 in a "camera obscura". This was a small dark room with a lens let into one wall: the scene outside was projected on to the opposite wall. It took about eight hours to expose a pewter plate covered with chemicals that reacted to light. In 1837, a Frenchman, Louis Jacques Mandé Daguerre (1789–1851), invented the daguerreotype process in which silver-plated copper sheets treated with iodine vapour replaced Niepce's pewter plate.

Development of the latent image (the picture held invisibly in the chemicals) required treatment with mercury vapour. The visible image produced was reversed, with the black parts white and the white parts black. The process became popular, but produced only one picture at a time. The multiple prints of today were impossible until William Fox Talbot (1800–77) developed the negative in 1839. But his calotype (later talbotype) was not as clear as the daguerreotype.

Talbot's paper negatives could be made transparent by wax or oil. They were soon replaced by glass negatives and in 1861 the first colour process was demonstrated.

The modern camera
In 1888 George Eastman (1854–1932) introduced the Kodak camera and brought photography to the man in the street. In 1924 the Leica was introduced as a miniature camera originally designed for testing 35mm motion picture film, and in 1925 the invention of the flash bulb released photography from dependence on sunlight or special artificial lighting.

The modern camera [Key] is a light-tight box with a mechanism that holds a piece of film flat and opposite a lens. The lens focuses on to the film a sharp upside-down image of the scene before the camera. A shutter, situated between the film and the lens, stops light reaching the film until the user decides to take a photograph. It then opens, usually for only a fraction of a second. The correct exposure is obtained by regulating the relationship between the shutter speed and the diameter of the lens – a factor that can be varied by adjustment of a diaphragm.

The diaphragm controls the amount of light passing through the lens and the shutter determines how long the film is exposed to the light. A fast shutter speed and a wide diaphragm opening will give the equivalent exposure of a slow shutter speed and a small opening. All cameras have a viewfinder – from a simple wire frame to a complex optical system – that enables the user to see what the camera "sees".

These features are common to all cameras, but there is great variation in their complexity and operation. The simplest cameras [3] have a single shutter speed and fixed diaphragms, both so chosen that on a

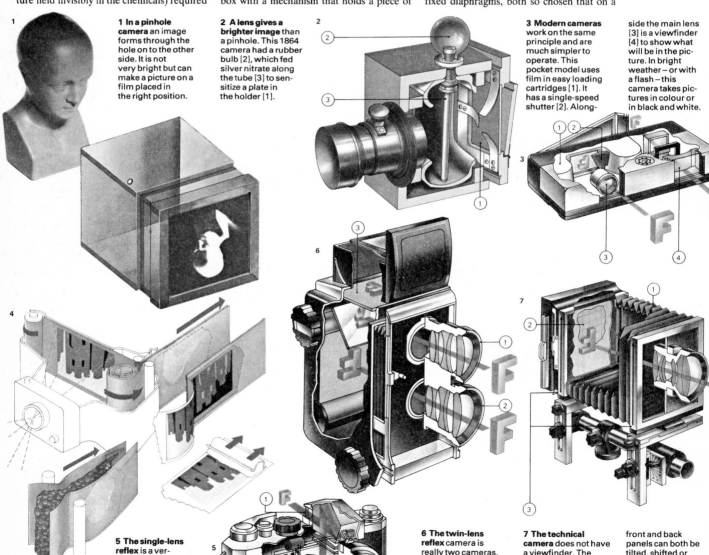

1 In a pinhole camera an image forms through the hole on to the other side. It is not very bright but can make a picture on a film placed in the right position.

2 A lens gives a brighter image than a pinhole. This 1864 camera had a rubber bulb [2], which fed silver nitrate along the tube [3] to sensitize a plate in the holder [1].

3 Modern cameras work on the same principle and are much simpler to operate. This pocket model uses film in easy loading cartridges [1]. It has a single-speed shutter [2]. Along-side the main lens [3] is a viewfinder [4] to show what will be in the picture. In bright weather – or with a flash – this camera takes pictures in colour or in black and white.

4 Polaroid cameras take composite "film and paper" packs which incorporate the necessary processing chemicals.

5 The single-lens reflex is a versatile camera design. The viewfinder [1] reveals an image formed via a mirror [2] by light from the main lens [3], showing exactly what is being focused upon.

6 The twin-lens reflex camera is really two cameras, one for focusing and viewfinding [1] and one for photography [2]. The lenses focus with a focusing screen [3].

7 The technical camera does not have a viewfinder. The image is focused by means of bellows [1] on a ground-glass sheet [2] at the back. Just before exposure this is replaced by a piece of film held in a dark slide. The front and back panels can both be tilted, shifted or swivelled independently [3]. This allows the professional photographer to manipulate subject angles and planes of sharp focus. It is ideal for static subjects.

sunny day the correct amount of light is admitted. Complex cameras, designed to take perfect photographs in all kinds of lighting conditions, have shutters with a wide variety of speeds, from hours to perhaps 1/2000th of a second; lenses that can admit a much greater amount of light (and still focus precisely and clearly); and built-in accessories of many kinds.

Generally the principal built-in accessory is an electronic exposure meter, which can automatically adjust shutter and diaphragm to the correct relationship. In many miniature (and some other) cameras the shutter is not built into the lens, or set just behind it, but lies almost against the film. These shutters are known as focal-plane shutters.

Film, developing and printing

Film may be cut into sheets, loaded into a light-tight cartridge or cassette, or wound (backed with paper) on to a metal spool. It is thin transparent plastic coated with a photographic emulsion made of grains of silver salts suspended in gelatine. The grains are relatively large in highly sensitive (fast) film

and small in slow film. Correct exposure is affected by film speed as well as by shutter speed and diaphragm opening.

The latent image formed on the film [13] is made visible and permanent by chemical processing in four main stages – developing, stopping development, fixing and washing. With negative film, developers darken the film in proportion to the light that reached it, so that the brighter parts of the scene that was photographed appear dark. In colour negative film [14] the colours of the original subject are also reversed, each colour being represented by its complement. Thus yellow appears as blue and red as cyan.

Fixing simply removes from the emulsion all the chemicals not affected by light, leaving areas of clear film. These portions print black in the final photograph. A "stop bath" between developer and fixer stops development at the correct point. Washing removes unwanted fixer, which would otherwise eventually spoil the negative. The printing process [10] is identical, except that light-sensitive paper is used (although film may be used if the photograph is to be projected).

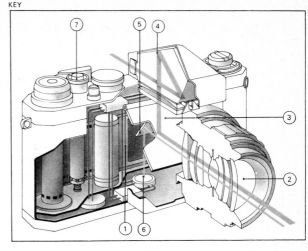

When the shutter [1] is released light reflected from a scene is focused on to film. Before the photo is taken, light entering the lens [2] is

split along two paths. Most is reflected upwards from a mirror [3] into a viewfinder [4]. A little is either reflected downwards from a smaller mirror

[5] into the photo-electric cell of an exposure meter [6], or directed to a cell in the base of the viewfinder. The release [7] opens the shutter.

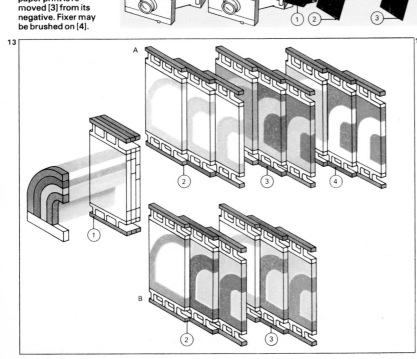

8 A black-and-white film is processed by immersion in a suitable developer [1]. The image is then washed [2] and made permanent by "fixing" [3], and the negative is washed again [4] and dried [5].

9 After drying, the negative is seen as a picture with reversed tones; the blacks are recorded as clear, the whites as black, with the intermediate tones as their complementary tones.

10 To make a print, light-sensitive paper is exposed to a same-size or enlarged image of the negative [1], then processed as is a film [2–6]. The paper is not as sensitive as film.

11 When it is washed and dried the paper has a permanent black-and-white image of the subject. The exact range from black to white depends on the paper's contrast and the surface.

12 The processing chemicals are spread on to Polaroid film as it is pulled from the camera [1]. After 15 seconds [2] the paper print is removed [3] from its negative. Fixer may be brushed on [4].

14 When light falls [1] on the light-sensitive emulsion of a film [2] it forms a latent image [3]. Grains of silver halide are slightly altered; the more light reaching the film, the more

grains are affected [4]. In developer the grains are converted back to black metallic silver. At first a few are changed [5]; later a denser image forms [6, 7] consisting of clumps of silver grains [8].

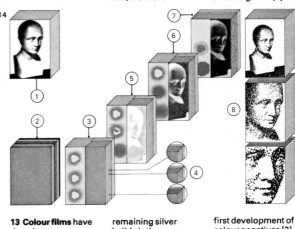

13 Colour films have three layers sensitive to blue, green and red light respectively; each forms a latent image on exposure [1]. [A] Most transparency film is first developed to a black-and-white negative [2]. All

remaining silver halide is then exposed and colour developed. Now the film is opaque, as all silver has been blackened [3]. The silver is bleached out leaving a naturally coloured dye image [4]. [B] Dyes form in the

first development of colour negatives [2]. After bleaching the negative image is in complementary colours [3], and it also has residual yellow and orange dyes. This ensures the correct colours in the subsequent printing process.

Taking pictures

In the modern world, photography has replaced painting and drawing as the chief means of making pictures. It lets men capture images without the need for graphic skills.

Using a camera

Even with the simplest camera there are rules to be followed. For example, a suitable film must be used, and the camera must be properly positioned so that the subject is not too close and out of focus, nor too far away and too small in the finished picture. A live subject must keep reasonably still, the camera must be held level and steady, and the shutter release pressed gently.

With a more complicated camera the right exposure must be selected. On some cameras the photographer simply sets a pointer to the appropriate weather symbol. With others, the camera automatically sets its own aperture or shutter speed, or both. In the most sophisticated equipment the exposure is set manually, or by overriding the automatic system, to give creative control.

Lens apertures, or "stops", are normally expressed as f-numbers [2]. These are so calculated that the light-passing ability of any lens is the same at the same f-number, within the limits set by manufacturing tolerances and lens efficiency. The smaller the number, the more light reaches the film. Most cameras have apertures indicated by numbers from the scale: 1, 1.4, 2.8, 4, 5.6, 8, 11, 16, 22, 32. Each number symbolizes half the light-passing ability of the one before it on the scale. Some cameras have maximum apertures that fall between the scale figures.

Shutter speeds [1] may also be set on a scale that halves the light reaching the film with each step. The commonly used speeds are all fractions of a second, usually on the scale: 1, $\frac{1}{2}$, $\frac{1}{4}$, $\frac{1}{8}$, $\frac{1}{15}$, $\frac{1}{30}$, $\frac{1}{60}$, $\frac{1}{125}$, $\frac{1}{250}$, $\frac{1}{500}$, $\frac{1}{1000}$. Any one of a number of combinations of aperture and shutter speed can give the same exposure. For example, many colour films need an exposure of $\frac{1}{125}$ at f11 in bright sun. They receive the same amount of light with $\frac{1}{30}$ at f22, and $\frac{1}{500}$ at f5.6.

Filters and focusing

The way in which a film records colours as monochrome tone values can be modified by using filters. They are discs of coloured glass and when placed in front of the camera lens they transmit light of their own colour and absorb light of other colours. A yellow filter can be used in landscape photography to prevent over-exposure of the blue sky and to highlight detail in cloud formation.

The chosen combination of aperture and shutter speed is decided by the amount of light available. The aperture determines how much of the picture is in sharp focus. The distance between the nearest and farthest parts of the subject that come out sharp is called the depth of field. It is not only affected by the f-number. It is smaller with longer-focus lenses, often called telephoto lenses, and greater with shorter-focus (generally wide-angle) lenses. The depth of field also decreases or increases as the distance between camera and subject is decreased or increased [7].

Shutter speed determines how sharply moving subjects come out. Slow speeds carry the risk that the picture will be spoiled by camera shake. Few people can hand-hold a camera steadily enough to use times longer

1 Shutter speed determines how sharply moving subjects come out. At a slow speed (such as $\frac{1}{15}$ second), moving things are blurred. This gives emphasis to movement, as in this waterfall [A]. At intermediate speeds, $\frac{1}{125}$ or $\frac{1}{250}$, ordinary movements do not affect the picture, but really fast objects still blur. Fast speeds, such as $\frac{1}{500}$ or $\frac{1}{1000}$ second can freeze most movement and reveal details that are normally unseen, as shown in [B].

2 When the lens is set to a large aperture (such as f4) it has little depth of field. Only part of the subject is in sharp focus. The actual plane of the sharp image depends on how close [A] or distant [B] the lens is focused. At small apertures (large f-numbers such as f16) the depth of field is much larger and most of the subject comes out sharp [C]. Choosing the aperture can concentrate attention on selected parts of the subject.

than $^1/_{30}$ second, and for hand cameras $^1/_{60}$ or $^1/_{125}$ is preferable.

Simple cameras are pre-set to give about $^1/_{60}$ second at f11. They have enough depth of field to take sharp pictures of anything more than about 1.5m (5ft) from the camera.

The professionals
Professional photographers work in a wide range of fields. Some record life as it is for newspapers, magazines and similar publications. Others set up the situation they want in a studio or on a carefully chosen location. Their pictures are usually used as decorative illustrations or in advertising to show a product to its best advantage.

Photo-journalists and other reporting photographers have to take scenes as they find them. They create their pictures by choosing a suitable viewpoint and manipulating the shutter speed and aperture. They may have some simple portable lighting, such as an electronic flash gun. But this is normally used merely to illuminate a subject that is not well enough lit.

On the other hand, advertising, portrait

and industrial photographers manipulate their lighting to make the most of the subject. A studio set may be lit by several electronic flashes [6], or by a series of theatrical spotlights and floodlights [3]. The first consideration is the angle of the main or key light, followed by the amount of fill-in light used to keep the shadows from being too dark. There may also be background lighting, or special effects, such as a backlight to make a model's hair glow.

Professional photographers understand how to get sharp, grain-free, perfectly lit and accurately coloured pictures. But much of the impact of good, exciting photography depends occasionally on breaking the rules to create something more than a mere record of what is in front of the camera.

Whether he breaks rules, or follows them, has sophisticated or simple equipment, a photographer creates his picture in the viewfinder the instant he presses the shutter release. Before this vital moment arrives the most important lesson is to make a critical examination of the whole composition of the prospective picture.

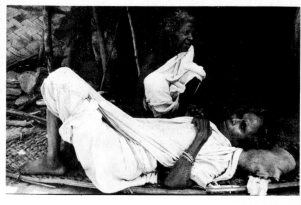

One good picture is worth 1,000 words – this maxim is known and understood by every newspaper editor. For example, this photograph, taken by Chris Steele-Perkins, shows all the agony and despair of the terrible conflict in Bangladesh. It says far more about human suffering than the most eloquent of reports could achieve with descriptive prose. The recent history of war and revolution in Asia, Africa, the Middle East, South-East Asia and Northern Ireland has brought to the fore photo-journalists able to capture the violence and compassion of the modern age, often risking their own safety in order to take good pictures.

3 The angle at which light falls on the subject changes its appearance in the photograph. Direct lighting from the front gives a flat look. If the key light is moved to the side [A], above [B], or below [C] it creates a more interesting picture. The effect can be harsh with a "hard" light source. To soften it, a fill light is used. It is placed in a more-or-less frontal position.

4 Camera lenses consist of glass or plastic elements in a tube. Number, shape and position of the elements determine the focal length and maximum aperture. On a 35mm camera, a 35mm lens covers a wide field of view; a 50mm lens covers a standard field. Some lenses can zoom through a range of focal lengths between two fixed points, as in an extremely long focus or telephoto lens of 200–600mm.

50mm

35mm

200-600mm

5 Simple cameras often take battery-fired flash cubes, with disposable flash bulbs mounted in reflectors, which rotate between flashes.

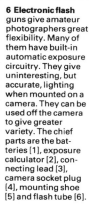

6 Electronic flash guns give amateur photographers great flexibility. Many of them have built-in automatic exposure circuitry. They give uninteresting, but accurate, lighting when mounted on a camera. They can be used off the camera to give greater variety. The chief parts are the batteries [1], exposure calculator [2], connecting lead [3], camera socket plug [4], mounting shoe [5] and flash tube [6].

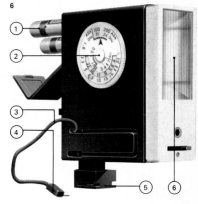

7 Altering the focal length alters the subject's size, pictured from a fixed camera position. (If the camera is moved so that the subject stays the same size, it comes out a different shape with different angles of view.) A wide-angle lens [A] enlarges the nose and chin, while a narrow angle, long focus, lens [C] tends to flatten them, but is preferred for portraits. A standard lens is in between [B], and intended to give a normal view.

Cine photography

A movie camera [Key] works just like a still camera, with one major exception: instead of taking just one picture of a scene, it rapidly takes a series of pictures or frames [7]. The usual rate for taking and projecting amateur movies is 18 pictures a second and for professional movies 24. Older silent movies were shot at 16 pictures a second. Each exposure produces a static view of the scene; but anything that moves is in a slightly different place in each succeeding frame. When the pictures are projected in sequence the movement is re-created. If pictures are taken at a faster rate, such as 48 or 72 a second, they produce slow motion when projected at normal speed; pictures taken at longer intervals, such as 16 or 8 a second, produce a speeded-up motion at normal projection speed.

The camera

All movie cameras have a motor – usually electric, occasionally clockwork – to drive the film from one spool to another; and they all have a lens, shutter and gate mechanism. Apart from these features, they vary enormously. The simplest cameras have a fixed-focus lens and simple automatic exposure systems – ensuring acceptable results in most outdoor conditions. More versatile cameras are fitted with zoom lenses that allow a range of image sizes. These lenses generally have a focus control and often a built-in rangefinder system. Only in the most sophisticated cameras can the lens be removed and replaced with another. Super 8 cameras range in sophistication from the movie equivalents of box-cameras to complex machines hardly distinguishable from 16mm professional equipment.

Cine camera film

Cine camera film is used in five widths – 70mm, 35mm, 16mm, 9.5mm and 8mm. The 70mm and 35mm sizes are used by major film companies in cameras that are highly complex and expensive. Such cameras are often used with special image-squeezing "anamorphic" lenses to produce wide-screen pictures. 16mm film is used for smaller-budget commercial pictures, documentary films, much television filming and by serious amateurs. A special format with a larger pic-ture area, Super 16, is made for wide-screen filming to be printed on to 35mm film stock. Although apparently superseded for a quarter of a century, 9.5mm still has its adherents. 8mm is the popular amateur format and is beginning to be used for low-budget television work. There are two picture sizes – Standard 8 and Super 8. With Standard 8 the camera is loaded with special 16mm film either on simple spools or in reloadable magazines. After half the width (that is, an 8mm-wide strip down one side) has been exposed, the film is turned over to expose the other half. It is cut along the middle after processing. Super 8 film in plastic cartridges has virtually superseded Standard 8. It has a larger picture area than Standard 8 and is not as subject to light leakage.

Because the same piece of film is normally used both for filming and projection, almost all amateur movies are shot in colour reversal film – usually rated at 40 ASA (17 DIN) in artificial light or 25 ASA (15 DIN) in daylight. ASA and DIN ratings are a measure of the "speed" of the film – that is, its sensitivity to light. Super 8 cameras have a built-

1 Moving subjects were first pictured as a series of still photographs by Eadweard Muybridge (1830–1904) in 1877. He set up 12 and later 25 cameras fitted with high-speed shutters. As a horse galloped or trotted by, it set off each camera in turn by breaking a string or through electrical contacts. Later Muybridge extended his technique to a wide range of subjects, using the principles of moving picture toys (such as the zoetrope) to produce moving images.

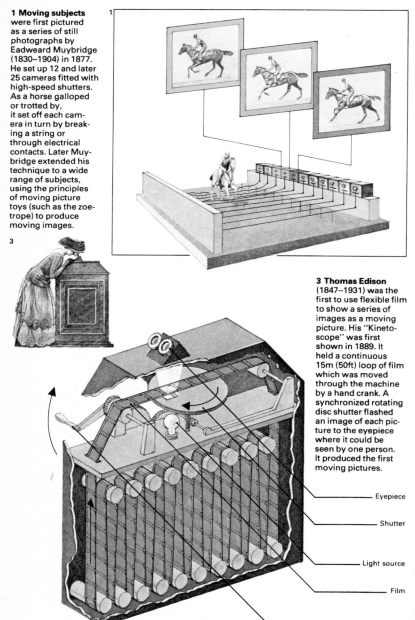

3 Thomas Edison (1847–1931) was the first to use flexible film to show a series of images as a moving picture. His "Kineto-scope" was first shown in 1889. It held a continuous 15m (50ft) loop of film which was moved through the machine by a hand crank. A synchronized rotating disc shutter flashed an image of each picture to the eyepiece where it could be seen by one person. It produced the first moving pictures.

- Eyepiece
- Shutter
- Light source
- Film
- Crank

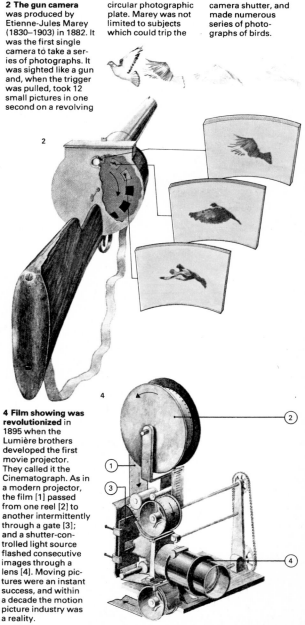

2 The gun camera was produced by Etienne-Jules Marey (1830–1903) in 1882. It was the first single camera to take a series of photographs. It was sighted like a gun and, when the trigger was pulled, took 12 small pictures in one second on a revolving circular photographic plate. Marey was not limited to subjects which could trip the camera shutter, and made numerous series of photographs of birds.

4 Film showing was revolutionized in 1895 when the Lumière brothers developed the first movie projector. They called it the Cinematograph. As in a modern projector, the film [1] passed from one reel [2] to another intermittently through a gate [3]; and a shutter-controlled light source flashed consecutive images through a lens [4]. Moving pictures were an instant success, and within a decade the motion picture industry was a reality.

in filter and normally use the 40 ASA (17 DIN) artificial light film with this filter in daylight. 160 ASA (23 DIN) films are available for poor lighting conditions and, with specially designed lowlight XL type cameras, can make films in ordinary domestic lighting.

Most professional moviemakers use negative film – either colour or black-and-white. The colours or tones of the final copies are determined in the processing laboratory. The films for projection are always positive – like colour transparencies, but negatives are used for some television transmissions and they are reversed electronically.

Projection and editing

For normal viewing, movies are projected at a suitable speed. The film is projected as a series of static images. If the images follow one another fast enough, the effect is a moving picture. To reduce flicker, the projector shutter closes and opens again during each frame. So at the cinema we see 48 pictures a second, each of which is repeated with a moment of blackness intervening.

For home movies, the original camera

film is projected. In professional work this hardly ever happens. Prints are made from the camera negatives and are edited and "cut together" to make a complete film. The camera negatives are then cut and joined together to match. Any optical effects are added at this stage. Such effects include "fades" to black or white, "dissolves" from one scene to the next, and "wipes" in which a new scene progressively displaces the old one. A master negative is then made from the complete film and used to produce all the prints for distribution. The prints need not be on the same size of film as the camera original. For the largest cinemas, 70mm film is used, although 35mm is more usual. 16mm copies are made for small cinemas, clubs and educational establishments.

Soundtracks on movies may be either magnetic or optical. Magnetic tracks are recorded on magnetic stripes coated on the film, just like a normal tape recording. Optical tracks record the sound as brightness variations in a dark stripe down the edge of the film. It is replayed by shining a light through it on to a photoelectric cell [7].

In a movie camera, fresh film [1] is fed from a spool to the gate [2]. A revolving shutter [3] controls exposure to light focused through a lens [4]. This produces an upside down image like that

in a still camera. While the shutter is closed, a claw mechanism [5] moves the film through the gate in measured steps. Between steps the film remains stationary and the shutter opens and closes again. So the scene is recorded as a series of pictures taken one after the other. The reflex viewfinder uses a mirror shutter [6]. When the shutter is closed, the image through the camera lens is reflected from its mirror surface to the viewfinder. As a result, the image directed through the prism and lens system is exactly the same as that passing through the lens. In the viewfinder, the cameraman sees exactly what the lens "sees".

5 Floor-mounted movie cameras are used in studios; lighter cameras such as this 35mm model are used outdoors. The camera can take most lenses and accessories. It can be carried on a cameraman's shoulder, but gives steadier pictures when fixed to a tripod. Film spools are mounted coaxially, so the balance remains constant; and to keep the noise to a minimum, the camera is sealed in a rigid

housing with a window in front of the lens. The gate is fitted with register pins to ensure that each frame is accurately located on the film.

Key
[1] Focus control
[2] Aperture control
[3] Mirror shutter
[4] Viewfinder eyepiece
[5] Take-up spool
[6] Feed spool
[7] Gate
[8] Sprocket drive
[9] Pull-down claw
[10] Register pins
[11] Indicator
[12] Viewfinder
[13] Footage indicator
[14] Lens

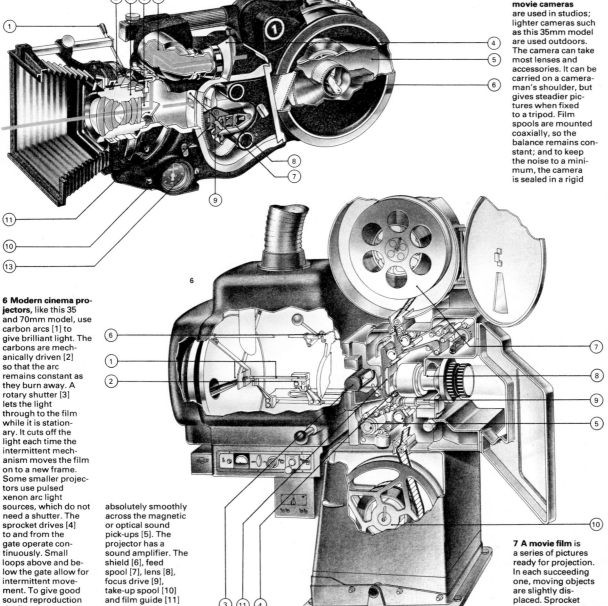

6 Modern cinema projectors, like this 35 and 70mm model, use carbon arcs [1] to give brilliant light. The carbons are mechanically driven [2] so that the arc remains constant as they burn away. A rotary shutter [3] lets the light through to the film while it is stationary. It cuts off the light each time the intermittent mechanism moves the film on to a new frame. Some smaller projectors use pulsed xenon arc light sources, which do not need a shutter. The sprocket drives [4] to and from the gate operate continuously. Small loops above and below the gate allow for intermittent movement. To give good sound reproduction the film must travel

absolutely smoothly across the magnetic or optical sound pick-ups [5]. The projector has a sound amplifier. The shield [6], feed spool [7], lens [8], focus drive [9], take-up spool [10] and film guide [11] are other main parts.

7 A movie film is a series of pictures ready for projection. In each succeeding one, moving objects are slightly displaced. Sprocket holes along the edge

ensure that each frame is held in just the right place in the projector. A variable area stripe along one edge carries the soundtrack. As this passes a light-sensitive cell, it modulates the light from a lamp and produces sound signals.

Communications: telegraph

Long-distance communications, which for thousands of years had depended on the slow and unreliable travel of messengers by foot, horseback or ship were transformed by telegraphy. Simple forms of semaphore had long been used, but the transmission of messages beyond the range of sight had to wait until the discovery of electricity. The idea was foreshadowed as early as 1753 by a Scottish doctor, Charles Morrison, in a letter to the *Scots Magazine*. In 1764 Georges Louis Lesages built and operated an experimental electric telegraph in Geneva using static electricity and an electroscope. The mutual repulsion of a pair of pith balls indicated the presence of an electric charge in a wire connected to them and a separate wire was used for each letter of the alphabet.

Single-wire telegraphy

At the end of the eighteenth century, Napoleon Bonaparte (1769-1821), who was the first to make use of a systematic telegraph, still had to rely on a visual system invented by a French merchant, Claude Chappe (1763-1805), to receive intelligence reports and send orders to his army [1]. It was not until 1816 that a single-wire telegraph was invented by an Englishman, Francis Ronalds (1788–1873). He set up discs turned by clockwork at each end of the wire. Each disc was initialled with the alphabet round its rim and, as the desired letter aligned with a pointer, the sender's wire was connected to an electroscope. With the discs synchronized, a man at the other end of the wire could note the letter indicated each time the wire received a charge.

Ten years later an American, Harrison Gray Dyer, built the first practical electrical telegraph by using the recently invented voltaic cell (battery) and a chemical solution that indicated the presence of an electric current by the formation of bubbles at two electrodes. Dyer sent messages along 12.5km (8 miles) of wire laid in Long Island, New York, using the earth to complete the circuit.

The final step in the evolution of the electric telegraph came in 1831 when another American, Joseph Henry (1797–1878), replaced Dyer's electrolytic indicator with an electric bell, using the principle of electromagnetism discovered in 1819 by the Danish physicist Hans Christian Oersted (1787-1851). Henry used a code to indicate the different letters of the alphabet.

Two Englishmen, William Cooke (1806-79) and Charles Wheatstone (1802-75), designed and installed the world's first commercial telegraph [2]. This was a five-wire system, first tested in 1837 between Euston and Camden Town on the London-Birmingham railway and installed two years later, between Paddington and West Drayton, for the Great Western Railway.

Morse code and later developments

Up to this time each inventor had devised his own means of coding messages. It was an American inventor and painter, Samuel Morse (1791–1872), who first recognized the practical and commercial inportance of devising a standard code. He demonstrated his own code in 1837 and it was the revised Morse code that eventually made possible the development of electric telegraphs throughout the world. Consisting essentially of a single wire, the telegraph circuit was

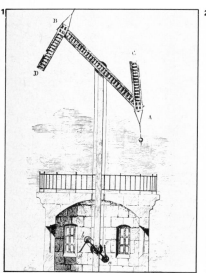

1 The earliest form of long-distance communication, apart from jungle drums, smoke signals and similar crude devices, was the visual semaphore invented by Claude Chappe and used by the French army from 1794. The Chappe telegraph consisted of pairs of hand-operated semaphore arms located on a chain of towers built on the tops of hills within sight of each other.

2 The world's first commercial telegraph was the five-wire system set up by Charles Wheatstone and William Cooke in England in 1839. Switch pairs made each needle deflect in either direction.

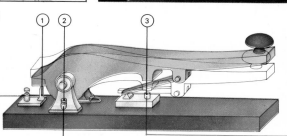
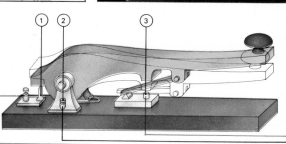

3 A Morse key is basically a switch. This early two-pole key has a closed circuit between points 1 and 2 when at rest. When the key is depressed contact [1] is broken and the circuit made instead through 3. Current entering via the black wire is switched from blue to red.

4 This early Morse receiver-printer is operated by closing the circuit of the transmitter (a simple key). The current energizes the coils [1]. The lever [2] is moved by magnetic attraction, bringing the printing disc [3] into contact with the paper tape for the duration of the current. The disc is linked by contact with a roller immersed in a bath of printer's ink. The movement of the paper tape is effected by clockwork wound by the handle [4]. It was found that a skilled operator could "read" a buzzer quicker than an inked tape.

5 Emile Baudot's multiplex system enabled several telegraph operators to send messages over the same line simultaneously. Each operator's set was connected in turn to the line by a distributor for just enough time to allow transmission of a single letter in the form of a five-unit code. By exact phase synchronization outgoing signals could be correctly separated and "read" on receivers at the other end.

completed by a battery and key between the wire and the earth at the sending end [3], and an electromagnetic sounder between the wire and the earth at the receiving end.

The laying of submarine cables [6, 8] was a natural development of the electric telegraph. A connection across the English Channel in 1850 encouraged engineers to attempt the more difficult task of laying a cable across the Atlantic. Success came in 1858 when a cable was laid from Ireland to Newfoundland, although a reliable link was not established until 1866 [Key].

Because wire is expensive inventors soon turned their minds to ways of sending a number of messages simultaneously along a single wire. The breakthrough came in 1874 when a Frenchman, Emile Baudot (1845–1903), designed an instrument which, when fully developed, could interlace six messages and unscramble them [5].

Automatic telegraphy
Baudot's system, in which every letter consisted of five pulses (or absence of pulses), was used successfully for about 50 years until replaced by a more sophisticated frequency division multiplex, invented in the 1890s by an American, Elisha Gray (1835-1901).

To reduce the time spent coding and decoding messages much effort was given, over many years, to the invention of an automatic printing telegraph. David Hughes (1831-1900), an American professor of music, built the first practical printing telegraph in 1854 [4], but it, too, was slow. In 1921 a Russian, N. P. Trusevich, invented what is called the "start-stop" system and the modern teleprinter became possible. The new invention solved the problem of keeping the receiving machine perfectly synchronized with the sending machine when the operator's typing speed varied slightly from letter to letter [9]. The modern teleprinter, using the five-unit code, can transmit up to 13 characters a second when working from punched paper tape which the operator first prepares, typing at his own speed. Telex [7] enables up to 26 teleprinter messages to be carried on a single telephone cable. Phototelegraphy [10] completes the range of modern telegraphic communications.

KEY

A cable-laying ship is specially designed so that miles of submarine telegraph cable can be fed out over sheaves in the bows. Today cable-laying is a routine task, but it took the American businessman Cyrus W. Field (1819–92) nine years and five attempts before the first successful transatlantic telegraph cable was laid in 1866. For the laying the engineers used the largest ship then afloat, the steam screw and paddle ship *Great Eastern* built by the British engineer Isambard Kingdom Brunel (1806–59).

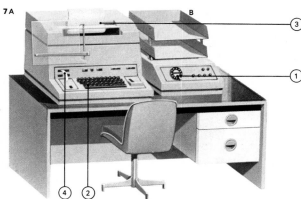

6 A typical early submarine cable was made up of a stranded copper conductor [3], usually of wires or copper tapes woven round a stout central strand; an insulating layer [2], originally of gutta percha; a layer of jute fibre [4] with galvanized steel wires embedded in it (for strength); another layer [1] of compounded jute; and an outer waterproof layer [5] tough enough to withstand chafing.

7 A modern telex installation comprises a teletypewriter [A] and a dialling unit [B], both often built into a single console. The operator uses the dial unit [1] to call the receiver's telex number and then types the message using conventional typewriter keys [2]. Alternatively, the message can be pre-typed on a punched tape [4] and fed in for extra speed in transmission or when a line is free. For checking, the transmitted message is automatically printed out above [3]. When not sending, the equipment is left ready for receiving. A buzzer can alert the receiving operator to an incoming message. If the operator is absent the teletypewriter is automatically activated to reproduce the message on the paper [3]. Incoming messages can thus be "stored" in typed form on the machine until the operator returns.

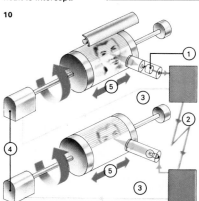

8 Telegraph cabling across the Atlantic first became fully successful in 1866. After this the world's oceans were soon crossed by a network of such cables. The map shows today's transatlantic routes. Cable communications were supplemented by radio in the 1920s and by satellite systems in the 1960s. Cables retain the advantage of privacy because, unlike radio signals, the messages they carry are difficult to intercept.

Shipping routes
Submarine cables

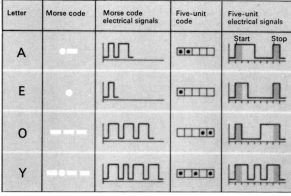

Letter	Morse code	Morse code electrical signals	Five-unit code	Five-unit electrical signals
A				Start / Stop
E				
O				
Y				

9 The teleprinter has a seven-unit code consisting of a start signal, a five-unit character signal and a stop signal. The start and stop signals enable the equipment to keep the five-unit signals in step for each transmitted letter, despite the fact that no two typists operate at the same precise speed or perfectly evenly. Morse signals, being of unequal length, cannot be so used.

10 In photo-telegraphy, used widely by newspapers, the picture is "scanned" by a spot of light that covers its area in a series of parallel lines. The brightness of each element is converted by the cell [1] into an electrical signal that is transmitted [2] by telegraph. A machine at the receiving end converts the signal back into a picture by printing it dot by dot according to the incoming signal. Pulses [3] synchronize the motors [4] and traverse [5].

Communications: telephone

Inventors working independently often arrive at very similar solutions to a problem. So it was in 1876 when Alexander Graham Bell (1847–1922), a Scottish professor of vocal physiology living in the United States, applied for a patent for his electric telephone only a few hours before an American from Chicago, Elisha Gray (1835–1901), filed a similar application. Bell was granted the patent and has since generally been credited as the sole inventor of the telephone.

Bell's instrument [2] was used both as transmitter and receiver and needed no battery. But the current generated when sound vibrated the diaphragm in its "microphone" was small and the instrument was therefore unsuitable for telephone communications over long distances.

The microphone and telephone exchange
In 1877 the American Thomas Edison (1847–1931) invented the carbon microphone. By another coincidence a similar microphone was developed independently a year later by the English scientist David Hughes (1831–1900), who is now generally

credited as the inventor. The carbon microphone [4] modulates an electric current from a DC source creating a voltage that varies in step with the sound waves. It is used to this day as the transmitter in modern telephones, the receiver being an electromagnetic earphone similar to that patented by Bell. A varying voltage in the earphone's coil causes a metal diaphragm to vibrate and produce sounds at low volume.

For the telephone to become a practical proposition it was necessary to find a means of interconnecting any pair of a number of instruments. The first telephone exchange was opened at New Haven, Connecticut, in 1878 and a similar eight-line exchange was set up in London a year later. In the early exchanges, an operator used plugs and sockets to connect callers.

In 1889 an American undertaker, Almon Strowger, annoyed by the inefficient service from his local exchange, designed an automatic selector. The first automatic exchange was opened in La Porte, Indiana, in 1892. The Strowger electromechanical selector [5] became standard equipment for

telephone exchanges throughout the world during the next half century.

Since 1926 an American invention, the crossbar switch, has replaced the Strowger selector in Sweden. It is in use today in both the United States and Great Britain, although an even more efficient all-electronic exchange was developed in 1960.

Telephone cables
The largest single expense in any long-distance telephone system is the cost of the wires that connect subscribers to each other. Research into the problem of using a single cable for more than one simultaneous telephone call bore fruit in 1936 when the first 12-channel coaxial cable was laid between Bristol and Plymouth in southwest England. The system uses electric carrier waves of different frequencies, which can be transmitted simultaneously along the metal core of the cable and separated at the other end by a series of electronic "filters", each of which accepts signals of one frequency only.

The longer a telephone line, the weaker the electrical signal reaching the end; this is

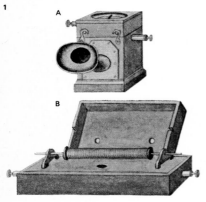

3 An exchange network allows telephone subscribers to dial any number in a national system. The lines and numbers indicate the direction in which calls can be routed and the dialling code for each route. The squares, always in pairs, are main exchanges, one part for local, the other for long-distance calls. The circles are subexchanges – those top right being directly

interconnected exchanges in a city. All city, local and main exchanges have lines to subscribers. A caller on exchange P can call numbers on exchange N by first dialling the code "9", or numbers on exchange Q by dialling code "987". To call

exchange S he must first dial code "991", and to call a number on exchange T the code is "99186".

1 An early telephone designed by a German, Philipp Reis, in about 1861 has a transmitter [A] with a metal point in light contact with a metal strip fixed to a membrane. Reis believed that the intermittent circuit caused when the membrane vibrated would produce a varying electric current which could be reconverted into sound. The receiver [B] was based on – the change in length of an iron needle in a magnetic field.

2 Bell's first telephone used a parchment drum, which vibrated when sound waves reached it. A piece of iron was supported by a short length of clock spring so that it rested lightly on the parchment [A]. An electromagnet [B] was placed so that one pole was close to the iron piece. When the parchment and the iron vibrated a small varying electric current was induced in the coil. When two such instru-

ments were connected the current produced by one energized the magnet of the other, causing the iron piece and the parchment to vibrate in step with the first. By this means a voice or any other sound that vibrated one parchment diaphragm was reproduced by similar vibrations of the other. Alexander Bell obtained the publicity he needed for his invention when it was seen by the Emperor of Brazil.

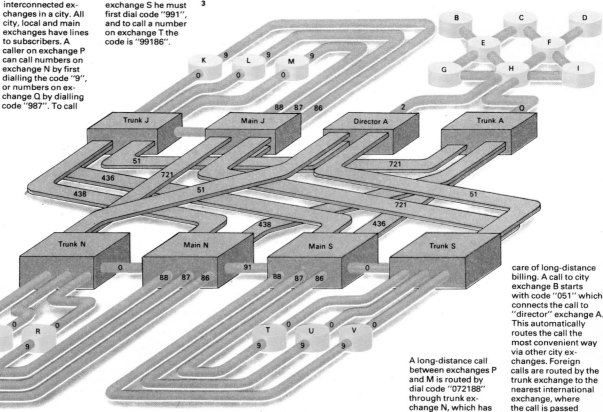

A long-distance call between exchanges P and M is routed by dial code "072188" through trunk exchange N, which has equipment to take

care of long-distance billing. A call to city exchange B starts with code "051" which connects the call to "director" exchange A. This automatically routes the call the most convenient way via other city exchanges. Foreign calls are routed by the trunk exchange to the nearest international exchange, where the call is passed to the other country.

due to the resistance of the wire. Automatic amplifiers (called repeaters) overcame this problem and today these are incorporated in multi-channel cables every 16km (10 miles). The first transatlantic multi-channel telephone cable, called TAT 1, was laid in 1956. It was a twin coaxial cable – one for speech in each direction – running from Scotland to Newfoundland and included 51 repeaters in each cable. Today, submarine telephone cables with two-way repeaters encircle the world. The repeaters are powered by alternating current from the same cable core that carries the modulated carriers. The power frequency is much lower than the carrier frequencies, so there is no interference.

For many years automatic dialling could be used only for calling a subscriber connected to one's own exchange. The problem of extending the system was largely one of designing a means of automatic billing that would charge according to distance and time.

Today, when a call is dialled the equipment connects the line to an electronic pulse generator. Each pulse records a fixed unit charge on the subscriber's account. The pulse generator selected depends on the distance of the called exchange.

Modern coaxial cables can carry an increasingly large number of simultaneous conversations – current research is producing multiple cables capable of handling up to 3,000 channels – but microwave radio has been playing a rapidly growing part in telecommunications since the early 1960s.

Microwave telephony
Modern microwave systems use relay towers at 40–50km (25–30 mile) intervals. Telephone signals are used to modulate microwave radio carriers instead of the electrical carriers used in coaxial cables [6]. The British microwave system [Key], which has about 120 relay stations throughout the United Kingdom, is typical. It operates with 132 separate microwave carriers, each able to accommodate 2,700 simultaneous telephone conversations (many of the channels are used to relay television signals). For intercontinental telecommunications microwave carriers are beamed up to satellites, amplified and beamed down to ground stations.

London's Post Office Tower is the hub of the United Kingdom microwave network. This provides thousands of telephone circuits and up to forty television channels connecting all parts of the British Isles, and links them with the international satellite station at Goonhilly Downs in Cornwall and a cross-Channel link station near Dover. The tower is 189m (620ft) tall, to the top of the aerials, and has a mass of radio equipment on most of its lower 16 floors. Above is a series of open galleries around which stand an array of parabolic dish and horn aerials for microwave signals. Above are public observation galleries and a restaurant.

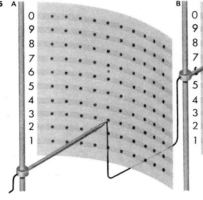

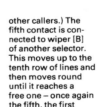

4 The heart of a carbon microphone is a small insulating cylinder packed with carbon granules. The centre of a metal diaphragm presses against the open end of the cylinder. When the diaphragm vibrates, the pressure on the granules, and thus the electrical resistance through them, varies. With a DC source connected, a variable current passes. This current will operate a magnetic earpiece.

5 Imagine a caller's telephone is connected to a wiper [A] of a Strowger selector. He dials 3064. In response to the three electrical impulses produced by dialling the digit 3, the wiper moves up to the third line of contacts and then moves along until a free line is found. (In the illustration the wiper has stopped at the fifth contact because the first four lines are already in use by other callers.) The fifth contact is connected to wiper [B] of another selector. This moves up to the tenth row of lines and then moves round until it reaches a free one – once again the fifth, the first four being busy. This line is connected to wiper [C] of a third Strowger selector. This, unlike the first two, which are "number-line" selectors, is a "double-number" selector. The wiper moves up to the sixth row of contacts in response to the dialled third digit 6 and then waits until the final digit 4 is dialled. It then moves round to the fourth contact leading to telephone number 3064.

Coaxial cable

6 Coaxial cables enable a number of telephone calls to be made simultaneously over a single circuit. Six calls, on lines A–F, are each passed through one of six modulators M1–M6, which vary six different carrier waves according to the audio signals. The six modulated carriers are then fed into a coaxial cable. At the other end, six filters F1–F6 are each tuned to accept one only of the six carrier frequencies. Only one of the six carriers is thus fed into each of six detectors, which separate the audio signals from the carriers, passing the former to the six subscribers, G–L. All the circuits are duplicated for two-way communication.

7 An up-to-date telephone has a set of numbered push buttons in place of the traditional dial. A number can be selected more quickly by push button and cross-bar and electronic exchanges can work as fast as a user can "dial". If a push button telephone is used with a Strowger exchange, the number has to be stored in a memory and converted into pulses at a speed the selectors can handle. Despite this limitation the push button system is more convenient.

Communications: radio

Radio waves were predicted before they were discovered. In 1865, James Clerk Maxwell (1831–79), a Scottish theoretical physicist, argued the existence of an unseen form of radiation. But his mathematics was so complex that his theory was at first rejected by some scientists. About 25 years later experiments showed that electromagnetic waves, which include gamma-rays, X-rays, and visible light and radio waves, all conformed to his formulae.

The first practical demonstration of what we now call radio waves took place in 1879, when the Anglo-American inventor David Edward Hughes (1831–1900) built a crude radio transmitter and receiver and passed signals without wires along Great Portland Street in London. Hughes failed to realize the full significance of his experiment and did not publish his findings for 20 years.

Successful transmission
In about 1887 the German scientist Heinrich Hertz (1857–94) built a spark generator [Key] that produced radio waves and a receiver that detected their presence at a dis-

tance. In a series of experiments he proved conclusively that energy could be transferred over a distance in a way that could not be accounted for by induction and he is generally credited with the discovery of radio.

Oliver Lodge, an Englishman, was the first to build a radio receiver – more sensitive than Hertz's coil and spark gap – that could be used for practical radio communication. It used a coherer [2], a device invented by a Parisian Edouard Branly (1844–1940). In an experiment in 1894, Lodge used his radio to operate at a distance of 137m (450ft).

The man who was to take wireless out of the purely experimental field was the Italian Guglielmo Marconi (1874–1937). After failing to interest the Italian government in his work he moved to England. In 1898 he set up a radio link between the mainland near Dover and the East Goodwin light vessel moored 19km (12 miles) offshore. A year later Marconi fitted the American liner *St Paul* with radio. The first message received was transmitted from 97km (60 miles) away.

In 1901 Marconi astonished the world by transmitting a radio signal across the Atlantic

Ocean [1] in Morse code. In 1906 a Canadian, R. A. Fessenden (1886–1932), transmitted from Brant Rock, Massachusetts, a signal in which operators at sea heard a voice and music in their headphones. This was the first audio-modulated transmission.

The nature of radio waves
When electrons oscillate in an electric circuit, some of their energy is converted into electromagnetic radiation. The frequency (the rate of oscillation) has to be very high to produce waves of useful intensity, but once formed they travel through space at the speed of light – 300 million metres a second (186,000 miles a second). When such a wave meets a metal aerial, some of its energy is transferred to free electrons in the metal, causing them to flow as an alternating electric current having the frequency of the wave. This, in the simplest terms, is the principle of radio communication. A radio transmitter produces concentrated electromagnetic radiation of a chosen frequency. The waves so generated are picked up by an aerial. From all the waves that come into contact with its

3 A 1920s crystal set, forerunner of the modern transistor, used a crystal of carborundum or lead sulphide, a semiconductor that rectified a radio carrier wave. This crystal produced an alternating current of the same frequency as the sound "carried" on the wave. The low frequency electric current had sufficient power to produce sound from sensitive earphones.

1 Three dots – the Morse code "S" – signalled success for Guglielmo Marconi and for the future of wireless telegraphy in 1901. They were transmitted from Cornwall, England, and received 3,520km (2,200 miles) away in Newfoundland by the inventor himself. The transmitter, using electricity generated by a 25hp oil engine, had an aerial supported by four 61m (200ft) masts. Marconi's receiver was connected to a 122m (400ft) aerial supported by a kite. Marconi had proved to doubting science his firm belief that radio waves were capable of travelling around the curvature of the earth.

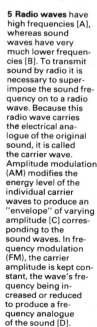

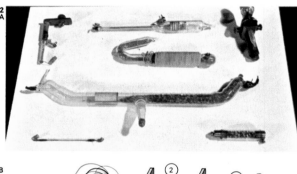

4 The modern transistor radio, like the old crystal set, "detects" (or demodulates) the radio carrier wave, although the process it uses is far more sophisticated. Having created an electrical analogue of the original sound waves, a series of amplifying circuits then produce a signal that has sufficient power to drive a small loudspeaker. Whereas radio wave energy was enough to operate earphones, the transistor set needs a battery.

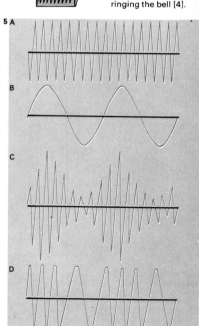

2 The first practical radio detectors were coherers [A], developed by Oliver Lodge (1851–1940). Each of those shown consists of a long glass tube with iron filings packed between two metal plates. In their loose condition the filings did not conduct electricity but when subjected to a vibrating electric wave they cohered (adhered to each other), making a conducting path between the plates. In the circuit shown [B] the coherer [1] acts as a switch in an electric bell circuit. As soon as streams of radio waves [2] reach the aerial plates [3], the coherer filings adhere, thus ringing the bell [4].

5 Radio waves have high frequencies [A], whereas sound waves have very much lower frequencies [B]. To transmit sound by radio it is necessary to superimpose the sound frequency on to a radio wave. Because this radio wave carries the electrical analogue of the original sound, it is called the carrier wave. Amplitude modulation (AM) modifies the energy level of the individual carrier waves to produce an "envelope" of varying amplitude [C] corresponding to the sound waves. In frequency modulation (FM) the carrier amplitude is kept constant, the wave's frequency being increased or reduced to produce a frequency analogue of the sound [D].

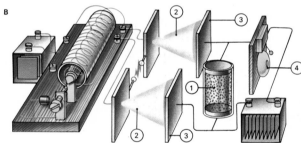

aerial, the radio receiver amplifies those of a selected frequency to which it is "tuned" and eliminates all others.

To transmit voice and music by radio the waves of a regular "carrier" signal must be modulated (varied) by the audio signal [5]. The waves may vary either in strength (amplitude modulation, AM) or in frequency (frequency modulation, FM). The receiver is then able to eliminate the high-frequency carrier waves, leaving only electrical waves of the same frequencies as those of the original sound. Finally, after amplification, the electrical waves are fed into earphones or a loudspeaker, which are able to convert electrical vibrations back into sound waves.

Frequencies, wavelengths and channels

Electromagnetic radiation can vary enormously in frequency. It includes gamma-rays, X-rays and ultra-violet, visible and infra-red light rays, all of which have very high frequencies. Electromagnetic radiation of lower frequencies is radio waves. Those waves next in frequency to infra-red rays are known as microwaves and are used mainly

for telecommunications between towers within visible range, but also for communication with satellites. These waves are followed in order of lower frequency (and so of longer wavelength) by ultra high frequency (UHF) – used for television broadcasts; very high frequency (VHF), for radio broadcasting and for local communication, such as between aircraft and ground control; short waves that, at high power, are used for worldwide broadcasting; medium waves for regional broadcasting; and the relatively little used long waves. The whole radio spectrum is divided by international agreement into bands reserved for specific uses and each band is generally further subdivided into channels spaced so that they do not overlap.

Stereophonic sound requires the reproduction of two separate sound signals that correspond to those received by the two ears of the listener. In radio this could mean doubling the channel width for every stereo transmission. Because radio space is already congested, engineers have devised a method of transmitting two separate audio signals over one radio channel.

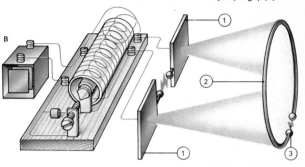

The first radio transmitters [A], as used by Heinrich Hertz and Oliver Lodge, made use of the radio waves generated when a high-voltage spark jumped between contacts [B]. Hertz beamed the waves from aerial plates [1] and detected them with a loop of wire [2] in which they caused a small spark to jump a gap [3].

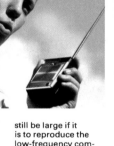

6 The non-stop trend towards miniaturization in electronics is shown in this comparison of a typical wireless set of the 1930s [A] and a transistor radio of today [B]. A loudspeaker must still be large if it is to reproduce the low-frequency components of sound, but now modern technology (much of it space technology "spin-off") has led to the design of smaller and smaller components of nearly all other kinds. The transistor [C, left] has almost entirely superseded the old thermionic valve [right]. Individual electronic components have been growing steadily smaller; more- over new developments have taken the process further, with the introduction of the integrated circuits (IC) in which a complete wired set of components is replaced by one minute IC.

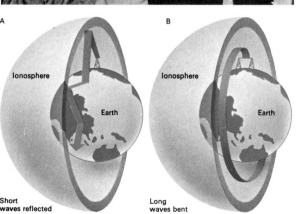

Ionosphere

Earth

Short waves reflected

Ionosphere

Earth

Long waves bent

7 The ionosphere (a layer of ionized gas in the earth's upper atmosphere) and the curved surface of the earth below act together as a kind of "waveguide", which bends the path of long radio waves [B] around the earth. The path

of waves of the medium band is not as bent, which is why they cannot normally be received more than a few hundred kilometres from the transmitter. All radio waves travel strictly in straight lines in free space but short waves are used

for round-the-world communication because they are reflected by the ionosphere and also by the earth's surface, as though these were mirrors [A]. Even shorter waves pass through the ionosphere and so are used for space communications.

8 Communications satellites, owned by an international consortium of over 80 nations, provide a major part of the world's global communications. Placed in synchronous orbit [A] 35,800km (22,375 miles) above the Equator over the Pacific [1], Atlantic [2] and Indian oceans [3], the Intelsat IV satellites remain in fixed positions in relation to the earth, each capable of relaying thousands of VHF radio signals to and from approximately one-third of the earth's surface. Together they cover most of the earth with some overlapping [B]. There are more than 70 earth stations (dots in [C]) capable of communication via the satellites, although submarine cables (red lines) are still used.

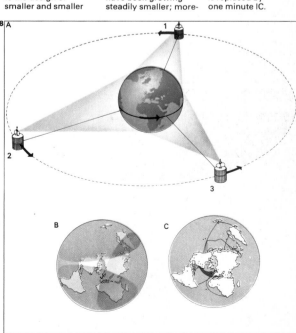
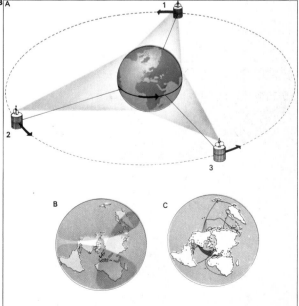

Communications: television

Unlike the telegraph, telephone and radio, television is unique among forms of telecommunications because it was originally developed purely as an entertainment medium. Today it has many other applications, particularly for remote surveillance.

The dawning image
V. K. Zworykin (1889–), a Russian emigrant to the United States, patented the iconoscope in 1923. A similar device was invented independently in Britain. Forerunners of modern television camera tubes, these were electronic devices in each of which a lens focused an optical image on to a screen inside a glass container. The image was scanned by an electron beam that covered the area in a continually repeated series of parallel lines. When the beam struck a bright part of the image the electron current flowing back was greater than when it fell on a darker part of the scene. By using this varying electric current to control the intensity of another electron beam in a cathode ray tube (a beam made to scan the face of the tube in step with the beam in the iconoscope), a replica of the original scene was built up spot by spot and line by line. The scanning covered the entire screen several times a second, the glow caused did not die away instantaneously, and so the human eye could not tell that the image was built up of individual elements.

It was not until 1936 that the world's first high-definition public television service was started by the British Broadcasting Corporation (BBC) in London. British engineers had spent the previous five years developing electronic television [1] as an alternative to the 30-line mechanical system that was invented in 1923–8 by a Scotsman, John Logie Baird (1888–1946).

Television standards
The BBC originally adopted an interlaced scan of 405 lines repeated 25 times a second. Interlacing means that alternate lines are scanned first, followed by those between – like reading lines 1, 3, 5 down this column and then going back to read lines 2, 4, 6.

Other countries set up television services using various standards which made international programme exchange very complex.

Eventually it was agreed that 625 lines, 25 frames a second interlaced, should be standard in most European countries. Today only North and South America and Japan use a different standard.

The sideband theory of radio states that, in order that two radio signals do not interfere with each other, the difference between their frequencies must not be less than the highest frequency of the signal being broadcast. Television signals include very high frequencies, so a bandwidth of about 5MHz (5 million cycles/sec) has largely been accepted as the practical minimum. Because this is equal to the radio space occupied by more than 500 voice channels the entire short-wave radio band would accommodate only five television channels. Thus television is broadcast in the VHF and UHF bands (very and ultra high frequency), which can accommodate up to 80 channels.

Colour television
In theory the range of pure colours (called "hues") is continuous from violet of the shortest visible wavelength to red of the longest.

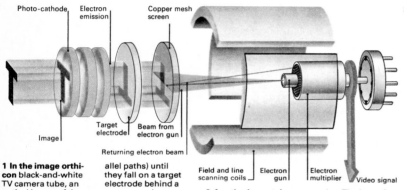

1 Photo-cathode · Electron emission · Copper mesh screen · Image · Target electrode · Beam from electron gun · Returning electron beam · Field and line scanning coils · Electron gun · Electron multiplier · Video signal

1 In the image orthicon black-and-white TV camera tube, an optical image of the studio scene is focused on a photocathode, which emits electrons in proportion to the amount of light falling on it. These electrons pass through magnetic and electrostatic fields (which keep them moving in parallel paths) until they fall on a target electrode behind a copper mesh screen. There a pattern of charges is formed, corresponding to the light and dark areas in the picture. A scanning electron beam from the other side is modulated by the charges, thus forming a varying transmission signal.

2 A cathode ray tube in a television receiver has a screen coated with a material that fluoresces when struck by an electron beam. The beam is produced by a cathode that emits electrons and is accelerated and focused by anodes. The beam is deflected by two scanning coils fed with signals so that it zig-zags across the screen. The velocity of the beam, and thus the intensity of each picture element, is controlled by a grid fed by another signal.

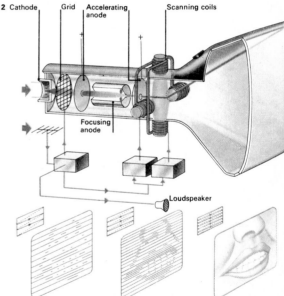

2 Cathode · Grid · Accelerating anode · Scanning coils · Focusing anode · Loudspeaker

3 A colour television camera first splits the picture into three primary colours using colour-separating mirrors. Each beam of coloured light enters one of three picture tubes, which convert the picture into electrical signals. The three signals are combined to form a monochrome signal and processed into a colour signal. This defines the hue (frequency) and saturation (intensity) of each colour.

3 Scene to be televised · Final encoder and amplifier · Unmodulated colour signal · First encoder · Picture tubes convert coloured light into signals · Composite signal to transmitter · Amplifier · Adder combines signals to form monochrome signal · Identical picture tubes · Final encoder and amplifier · Camera separates scene into three primary colours · Mirror · Lens focuses scene on to tubes · Dichroic mirrors · Mirror

4 In a colour television receiver a decoding circuit extracts the information of the original colour signals. This is used to modulate the beams from three electron guns. The screen has a pattern of tiny phosphor dots which glow red, green or blue when struck by electrons. Directly behind the screen is a shadowmask with thousands of holes arranged so that the beam from each gun can strike only dots of the colour from which its controlling signal was made.

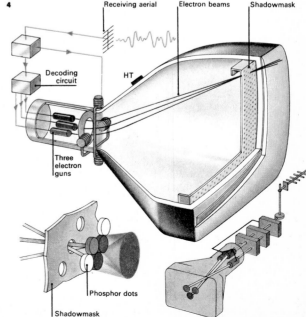

4 Receiving aerial · Electron beams · Shadowmask · Decoding circuit · HT · Three electron guns · Phosphor dots · Shadowmask

In practice the sensations perceived by the human eye in response to all these hues can be quite accurately matched by simple mixtures of red, green and blue light. Colour television [3] uses this principle by having three camera tubes to convert the red, green and blue light present in each televised scene into three simultaneous but separate electrical signals. In theory these three signals could be transmitted separately, received by three separate circuits in the television receiver and then combined to form a colour picture. But this idea has a major disadvantage. Because the minimum practical bandwidth for one television signal is 5MHz three simultaneous signals would occupy 15MHz – far too much of the already overcrowded radio space available.

Experiments have shown that, provided the black-and-white detail of a picture is sharply defined, the human eye does not require the colour definition to be as high. American engineers devised a clever system to use this information. First the three primary colour signals were added to form a detailed monochrome (black-and-white)

signal for transmission in the usual way. At the same time the three colour signals were converted into a second composite signal that defines the colour mixture in terms of hue and saturation (the amount of white used to dilute the pure hue). Because this colour signal does not need to be of high definition it is possible to sandwich it between the information giving the detail of each monochrome line without interfering with it. In this way a complete colour signal can be transmitted within a 5MHz monochrome signal bandwidth. The television receiver makes a detailed picture from the monochrome signal, extracts the colour information interleaved with it and uses this to deflect the three picture-tube electron beams on to those spots on its screen that will glow with the appropriate primary colours [4].

In the United States this system has been used since 1953 and is known as the National Television Systems Committee (NTSC) system. It works well but has the disadvantage that the colours produced on the receiver screen can be significantly altered by minor changes in the transmitted signal.

KEY

Electronic scanning is the basis of television. An electron beam (green) scans the screen [A] in a series of horizontal lines, which are kept in step with the lines scanning an optical image in the television camera in the studio from which the broadcast comes. This synchronization

of the scanning process is achieved by a set of timing pulses superimposed on the picture information in the transmitted signal. At the end [1] of each horizontal line [2], there is a pulse that triggers the instant return [3] of the electron beam to the opposite side [4], where it scans

the next line [5] below the previous one. After the final line of each picture a different pulse triggers the return (yellow) of the electron beam to the top of the picture. A saw-tooth current [B] through electromagnetic deflection coils (round the neck of the tube), controls the beam.

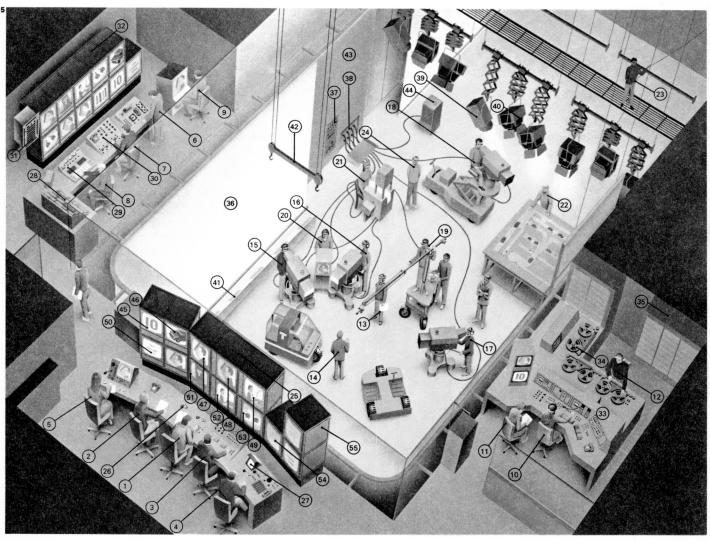

5 The transmission of a live television programme requires the combined efforts of a large, highly skilled team which can be divided into four groups: the studio floor, lighting and colour control,

and the sound and direction teams. All are shown in this illustration of the layout of a modern television studio.

1 Director
2 Assistant director

3 Vision mixer
4 Technical manager
5 Timekeeper
6 Lighting supervisor
7 Tariffer (controls iris settings of cameras)
8 Lighting engineer
9 Colour grader
10–12 Sound engineers
13 Floor manager

14 Presenter
15–18 Cameraman
19 Microphone-boom operator
20 Monitor pusher
21 Autocue operator
22 Props man
23–24 Electricians
25 Director's array
26 Microphone to studio
27 Test screen

28 Dimmer bank
29 Switchboard
30 Camera iris controls
31 Lighting display board
32 Picture quality control
33 Sound console
34 Tape decks
35 Amplifiers
36 Cyclorama
37 Hoist control panel

38 Output socket
39 Spotlight
40 Floodlight
41 Cyclorama lights
42 Scenery hoist
43 Soundproof wall
44 Studio speaker
45 Telecine
46 Videotape picture
47 Monochrome final trans-

mission picture
48 Colour final transmission picture
49 General monitor
50 Credit holder
51–54 Pictures from cameras 1–4
55 Monitor bank for extra cameras and outside broadcasts

Sound recording and reproducing

It was possible, at about the turn of the century, to reproduce the expression and "attack" of an actual piano performance on a pianola paper roll. But the story of sound recording and reproduction as the terms are now understood is the story of the gramophone, the "talking" motion picture and the tape recorder.

Thomas Edison (1847–1931) invented a hand-cranked phonograph [1] in 1877. The machine converted the air pressure variations of sound waves into a mechanical record consisting of a groove of varying depth in a sheet of tin-foil wrapped round a cylinder. The foil was soon replaced by a hard wax cylinder and in 1894 Charles Pathé (1863–1957) and his brother Emile (1860–1937) opened a phonograph factory.

The development of early sound systems
Meanwhile Emile Berliner (1851–1929), a German in Washington, DC, patented a "gramophone" in 1887. This used a flat disc instead of a cylinder, the sound groove being cut as a spiral. By 1900 the hill-and-dale recording was replaced by a groove that

made a stylus vibrate from side to side. And with the advent of a shellac disc pressed from a "negative" of the original recording the gramophone, known in the United States as the victrola, became widely popular [Key].

At first methods of recording and playback were entirely mechanical and the quality of reproduction was poor. The invention of the triode valve in 1906 opened the way to electrical recording and by the 1930s music of much improved quality was reproduced electronically from shellac discs running at 78 revolutions per minute (rpm).

In 1948 the American Columbia Company successfully demonstrated an "unbreakable" vinyl plastic disc and high-fidelity microgroove discs playing for 25–30 minutes a side at 33⅓rpm soon became popular. By 1958 the stereo disc had been introduced. It had separate twin soundtracks in a single groove (each corresponding to the sounds received by a listener's left and right ears) and provided a sense of musical presence hitherto unknown in a recording [2].

Once silent motion pictures had been developed, a system of synchronized sound

followed in the mid-1920s. Early "talkies" used an adaptation of the already popular shellac disc. The most successful system had a 40cm (16in) disc running at 33⅓rpm, with a motor linked mechanically to the film drive. By 1930, engineers had developed a far better system that recorded the sound optically on one edge of the film in the form of a transparent line varying either in density or in width [3]. A fine beam of light shone through the moving line on to a photoelectric cell, its varying electrical output being amplified and fed to loudspeakers.

Experiments in magnetic recording
The idea of converting the varying pressure waves of sound into a magnetic pattern on a continuous steel wire was developed in the 1920s. The British Broadcasting Corporation, which wanted to transmit the same programmes to different parts of the world at different times, installed an improved machine in 1931. This used a 6mm-wide steel tape running at 1.5m per second to record and replay programmes 20 minutes in length.

In 1929 Fritz Pfleumer patented a

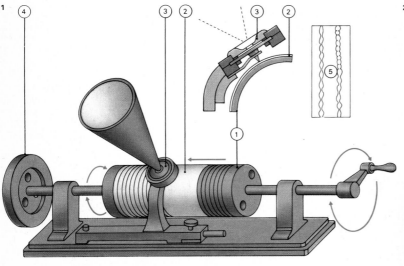

1 Thomas Edison's phonograph consisted of a brass cylinder [1] cut with a spiral groove. Over this was wrapped a sheet of tin foil [2]. A conical funnel focused sound on to a metal diaphragm [3], which touched a steel stylus held by a flat spring. The sharp tip of the stylus pressed on the foil. The cylinder was mounted on a screw of the same pitch as the groove, so that when the cylinder was turned the stylus pressed always over the groove. A flywheel [4] helped keep the cylinder speed steady. When sound caused the diaphragm to vibrate, the stylus pressed the foil into the groove in step with the vibrations. The cylinder was wound back to its original position, and the sound reproduced by turning the handle. The stylus and the diaphragm were then vibrated by the indentations [5] in the foil.

3 An optical system is used by the film industry for recording sound, the vibrations being reproduced in the form of a transparent line of varying thickness. In the projector, a light beam passes through the line on to a photoelectric cell. The width of the line controls the amount of light reaching the cell, the resulting electrical signal being amplified to produce sound. In home movie equipment the sound is recorded on a magnetic stripe as on tape.

4 In recording on magnetic tape [A], the tape first passes an erase head which leaves the magnetic particles on the tape in random disarray. Then the record/replay head, energized by a microphone signal, orientates the particles according to the signal's waveform. In playing back [B], the tape again passes the record/replay head. Magnetic variations reproduce in it the currents that formed them [C]. After amplification, the currents drive a loudspeaker.

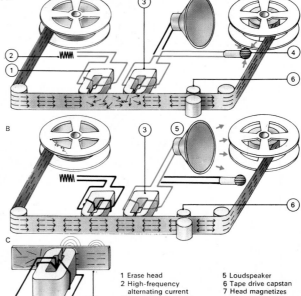

1 Erase head
2 High-frequency alternating current
3 Record/replay head
4 Microphone
5 Loudspeaker
6 Tape drive capstan
7 Head magnetizes tape coating

2 On a stereo disc, the groove walls are angled at 90° to each other. When a recording is made [A], sound from one microphone [1] produces a hill-and-dale contour on one groove wall. The second channel sound [2] contours the other groove wall. After being pressed between metal moulds [B], the final plastic disc is ready to be played back. The cartridge stylus of the play-back machine vibrates in two planes perpendicular to each other [C]. The movement in each of these planes actuates separate electromagnets, which are wired to two different amplifiers and separate loudspeakers. The sound recorded by the two original microphones is thus reproduced independently.

recording tape that had a flexible insulated base with a magnetic coating. The German AEG company developed this invention and in 1935 in Berlin exhibited the Magnetophone, the first modern tape recorder. But it was not until the end of World War II that the potential of the reel-to-reel tape recorder using 0.5cm (0.25in) plastic-based tape with an iron oxide coating [4], was fully realized. The tape can move at various speeds, with higher speeds providing greater fidelity. The most common speeds for domestic recording are 4.8cm/sec (1.875in/sec), 9.5cm/sec (3.75in/sec) and 19cm/sec (7.5in/sec). For stereo recording two separate soundtracks are recorded side by side using two microphones. Stereo reproduction or playback needs two amplifiers and speakers. The system of dividing the tape into four tracks permits two stereo recordings to be made: tracks 1 and 3 in one direction and 2 and 4 in the reverse.

The cartridge and cassette revolution

The main drawbacks of a reel-to-reel tape recorder are the vulnerability of the tape to damage during threading and the inconvenience of threading and storing it. To eliminate these, the tape cartridge and cassette were invented. The former contains a single loosely wound reel of continuous tape. The tape is fed out from the centre at an angle, guided by rollers to the gate where it touches the playback head of the equipment and then back to the outside of the reel.

A cassette recorder [7] has two spools like those of a reel-to-reel recorder, but much smaller, and is suitable for recording, automatic rewind and playback operations. The tape is only 3.8mm (0.15in) wide and runs at 4.88cm/sec (1.875in/sec). The cassette (plastic case) holds tape for 45, 60, 90 or 120 minutes' playing time and clicks into the cassette player without the need for threading the tape. High-frequency random noise called "tape-hiss" (a consequence of having four tracks recorded on the extremely narrow tape at a slow speed) can lower the quality of the cassette recording. But this blemish on the quality can often virtually be eliminated by using an electronic noise-reduction circuit.

KEY

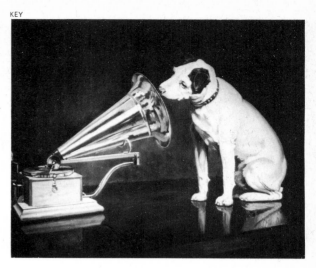

The marvel of sound reproduction was captured in a narrative painting which became a trade-mark as "His Master's Voice". In 1899 the British artist Francis Barraud portrayed a fox terrier called Nipper listening to the voice of his dead master from a phonograph. The Gramophone Co. later EMI, which bought the painting, got Barraud to paint in a gramophone.

5 The human hearing process, using a pair of ears, can sense the direction of a sound and so can discriminate between a sound from one direction and background noise from another. This is not so of a microphone, which combines all the sounds it "hears" into one electrical wave. To maintain a high signal-to-noise ratio it is therefore normal to place microphones as near as possible to the desired sound source. To record an orchestra and choir with proper balance between instruments and voices a single microphone would have to be roughly the same distance from each sound source. Except in a perfectly sound-proof studio this would result in an unacceptably low signal-to-noise ratio. The engineer solves this problem by providing separate microphones for each section of the choir and orchestra and for the soloists, the combined outputs then being mixed by electronic means. The balance can then also be adjusted.

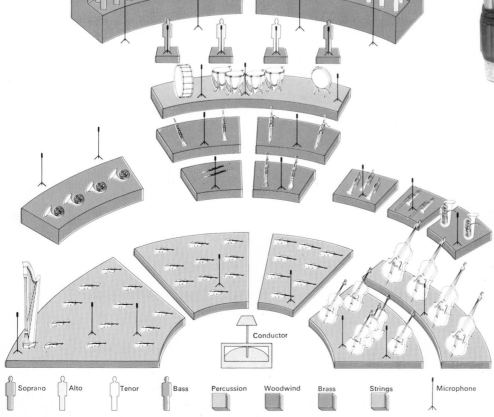

Conductor

| Soprano | Alto | Tenor | Bass | | Percussion | Woodwind | Brass | Strings | | Microphone |

6 A jukebox, an early example of which is shown here, is a coin-operated machine for selling music. Some modern versions hold 200 or more records and provide stereophonic sound reproduction.

7 A portable cassette player allows tape-recorded music to be heard almost anywhere. With transistorized circuits powered by batteries, it is light and compact and can be used with pre-recorded tapes.

Video recording and reproduction

From the earliest days of the television industry, there was a need for a method of recording programmes in such a way that they could be played back immediately. Cinema film is often unsuitable because the delay in processing prevents it being shown immediately, and the fact that film cannot be re-used makes it expensive.

A Scotsman, John Logie Baird (1888–1946), inventor of a mechanical television scanner, was the first man to record a moving picture by other than photographic means. In 1927 he used equipment designed for cutting 10in (25.4cm) 78rpm sound records to record pictures using the output of his 30-line TV scanner.

Magnetic tape recording

The development of magnetic tape recording meant that Baird's aim could be achieved more simply with immediate replay. In the meantime, however, television had progressed from the first 30-line format to a picture having 405 to 819 lines. The best of the early shellac records could reproduce audio (sound) signals up to a frequency of about 4,500 hertz (Hz), and high-fidelity LP records today reproduce musical overtones up to 15,000Hz or more. But a modern TV signal includes frequencies up to 5MHz.

The frequency response of a magnetic tape recorder is limited by the size of the head gap and the speed with which the tape passes the head. The finest equipment operating at 19cm (7.5in) per second cannot reproduce frequencies much above 25,000Hz. An increase in frequency response to 5MHz can be achieved only by increasing the tape-to-head speed to at least 1,270cm (500in) per second.

The earliest videotape recorders (which record pictures on magnetic tape just as a tape recorder records sound) were designed to operate at tape speeds of 254cm (100in) per second or more. They required enormous spools of tape and presented speed control problems; also constant head-to-tape contact was difficult to achieve. Research led to the introduction by Ampex, in 1956, of the first transverse-scan recorder – the system used professionally today. In this system, the tape, normally 5.08cm (2in) wide, moves at either 38cm (15in) or 19cm (7.5in) per second. Four record/replay heads mounted on a drum sweep across the tape producing transverse parallel record tracks for the video signal [2]. Linear tracks at the edges of the tape are used for tape-speed control, picture cueing and sound. Head-to-tape "writing" speeds of 3,810cm (1,500in) per second are achieved.

Helical scanning

The highly sophisticated transverse-scan colour videotape recorder is far too expensive for institutional and domestic use. A cheaper method uses what is termed helical scanning. Here the tape passes in a helix around a rotating drum into which one or more record/replay heads are built [2A,B]. The drum is rotated, usually in the opposite direction to the tape (it "slips" round within a loop of tape). As the tape rises by its own width in its journey around the drum, the heads sweep across the tape at an acute angle. Tape-to-head "writing" speeds of up to 2,540cm (1,000in) per second are achieved with helical-scan portable videotape recorders. In domestic applications, this system

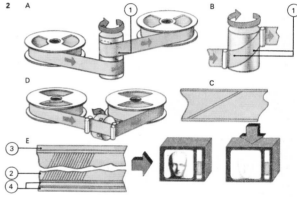

2 Videotape may move in a helix round a rotating drum having either one [A] or two [B] record/replay heads [1]. The combined motion of tape and head produces diagonal video tracks [C]. Transverse scanning [D] uses four heads on a horizontally spinning drum to produce tapes recorded as in [E] with video tracks [2], an audio track [3] and picture control tracks [4]. Both systems have high "writing" speeds.

1 The earliest video recorder worked in exactly the same way as an audio tape recorder, using spools of wide magnetic tape. The video track was recorded by a stationary head and the recording of the high frequencies required to produce pictures of acceptable quality was achieved by using very fast tape speeds. In the most highly developed of these machines, 914.4cm (360in) of tape 5.1cm (2in) wide passed the head each second. Even so, picture quality was poor by modern standards and the machines suitable only for black-and-white pictures.

3 The moving head was invented by a little-known company in Redwood, California, in 1956, as a means of achieving the high tape-to-head speed required for video recording without the tape itself having to move at unmanageably high speed. The latest Ampex machine [A] is a self-contained videotape recorder designed for colour television. The studio videotape recorder is expensive and heavy and many manufacturers, foreseeing a wide market for a cheaper and smaller machine suitable for home, school, police and other work, have made cassette videotape recorders that are compact and efficient, yet not too costly. This cassette player [B] is a typical example of such a model.

has the advantage that a conventional TV can be used as a combined picture and sound monitor, the signal produced on replay being fed into the aerial socket via a modulator. Tape 1.27cm (0.5in) wide is commonly used, although some recorders of this kind use 1.9cm (0.75in) or 2.5cm (1.0in) tape. The speed-control mechanisms on these machines are less sophisticated, and generally use servo motors in much the same way as those on studio machines.

Types of video disc

It is possible for magnetic tape to be replaced by magnetic discs in video recording, and the system has the advantage of giving rapid access to any part of the recording for immediate replay, in slow motion if necessary [5]. But a disadvantage is that playing time is short – generally 30–36 seconds using both sides – whereas a modern videotape recorder can accommodate a 90-minute colour TV programme on one spool of tape.

The production of pre-recorded TV tapes is expensive and so some manufacturers have been developing video machines that use discs similar to gramophone records. Such machines are not recorders, but replay programmes on mass-produced discs [4].

There are two kinds of such video discs, which differ in the "pick-up" used to extract the recorded information. In a system developed by Philips, MCA in the United States and other companies there are small elliptical depressions in the disc [6]. The disc revolves at 1,500 revolutions per minute (for a 50Hz electricity supply) or 1,800rpm (for a 60Hz supply). A laster beam scans the lower surface of the disc and the reflected beam becomes modulated and provides video and sound signals for 25 or 30 television pictures per minute (normal rates of transmission). A disc 30.5cm (12in) in diameter records up to half an hour's television. It can provide slow motion or "stationary" pictures.

The video disc developed by Telefunken and Decca is grooved like a long-playing gramophone record [7], although the grooves are finer and spaced much closer together. Playing speeds are again 1,500 or 1,800rpm but such discs record only about seven minutes of television.

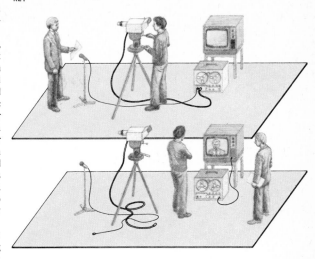

The recording and reproduction of moving pictures on magnetic tape has been developed to such an extent that reproduced television pictures are nearly indistinguishable from orginals. Even portable video-tape recorders that can be used domestically give remarkably good results.

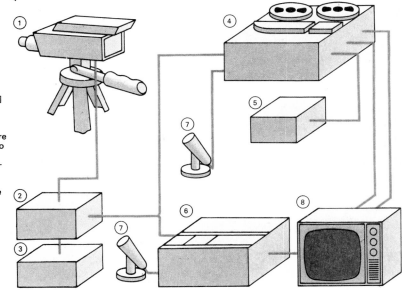

4 Live video re-cordings in black-and-white or colour can be made with ease today. The diagram shows a typical set-up using equipment that is readily available on the market. The camera [1] is connected via its control [2] and sync [3] units to the reel-to-reel colour video-tape recorder [4] (with colour pack [5]) or, more commonly, to the video cassette recorder [6]. A microphone is simultaneously connected to record the accompanying sound [7]. The colour TV set [8], has special sockets to enable it to be used as a monitor during recording. Recorded tape can be played back through the TV set immediately after the tape is wound back.

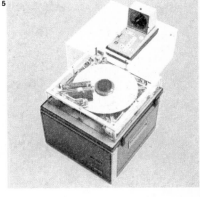

5 The slow-motion "action replay" seen frequently on sports programmes was made possible by the invention of a magnetic disc recorder that provides continuously variable slow-motion forward and reverse as well as stop, "freeze" and natural-speed replay. It records about 7.5 to 9 seconds of television programme material on a series of concentric magnetic tracks on each side of two discs.

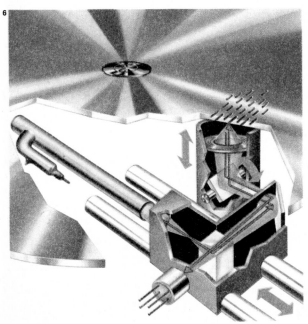

6 The non-magnetic video disc is used by several firms as an alternative to magnetic tape systems. Philips and other companies have designed systems that use minute ellipitcal depressions on a 30.5cm (12in) disc to record 30 minutes of colour video signals with sound. It is scanned using a laser beam.

7 Video discs are like sound records. The Teledisc, shown much magnified [right], has about 25 hairline grooves in the space occupied by each groove on a standard LP gramophone record (left). Like the Philips video disc (illustration 6) the Teledisc revolves at 1,500 rpm (UK) or 1,800 rpm (USA).

Radar and sonar

Sonar (formerly known as ASDIC in Britain) is a system of direction finding and rangefinding using sound waves under water. Radar uses the same principles, with radio waves instead of sound waves.

The essentials of the two systems are simple. Acoustic (sound) or electromagnetic (radio) waves are transmitted. When they meet a solid object, some are reflected and return – there is a sound or radio echo. The time that elapses between a wave's transmission and return, multiplied by the speed of the wave, gives the distance travelled. Normally this is twice the distance of the object. Early radars [Key] were mounted on trailers for portability. Some used a "lens" for directing the radar beam.

Development and uses

Sonar (from *SOund Navigation And Ranging*) was developed principally for the detection of submarines and to act as a submarine commander's "ear" for the detection of other vessels, minefields, submerged ice, wrecks and other underwater hazards. Sonar can be "active" or "passive". In active sonar, an acoustic wave is transmitted and its echo picked up [1]. In passive sonar, other vessels are detected by listening for noise generated by their engines. Today sonar is also used by fishing vessels seeking shoals of fish and for surveying the ocean bed.

In 1935 a British team headed by Robert Watson-Watt (1892–1973) started a programme of research aimed at adapting and developing radio location for military use [5]. By the outbreak of World War II in 1939, Britain had an aircraft detection system along its east coast. Known as RDF (radio direction finding) it was quickly extended to cover the south coast and was a major factor in Britain's ability to win the war in the air even though its aircraft were outnumbered.

The secrets of RDF were passed to the United States, where further intensive research was conducted and a new name, "radar" (*RAdio Detection And Ranging*), given to the new technology. German scientists conducted similar research during the early years of the war and achieved similar, although less technically advanced, results.

A radar installation consists of three separate units: a transmitter that radiates a special form of radio signal; a receiver that picks up and processes any reflected waves; and a presentation unit that gives a visual display from which the operator can immediately read the desired information.

Types of radar aerials

Radar aerials (antennas) vary in design according to their purpose. Many consist of a metal lattice in the shape of a flat dish or rectangular array, which can be steered at any angle to the vertical or horizontal to aim the radar in the required direction. Some can be "locked on" to a target so that they track it automatically. A location radar has a narrow searchlight-type beam, focused by a parabolic reflector, so that the bearing and elevation of reflected waves can be accurately measured. A search radar uses an aerial that radiates waves over a wide arc. The beam is kept relatively flat for a ship's radar, but covers a vertical arc in an aircraft search radar. In both cases, the aerial is sometimes made to revolve horizontally so that the radar sweeps round continuously. Most radar

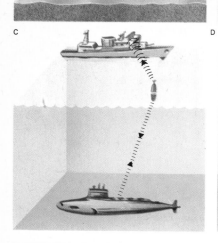

1 A B

C D

1 The time taken for a sound wave, transmitted from a device in the water under a ship, to travel to the sea-bed and echo back to the ship is measured to calculate the depth of the water. The acoustic generator [1] can be mounted directly under the ship [A], in which case the echo time multiplied by the speed of sound in water gives twice the depth. The signal-to-noise ratio of the echo picked up by the microphone [2] can be improved by lowering the sound generator into the water [B], so reducing the total distance that the sound waves must travel. The surface vessel may confuse an echo from a submarine and so a warship can use a sonar buoy [C]. For maximum mobility a ship makes use of its own helicopter which suspends a "dunking" sonar in the water [D] and transmits signals back to the mother ship by means of a short-wave radio.

2 The reflected wave of a radar beam that hits an approaching or receding object has a wavelength greater or less than the transmitted wave. If a wave of a given wavelength [a] is reflected from a planet [1] spinning about its pole [N], the wavelength [b] of the reflected wave from the approaching side [2] will be less than the wavelength [c] from the receding side [3]. The difference between b and c can be used to compute the planet's rate of spin and day length.

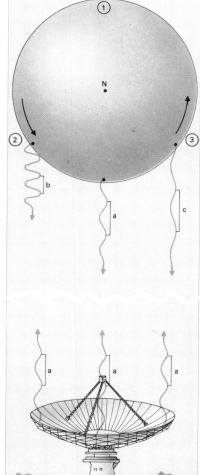

3

3 An aircraft's radar aerial may be hidden beneath a streamlined pod or radome made of a material that protects it from bad weather without seriously affecting the transmissions.

4 The presentation unit of a storm-detector radar has a cathode ray tube [1] that maps signals from a rotating aerial as glowing storm clouds. The function selector [2] controls observed range; paper tape [3] gives a record.

4

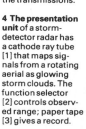

receivers have large aerial arrays designed to receive as much as possible of a reflected signal, which is usually very weak.

Processing and presentation

Radar signals, suitably processed and amplified, are passed to the presentation unit along with the original transmitted signal.

The signal presentation system is generally a cathode ray tube display, based on an oscilloscope, and can give either a simple read-out of range, or of elevation, or both. Alternatively it can display a complete electronic "map" of the position of wave-reflecting objects in all directions [4].

In a simple straight-line display, the direction and elevation of the located object (an aircraft in the sky, for example) are read from dials indicating the direction and elevation of the radar beam. The range is read off a pulsed straight-line oscilloscope trace in which the time between transmission and reception is twice the range.

The "map" or Plan Position Indicator (PPI) display is produced by a straight-line oscilloscope display arranged with a radial scan that begins at the centre of the tube and ends near its circumference. The scan is then made to rotate, with the start of the scan as the centre of rotation, in step with the rotation of the aerial. The oscilloscope screen is coated with a material having a long afterglow, so that an echo signal (a bright spot) on the screen remains visible during the time taken for one complete revolution of the aerial. The distance of an echo spot from the tube centre represents the range of the object, and its bearing on the screen conforms to its actual bearing.

Most radar installations depend entirely on the weak waves reflected by solid objects, although some systems use a relay receiver-transmitter to receive and retransmit a more powerful return wave. Such a system is known as secondary radar.

When an electromagnetic wave is reflected by an object moving towards or away from the radar installation, the frequency of the reflected wave is altered. This is the Doppler effect, well known in acoustics. The resulting frequency shift can be used to calculate the speed of an object [6].

During World War II, the British developed small, transportable radar sets so that their radar defence system was able to monitor any area of potential air-attack.

5 Six "bedspring" dipole arrays end-to-end on a radar mast

An aerial that gives a wide, flat radar beam

Rotating aerial for general search radar

Mobile radar for anti-aircraft gun control

Anti-missile rockets controlled by radar

Seaborne missile-tracking radar equipment

"Bedspring" dipole array for wide-search radar

Radar aerial protected against the weather by rigid radome

Early-warning radar

Seaborne radar

Target discrimination radar aerial gives accurate location

German World War II radar

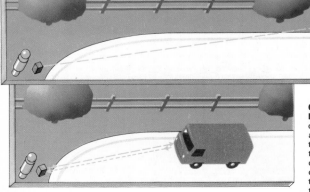

5 Radar was first used in the 1920s to demonstrate the existence and extent of the ionosphere, which was found to reflect radio waves. Research during the 1930s in Britain, USA, Germany and France developed radar for military purposes and it became a vital aid in both defence and attack during World War II when British and German electronic engineers designed and built similar installations. So greatly has its efficiency improved that radar is now regarded as an indispensable tool of modern warfare. It also proves valuable in many civil applications such as meteorology, navigation, airport traffic control and surveying. Military uses of radar include long-range aircraft and missile warning systems; location radar for automatic control of anti-aircraft guns; airborne radar for use as a night "eye" when attacking enemy bombers in darkness; and naval radar to give information about the presence of enemy shipping in conditions of poor visibility. Radar is also used in sophisticated weaponry as a homing device for steering anti-missile missiles.

6 Radar is used by the police to compute the speed of a passing car. If the speed exceeds the legal limit, the operator can warn a colleague by walkie-talkie radio in time to flag down the offending driver and charge him with speeding. The radar set continuously measures the car's distance from the set and the change in range is used to compute the speed by electronic means, giving an immediate visual display.

INDEX

How to use the index Each subject is listed alphabetically. A distinction is made between general entries and specific entries. Thus general information about aeroplanes, for example, is listed (in alphabetical order) before the names of specific aeroplanes. Page numbers in Roman type refer to text references, page numbers in italic type refer to illustrations or captions to illustrations.

Aeroplane,
  airborne control, 45
  control surfaces, *44*
  development, 40–3, *41*
  lift, 44–5
  propulsion, *45*
  stalling, *44*
  streamlines, *45*
  subsonic, *43*
  vertical take-off and landing, *45*
  wings, 44, *44*
Air Cushion Landing System, *3*
Beechcraft Super King Air 200, *42*
Blériot Type XI, *40*
Boeing 747, *43*
Concorde, *43*
De Havilland Dragonfly, *42*
Douglas DC-3, 41, *41*
GAF Nomad, *42*
Junkers F-13, *40*
Macchi MC72, *40*
Percival Gull, *42*
Wright Flyer III, *3*
Aerostat. *See* Airship, Balloon
Agriculture, 74
Aircraft. *See* Aeroplane, Airship, Helicopter
Air-cushion technique, *55*
Air-cushion vehicle, 8–9, *29*, 54–5
  first, *9*
  propulsion and steering, *9*
  skirt, *9*
  Swiss PT 150–DC, *8*
  types, *9*
Airport,
  and aircraft noise, *60*
  air-traffic control, 61
  location, 60–1
  navigational aids, *61*
  runways, 60
  terminal, *61*
  Heathrow, *61*
  O'Hare International, Chicago, *61*
  Schiphol, *60*
Airship,
  first flight, *2*
  non-rigid, *38*
  operation of, *39*
  relative sizes, *38*
  rigid, *38*
  semi-rigid, *38*
  uses, *39*
  Hansa, 38
  Hindenburg, 38, 39
  R101, *39*
  Skyship, 39
  Zeppelin, *38*

Alcantara Bridge, *65*
Alexander the Great, *64*
Alexandria, 68
Alum, 77
American Dictionary of the English Language, 89
Ampex videotape recorder, 108, *108*
Amplitude modulation (AM), *102,* 103
Anders, William, 51
Aniline dyes, 82
Animal Farm, 86
Appian Way, 56
Applegath, Augustus, 79
Aqueduct, 62, 71, *74,* 76
Archimedes, 54, *55*
Arno Bridge, 65
Artesian well, 74
Aston expressway, 67
Aswan High Dam, 72, 73
Audio tape recorder, 108
  See also Magnetic recording, Videotape recorder
Autobahn, 58
Autogyro, 46, *46*
Automobile. *See* Car
Autostrada, 58
Azo copier, 82

Babylon, 62
Bailey, Nathan, 88
Baird, John Logie, 104, 108
Balloon,
  construction, 38
  first hydrogen, *2*
  flight, 38, *39*
  gas, 39
  hot air, 39
Baltic Sea, link with White Sea, 70
Bandwidth, 103–5
Barge, Chinese, *31*
Barkentine, *5*
Barraud, Francis, *107*
Baudot, Emile, 99
Bauer, Andreas, 79
Bayle, Pierre, 88
Bayonne Bridge, New York, 67
BBC (British Broadcasting Corporation), 104, 106
Beaumont, Frederick, 62
Beechcraft Super King Air 200, 42
Bell, Alexander Graham, 8, 100, *100*
Bentley (1930), *21*
Benz, Karl, 14, 16, 18, *19*
Berliner, Emile, 106
Berte, Anthony, 78
Bible, the Gutenberg, 78, *78*
Bicycle,
  development, 14–15
  modern, 14–15, *15*
  penny-farthing, 14, *15*
  racing, *15*
  Dursley Pederson, *14*
  Moulton, *14*
  Raleigh Safety, *14*
  Swift ladies', *14*
  Velocino, *14*
  Whippet, *14*
Biochemical oxygen demand (BOD), 76–7
Biringuccio, Vanoccio, 78

Black, Joseph, 38
Black Lion Wharf, Wapping, etching, 79
Blériot, Louis, 40, *40*
Blériot Type XI, *40*
Blimp, *See* Airship
Blueprint, 82, *83*
BOD (biochemical oxygen demand), 76–7
Boeing 747, 43, *43*
Bonaparte, Napoleon, 98
Book,
  binding, 87
  first printed, 78, *78*
  hand produced, *86*
  production, 86–7
  publishing, 86–7
  reference, 88–9, *88–9*
  shops, 87
  text, *86*
  trade fair, 87
  world market, 87
  See also Encyclopaedia
Borman, Frank, 51
Bosporus, 64
Bosporus Bridge, Istanbul, *67*
Bourne, William, 10
Boyle, Robert, 10
Branly, Edouard, 102
Bridge,
  early types, *64, 65*
  low cost, 30–1
  timber, *65*
  types, 66–7, *66–7*
Brig, *5*
Brigantine, *5*
British Broadcasting Corporation (BBC), 104, 106
British Rail Advanced Passenger Train, 35
Brougham, Lord, 13
Brough Superior, *16*
Bruce, David, jr, 79
Brunel, Isambard Kingdom, 99
Brunel, Marc Isambard, *62,* 62
Bugatti Royale, *21*
Buggy, *13*
Building,
  bridge, 64–7, *64–7*
  canal, 70–1, *70–1*
  dam, 72–3, *72–3*
  road, 56–7, *56–7*
Bus, 27, *27*
Bushnell, David, 10
Butler, Edward, *17*

Cable,
  coaxial, 100–1, *101*
  laying submarine, 99, *99*
  submarine, 99
  transatlantic network, 99
Camera, 92–3, *92–3*
  aperture, 94, *94*
  cine, 97
  focus, 95
  lens, 95
  movie, 97
  pinhole, 92
  shutter speed, 94
  single-lens reflex, 92
  technical, 92
  twin-lens reflex, 92
  Polaroid, 92

Canal,
  construction, 70–1, *70–1*
  maintenance, *70*
  tunnels, 62
Canal du Midi, 70
Car,
  brakes, 22–3, *23*
  catalytic converters, 25
  clutch, 22
  construction, 23
  development, 18–19
  electric, 24
  electrical systems, 22, *22*
  gas turbine, 25
  gears, 22
  hybrid city, 25
  and pollution, 24–5
  and road accidents, 25
  and safety, 25
  racing, *29*
  research and future planning, 24–5
  stratified-charge engine, 24
  steering, 23, *23*
  suspension, 23, *23*
  terms, 22
  transmission, 22
  tyres, *22, 25*
  Auburn 851, *21*
  Bentley (1930), *21*
  Bugatti Royale, *21*
  Chrysler Airflow, *21*
  Citroen 15CV, 19, *19*
  Daimler (1897), *3*
  Duesenberg, *20*
  Fiat, *19,* 20
  Hispano-Suiza, *20*
  Isotta-Fraschini A, *20*
  Mercedes, 20
  Mercedes (1901), *18*
  Mercedes (1914), *20*
  Mini, 19, *19*
  Model T Ford, 18, *18*
  Panhard and Levassor, *18*
  Rolls-Royce Silver Ghost, *18*
  SS Jaguar, *21*
  Vauxhall 30/98, *19*
  Volkswagen, 19, *19*
Carbon microphone, 100, *101*
Cargo ship, *6*
Carrier wave technique, *102,* 103
Caterpillar crawler, *54*
Cathode ray tube, *104*
Cawdrey, Robert, 88
Cement, 66
Chambers, Ephraim, 88
Chandler, Raymond, 86
Channel Tunnel, 62, *63*
Chappe, Claude, 98, *98*
Charabanc, *13*
Chariot, *2*
Charles, Jacques, 38
China, 70
Chrysler Airflow, *21*
Cine photography,
  cameras, 96–7, *97*
  editing, *97*
  film, 96–7, *97*
  projection, 97, *96–7*
Citroen 15 CV (1939), *19*
Classification system,
  Dewey, 90
  faceted, 90
  Library of Congress, 91

Clipper, 5, *5*
Cockerell, Christopher, 8
Coefficient of friction, 54
Coles Colossus, *29*
Computer, *85, 90,* 91, *91*
Concorde, 43, *43*
Concrete, 57, 66
Concrete carrier, *28*
Concrete paving machine, 57, *57*
Constantinople, 68
Container ship, 6, *6*
Cooke, William, 98
Copper, 62
Corinth Canal, *71*
Cornu, Paul, *3*
Corps des Ingénieurs des Ponts et Chaussées, 56, 65
Corps of Bridge and Road Engineers, 56, 65
Cowper, Edward, 78
Crane, portal, *54,* 55
Cruise liner, 7
Cubuk Dam, *73*
Cugnot, Nicolas, 18
Cyclopaedia, 88, *88*

Daguerre, Louis Jacques Mandé, 92
Daily Mail, 84
Daimler, Gottlieb, 14, 16, *17,* 18, *19*
Dam, 62, 72–3, *72–3*
Darby, Abraham, 65
Darius, King, 64
Data processing, 90–1, *90*
Da Vinci, Leonardo, 59, 70 aircraft design, *47*
Decca, 109
De Colechurch, Peter, 65
De Dion Bouton, 16
De Havilland Dragon-Fly, *42*
De la Cierva, Juan, 46
De Lana, Francesco, 38
De La Pyrotechnica, 78
De Lesseps, Ferdinand, *71*
Desalination, 75, *75*
De Sivrac, Comte, 14
Dewey, Melvil, 90 classification system, 90–1
Dictionary, 88–9
Dictionnaire Historique et Critique, 88
Diderot, Denis, 88, *88*
Didot, Firmin, 78
Diesel, Rudolf, 33
Diesel fuel, exhaust emission, *24*
Digger, 52, *53*
Dirigible. *See* Airship, Balloon
Disc, gramophone, 106
Dock, 68–9 container, *68* dry, 68, *68* floating, *68*
Dog cart, *13*
Douglas DC-3, 41, *41*
Dover, 68
Drag, *13*
Drainage. *See* Sewage
Dredger, 52 bucket, 52, *53* grab and dipper, 52–3 suction, 52–3, *53*

Duesenberg, *20*
Dumper truck, 53
Dunlop, John B., 14, 16
Duplicator, spirit, 82, *83*
Dutch East Indiaman, *5*
Dyer, Harrison Gray, 98

Eads, James, 65, *65*
Eastman, George, 92
Ecole des Ponts et Chaussées, 56
Edison, Thomas, *96,* 100, 106, *106*
Egypt, 62, 68
Electromagnetic spectrum, 102–3
Elementary Education Act, 84
Encounter Bay, 6
Encyclopaedia Britannica, 88
Encyclopaedia, 88–9 and audio-visual technique, 89 first, 88
Encyclopédie, 88, *88*
Encyclopédie Française, 88
Estuary, 68
Etching, *79*
Etymologiae, 88
Euphrates, River, 62
Euphrates Bridge, 64, *64*
Excavator, 52, *52*
Exchange, automatic telephone, 100, *100–1*

Fâ-Hsien, 64
Far East, 68
Ferry, 7
Fertilizer, *76–7*
Fessenden, R. A., 102
Fiat, *19,* 20
Field, Cyrus W., *99*
Film, colour, 93 printing, 93, *93* processing, 93, *93* Polaroid, 92
Fingerprint, *91*
Flood control, 72
Florio, John, 88
"Flying crane", *47*
Ford, Henry, 18
Forlanini, Enrico, 8
Forth railway bridge, *66*
Frankfurt Book Fair, 87
Free Enterprise IV, 7
Freeway, 58–9 elevated, *59* proportional expenditure, *56* urban, *59*
Frequency modulation (FM), *102,* 103
Frères du Pont, 64
Freyssinet, Eugene, 66
Friction, 54
Fulcrum, 54
Funeral coach, 17th century, *12*

Gaddi, Taddeo, 65
GAF Nomad, *42*
Gagarin, Yuri, 50
Galleon, *4, 5*
Golden Hind, 5

Genoa, 68
Genoux, Claud, 79
Gibbon, Edward, 86
Gibraltar, Straits of, 68
Giffard, Henri, 38
Giocondo, Giovanni, 65
Gladesville Bridge, *66,* 67
Goddard, Robert, 48
Godfather, The, 86
Grader, 53
Gradient, 58
Gramophone, 106, *107*
Gramophone record, frequency response, 108
Graphic reproduction, 82–3, *82–3*
Gravelly Hill junction, Birmingham, *67*
Gray, Elisha, 99–100
Great Eastern, 99
Ground loading, 55
Gutenberg, Johannes, 78, *78*

Hansa, 38
Hansom, Joseph, 13
Harbour, 68–9, *68* engineering, 68–9, *69*
Harley Davidson WLA and WLC, *16*
Harmsworth, Alfred, 84
Harris, John, 88
Heathrow Airport, *61*
Hectograph, *83*
Helicopter, development, 46–7 first, *3* flight, *46* "flying crane", *47* rescue, *46* tail-rotor, *46* tandem, *47* twin-rotor, *47* versatility, 47 Mi-12, *47* VS-300, *47*
Hellespont, 64, *64*
Henry, Joseph, 98
Herodotus, 64
Hertz, Heinrich, 102
Hildebrand, Henry, *17*
Hildebrand, Wilhelm, *17*
Hill, Rowland, *79*
Hindenburg, 38, 39
His Master's Voice, *107*
Hispano-Suiza, *20*
Historia Naturalis, 88
Hitler, Adolf, 58
Holden, Capel, 16
Holland, John P., 10
Hoover Dam, 72
Horatius, 64
Hovercraft. *See* Air-cushion vehicle
Hovertrain, *37*
Howrah Bridge, *66*
Hughes, David, 99, 100, 102
Humber Bridge, 67
Hydraulic jack, 55
Hydraulic loader (mechanical shovel), 52, 53
Hydroelectricity, 72, *73*
Hydrofoil, 8, *9* classes, *8* first, *8* propulsion, *8*
Hydrologic cycle, 75

Iconoscope, 104
Incas, 64
India, 64
Indian motor cycle, *16*
Industrial Revolution, 68, 75
Information retrieval, 90–1
Intaglio printing, 78–80, *79*
Intelsat IV, *103*
Interchange, motorway, *58*
International Federation of Documentation, 90
International Institute of Bibliography, 90
Ionosphere, *103*
Irrigation, *71,* 71–2
Isotta-Fraschini A, *20*
Issigonis, Alec, *19*

Jacquard, Joseph, *90*
Jeep, *28*
Jericho, 62
Johnson, Samuel, *86,* 89
Jordan Canal, *71*
Joy of Knowledge, The, 88–9, *89*
Jukebox, *107*
Julius Caesar, 64
Junkers, Hugo, 40, *41*
Junkers, F-13, 40
Junkers Ju 52/3m, *41*

K-class submarine, *11*
König, Friedrich, 78

Land reclamation, 72
Lanka Devi, 6
Lanston, Tolbert, *81*
Lawson, H. J., 14
Lemercier, Alfred, 79
Leonov, Alexei, 50, *50*
Lesages, Georges Louis, 98
Letterpress printing, *78, 80,* 81, *81*
Lever, 54
Lexicon, 88
Lexicon Technicum, 88
Library, 90–1 security in, *90*
Library of Congress, 91
Licensing Act, 84
Lighthouse, 68
Linotype, 79, 81
Lithography, 78, 79, 80–1, *81*
Load, 54, 67
Lock, 70, *70* pound, 70
Locomotive, diesel, 33 diesel-electric, *33* electric, 32–3 first commercial, *32* steam, 32 underground, *34* Bavarian Class 53/6, *32* *Beyer-Garratt, 33* "Big Boy", *33* French Class CC7100, *33* *General, 32* High Speed Train, *33* *Mallard, 32* *Rocket, 32* Tokaido, *33* *See also* Railway
Lodge, Oliver, 102

London Bridge, *64*, 65
Long-wagon, medieval, 12, *12*
Lovell, James, 51
Lunokhod I, *48*
Luppis, G., *10*
Lusitania, 6

McAdam, John, 13, 56
Macchi MC72, *40*
Machine,
    earth-moving, 52–3, *52–3*
    lifting, 54–5, *54–5*
Machine communication,
    punched-card method, *90*, 91
Machinery,
    tunnelling, 62–3, *62–3*
    typesetting, *85*
Macmillan, Kirkpatrick, 14
Magazine, 84–5
    delivery, *85*
Magnetic recording, 106–9, *106–9*
Magnetophone, 107
Mail coach, 12
Marconi, Guglielmo, 102
Marey, Etienne-Jules, *96*
Maxwell, James Clerk, 102
Maybach, Wilhelm, 16
Mechanical advantage, 54
Mechanical shovel (hydraulic loader), *52*, 53
Medway Bridge, *66*
Menai Bridge, 65
Mercedes (1901), *18*
Mercedes (1914), *20*
Mergenthaler, Ottmar, *79*
Mersey Mole, *63*
Metropolitan Vickers, 43
Michaux, Ernest, 14, 16
Michaux, Pierre, 14, 16
Microphone, *106*–7, 107
Mil, Mikhail, *47*
Mimeograph, 82, *82*
Mini, *19*
Mining, 62
Missile,
    Polaris, 10
    Poseidon, 10
Mitsubishi shipyards, Koyagi, *6*
Mi-12, *47*
Model T Ford, *18*
Monotype, 81, *81*
Montgolfier, Etienne, 38, *39*
Montgolfier, Joseph, 38, *39*
Morrison, Charles, 98
Morse, Samuel, 98
Morse code, 98–9, *98*
Motion picture, sound with, 106–7, *106*
Motor cycle,
    development, 16–17
    first, *17*
    modern types of, 17, *17*
    Brough Superior, *16*
    Butler spray carburettor, 16
    De Dion Bouton, 16
    Harley Davidson WLA and WLC, *16*
    Indian, *16*
    MV Augusta, *17*
    Vincent Rapide, *17*
    Wankel engine, *17*

Motorway, 58–9
    elevated, *59*
    proportional expenditure, *56*
    urban, *59*
Muybridge, Edward, *96*
MV Augusta, *17*

National Television Systems
    Committee (NTSC) system, 105
News of the World, 84
Newspaper, 84–5, *84–5*
    production, *80*
New York Tribune, 79
Niagara Falls, suspension bridge, 65
Niepce, J. Nicéphore, 14, 92
Nieuwe Tijdingen, 84
Nile, 70
Nineteen Eighty-Four, 86
Northcliffe, Lord, 84
NTSC (National Television Systems Committee) system, 105

Oersted, Hans Christian, 98
Offset lithography, 83
O'Hare International Airport, Chicago, *61*
Ohau Stadium, Hawaii, *55*
Oil tanker, *6*
Omnibus, *13*
Orwell, George, 86, *86*
Otto, Nikolaus August, 18
Ox-cart, *12, 31*
Oxford English Dictionary, 89
Oxford Junior Encyclopedia, 88

Panama Canal, 70, *71*
Panhard and Levassor, *18*
Patent, *91*
Pathé, Charles, 106
Pathé, Emile, 106
Pavement. *See* Road
Penny-farthing, *15*
Percival Gull, *42*
Perronet, Jean Rodolph, 65, *65*
Pfleumer, Fritz, 106
Pharos lighthouse, 68
Philips, MCA, 109, *109*
Phoenicians, 68
Phonograph, 106, *106*
Photocopying, 83
Photography,
    cine. *See* Cine photography
    development of photographic processes, 92–3
    lighting, *95*
    of moving subjects, *96*
    professional, *95*
    reportage, *95*
    space, *49*
    See also Camera
Photogravure, 80
Photolithography, 79, *80*
Photosetting, 81, *81*
Photostatic copying, *83*
Photo-telegraphy, *99*
Physical communications, in underdeveloped countries, 30–1, *30–1*
See also Canal, Railway, Road

Pianola, 106
Piasecki, Frank, *47*
Planographic printing, 80
Plant,
    sewage treatment, *77*
    water treatment, *74*
Pliny the Elder, 88
Pollution, 75–7, *75*
    of River Thames, 76–7, *77*
Polytetrafluorethylene (PTFE), 54
Pons Fabricius, 64
Pons Sublicius, 64
Pont d'Avignon, 65
Pont de la Concorde, Paris, *65*
Ponte Quattro Capi, 64
Ponte Vecchio, 59
Porsche, Ferdinand, *19*
Port, 68–9
    cargo-handling, *69*
    multi-purpose, *69*
Post Office Tower, London, *101*
Printing, 82–3
    books, 86
    colour production, *81*
    equipment, *82*
    newspaper, *80*
Printing press, 84
    early, *78–9*
PTFE (polytera-fluorethylene), 54
Ptolemy II, 68, 70
Public transport system, development, 26–7
Publishing, 86–7
Pulley, block, *54*
Pump, *74*
Punched-card method of machine communication, *90*, 91
Puzo, Mario, *86*

Quebec Bridge, Canada, 67
Queen Elizabeth II, 7

Radar,
    antennas, 110–11
    development and uses, 110, *111*
    processing and presentation, 111
Radio, *102–3*
Radio wave, 102–3, *102–3*
Railway,
    first, *53*
    freight stock, *35*
    future developments, 36–7
    marshalling yards, 36, *36*
    and passenger transport, *34*
    rail gauges, 34–5, *34*
    rolling stock, 34–5, *35*
    track, *36*
    tunnels, 62–3
    types of, *37*
    underground, *34–5, 35, 62*
    wagon couplings, *35*
    See also Locomotive
Recording,
    electrical, 106, *107*
    magnetic, 106–9, *106–9*
    mechanical, 106
Record storage, *91*
Red Sea, 70
Relief printing, 78–80
Renaissance, 58

Rennie, John, 69
Repeater (electronic amplifier), 101
Reproduction,
    print, 82–3, *82–3*
    sound, 106–7, *106–7*
    video, 108–9, *108–9*
Rhine Bridge, 64
Rickshaw, *31*
Ridout, Ronald, 87
River boat, *3*
Road, 58–9
    construction, 56–7, *56*
    design, 30
    low-cost construction, 30, *30–1*
    machinery, *57*
    modern, *57*
    McAdam's, 56–7, *57*
    Roman, 56, *57*
    Tresaguet's, *57*
Road Act 1861, 16
Road Act 1865, 16
Rocket,
    multi-stage, *48*
    American Vanguard, *48*
Roebling, John, 65
Rolls-Royce Silver Ghost (1907), *18*
Romans,
    bridges, 64, *65*
    engineering of, 58–9, 62, *74, 76*
    roads, 56, *57*
Ronalds, Francis, 98
Royal Type Foundry, Korea, 78
Ruggles, Stephen, *78*

Sail, *5*
Sailing ship, mercantile,
    aerodynamics, *4*
    ancient Egyptian, *4*
    barkentine, *5*
    brig, *5*
    brigantine, *5*
    clipper, 5, *5*
    development, 4–5, *5*
    steel bark, *5*
    Dutch East Indiaman, *5*
    Egyptian, *2*
    galleon (*Golden Hind*), 4, *5*
    Roman grain, *4*
St Lawrence Seaway, 70, *70*
St Louis Bridge, 65, *65*
St Paul, 102
Salinity, 75
Satellite, 48–9, *48–9*
    communications, *103*
    orbit, *49*
    photography, *49*
    Sputnik I, *49*
Schiphol Airport, Amsterdam, *60*
Schneider Trophy, *40*
Scots Magazine, 98
Scraper, 53, *53*
Seaplane, Supermarine S-6B, *40*
Semaphore, *98*
Semiramis, Queen, 62
Senefelder, Aloys, 78
Septic tank, *77*
Severn Bridge, Coalbrookdale, 65
Sewage, 75, 76–7
    treatment plant, 76–7
    works, 76, *77*

Shepard, Alan, 50
Shield, tunnelling, 62, *62*
Shillibeer, George, 13
Ships and shipping,
    cargo vessel, *6*
    container, *6*
    cruise liner, *7*
    development, 6–7
    engines, 7
    ferry, *7*
    launching, 7
    nautical terms, 7
    oil tanker, production line
        assembly of, *6*
    sailing. *See* Sailing ship
    tug, *7*
Shovel dozer, *52*, 53
Sidon, 68
Sikorsky, Igor, 46, *47*
Silk, loom, *90*
Simenon, Georges, 87
Skyship, 39
Sled, 12, *12*
Smeaton, John, 68
Sonar, 110, *110*
Sound, recording and
    reproduction, 106–7
Space-flight, manned,
    first, 50
    first Moon landing, *51*
    free fall, *50*
    Apollo programme, 48,
        51, *51*
    Apollo-Soyuz, 50
    Gemini programme, *50*
Space probe, 48–9, *49*
"Spaghetti Junction", 67
Specialist vehicle,
    design, 28
    riot, *29*
    steering, 29
    suspension, 28–9
    tracked commercial, *28*
Spirit of London, 7
SS *Great Britain*, 6, *6*
SS Jaguar (1938), *21*
Stackgarth (tug), 7
Stage-coach, 12
Stamp tax, 84
Stanhope, Charles, 78
Starley, James, 14
Star III, 11
Steel, 66, 74
Steel bark, *5*
Steelmaking, 74
Stephenson, George, 32
Stephenson, Robert, 65
Stereo, recording, 106, *106–7*
    See also Magnetic recording
Stonehenge, 54, *54*

Strowger, Almon, 100
    system, 100, *101*
Submarine,
    development, 10–11
    diving, 10
    K-class, *11*
    navigation, 11
    nuclear, *10*, 11
    nuclear missiles, *10*
    weapons, *10*
    Turtle, 10, *11*
    U-boat, *11*
    USS *Nautilus,* 11
Submarine telephone cable,
    99, *99*
Submersible, 11
Suez Canal, 70, *71*
Supermarine S-6B, *40*
Swamp buggy, *29*
Sydney Harbour Bridge, *67*

Table Alphabeticall, 88
Talbot, William Fox, 92
Tape recorder, 108–9, *108–9*
    See also Magnetic recording
Tarmac, 57
TAT I, 101
Technology, small, 30–1,
    30–1
Telecommunications,
    98–105
Telefunken, 109
Telegraphy,
    electric, 98–9, *98*
    radio, 102–3, *102–3*
Telephone, 100, *100–1*
Telephony, microwave, 101
    British system, *101*
Teleprinter, 99, *99*
Television,
    colour, 104–5, *104*
    electronic system, 104,
        104–5
    frequencies used, 104
    mechanical system, 104
    programme production
        team *105*
Telex, 99, *99*
Telford, Thomas, 56, 58,
    65, 68
Thames, pollution of, 76, *77*
The Godfather, 86
The Joy of Knowledge, 88–9,
    89
Thermionic valve, 103
The Times, 84
Thornycroft, John, 8
Torpedo, *10,* 11
Tower Bridge, London, *66*

Tractor
    combat engineer, *29*
    steam powered, *28*
Traffic,
    air, 60–1, *60–1*
    in cities, 59, *59*
    controls, 58-9
    engineering, 58–9
    signs, *58*
Train,
    electric, 35
    hovertrain, *37*
    underground, *34*
    *British Rail Advanced
        Passenger Train, 35*
    See also Railway
Tram, 26–7
Transistor, *103*
Transistor radio, *102–3*
Transport,
    history, 2–3
    railway, 34–5, *34–5*
    technology, 30–1, *30–1*
    wheeled, development,
        12–13
    See also Bus, Car, etc.
Travois, *2*
Tresaguet, Pierre, 56
Trevithick, Richard, 32
Tring Cutting, *53*
Trolleybus, 26–7, *26*
Truck,
    body types, *29*
    tipper, *29*
Trusevich, N. P., 99
Tsiolkovsky, Konstantin, 48
Tug, *7*
Tunnel,
    engineering, 62–3, *62–3*
    underwater, 62–3, *63*
Turbofan engine, *45*
Turboprop engine, *45*
Typefounding, 78, *78*
Typesetting, 78
Typewriter, 83

U-boat, *11*
UDC (Universal Decimal
    System), 90
Universal Decimal System
    (UDC), 90
*Universal Etymological
    English Dictionary,* 88
Universal Lexicon, 88
USS *Nautilus,* 11

Van Drebbel, Cornelius, 10
Varro, 88

Vauxhall 30/98, *19*
Verrazano-Narrows Bridge,
    New York, 67
Victory printing press, *79*
Victrola, 106
Video recording and
    reproducing, 108–9
Videotape recorder, 108–9,
    108–9
Vincent Rapide, *17*
Volkswagen, *19*
Von Braun, Werner, 48
Von Drais, Karl, 14
VS-300, *47*

Wagonette, *13*
Walking beam, 55
Wankel engine, *17*
Water,
    collection, 74
    consumption, 74
    storage, 72, 74–5
    supply, 72–5
    treatment plant, *74*
Waterways, 70–1
Waterwheel, *74*
Waterworks, *74*
Watson-Watt, Robert, 110
*Webster's Third New
    International Dictionary,*
    89
Westinghouse, George, 34
Wheatstone, Charles, 98
Wheel and wheeled transport,
    development, 12
    See also individual vehicles
Wheelbarrow, 52
Whistler, James, *79*
White, Edward, *50*
Whitehead, Robert, *10*
White Sea to Baltic canal,
    70
Whittle, Frank, 43
Woodcut, *78*
Worden, Alfred M., *50*
World of Words, 88
Worms and Phillipe, *79*
Wright, Orville, 40, 60
Wright, Wilbur, 40, 60
Wright Flyer III, *2*

Xerography, 83
Xerxes, 64, *64*

Zeppelin, Ferdinand von, *38*
Zeppelin, *38*
Zworykin, V. K., 104

Bibliography

Transport
Bagwell, P. S.; *Transport Revolution from 1770*; Batsford, 1974
Brown, B.; *Transport Through the Ages: Drawings*; Barker, 1971
Clarke, D. (Ed.); *Encyclopaedia of Transport*; Marshall Cavendish, 1976
Ridley, A.; *Illustrated History of Transport*; Heinemann, 1969
Gunston, B.; *Transport: Problems and Prospects*; Thames & Hudson, 1972
Angelucci, E. and A. Culari; *Ships*; Macdonald, 1977
Howarth, D.; *Sovereign of the Seas*; Collins, 1974
Larsen, E.; *Hovercraft and Hydrofoils*; Dent, 1970
McLeavy, R.; *Hovercraft and Hydrofoils*; Blandford, 1976
Watts, A. J.; *Submarines and Submersibles*; Ward Lock, 1976
Horton, E.; *Illustrated History of the Submarine*; Sidgwick & Jackson, 1974
Roscoe, K.; *Undersea Exploration*; Hamlyn, 1971
Bendixon, T.; *Instead of Cars*; Penguin, 1977
Cardy, A. C. C.; *History of Modern Road Transport*; Macmillan, 1970
Tarr, L.; *History of the Carriage*; Vision, 1970
Tristram, W. O.; *Coaching Days and Coaching Ways*; E. P., 1973
Ritchie, A.; *Kings of the Road: Illustrated History*; Wildwood, 1975
Woodforde, J.; *Story of the Bicycle*; Routledge, 1970
Connolly, H.; *Pioneer Motorcycles (1875–1905)*; Main-Smith, 1974
Hough, R. & L. J. K. Setright; *History of the World's Motorcycles*; Allen & Unwin, 1973
Louis, H. & B. Currie; *Classic Motorcycles*; P. Stephens, 1977
Vanderveen, B. H. (Ed.); *Motorcycles and Scooters from 1945*; Warne, 1976
Posthumus, C.; *Vintage Cars (1919–30)*; Hamlyn, 1977
Sedgwick, M.; *Cars of the 1930s*; Batsford, 1970
Nicholson, T. R.; *Passenger Cars*; Blandford Press, 1970–72 (3 vols)
Sedgwick, M.; *Passenger Cars (1924–42)*; Blandford Press, 1975
Nicholson, T. R.; *Sports Cars*; Blandford Press, 1969–70 (2 vols)
Day, J.; *Bosch Book of the Motor Car*; Collins, 1975
Young, F.; *Complete Motorist*; E. P., 1973
Plowden, W.; *Motor Car and Politics*; Penguin, 1973
Turner, G.; *Car Makers*; Eyre & Spottiswood, 1963
Kaye, D.; *Pocket Encyclopaedia of Buses and Trolleybuses Before 1919*; Blandford, 1972
Joyce, J.; *Trams in Colour (since 1945)*; Blandford, 1970
Kaye, D.; *Buses and Trolleybuses 1919–45*; Blandford, 1970
Booth, G.; *British Motor Bus: Illustrated History*; I. Allan, 1977
Newton, K. et al.; *Motor Vehicle*; Newnes-Butterworth, 1972
Champion, R. C. & E. C. Arnold; *Motor Vehicle Calculations and Science*; Arnold, 1970
Schumacher, E. F.; *Small is Beautiful*; Sphere, 1974
Nock, O. S.; *Locomotion*; Routledge, 1975
Reed, B.; *150 Years of Steam (British) Locomotives*; David & Charles, 1975
Ferneyhough, F.; *History of Railways in Britain*; Osprey, 1975
Simmons, F. (Ed.); *Rail 150*; Eyre Methuen, 1975
Nock, O. S.; *Encyclopaedia of Railways*; Octopus, 1978
Nock, O. S.; *Railways Then and Now*; Elek, 1975
Kichenside, G. & A. Williams; *British Railway Signalling*; I. Allan, 1975
Whitehouse, P. B.; *Britain's Main-Line Railways*; New English Library, 1977
Nock, O. S.; *Out the Line*; Elek, 1970
Nock, O. S.; *Railways of the Modern Age since 1963*; Blandford, 1975
Brooks, P. W.; *Historic Airships*; Evelyn, 1973
Robinson, D. H.; *Zeppelin in Combat*; G. T. Foulis, 1971
Taylor, J. W. R. (Ed); *Guinness Book of Air Facts and Feats;* Guinness, 1973
Taylor, J. W. R. & K. Munson; *History of Aviation*; New English Library 1971–77
Mondey, D.; *Aircraft: A Colour History of Aviation*; Octopus, 1974
Taylor, J. W. R.; *Jets*; Dent, 1976
Arkell, B. & J. W. R. Taylor; *Helicopters and VTOL Aircraft Work Like This*; Dent, 1972
Bono, P.; *Frontiers of Space*; Blandford, 1977
Gatland, K.; *Manned Spacecraft*; Blandford, 1976
Porter, R.; *Versatile Satellite*; Oxford U.P., 1977
Gatland, K.; *Missiles and Rockets*; Blandford, 1975
Ryan, P.; *Invasion of the Moon (1957–70)*; Penguin, 1971
Gatland, K.; *Robot Explorers*; Blandford, 1972
Smolders, P. L.; *Soviets in Space*; Lutterworth, 1973

Transport engineering
O'Flaherty, C. A.; *Highway Engineering*; Arnold, 1974
Overman, M.; *Roads, Bridges and Tunnels*; Aldus, 1968

O'Flaherty, C. A.; *Highways and Traffic*; Arnold, 1974
Kefford, C. W.; *Traffic*; Blandford, 1969
Henry, B.; *Heathrow Airport, London*; Dent, 1975
Beaver, P.; *History of Tunnels*; P. Davies, 1972
Mare, E. de; *Bridges of Britain*; Batsford, 1975
Metcalfe, L.; *Bridges and Bridge-Building*; Blandford, 1970
Henry, D. & J. A. Jerome; *Modern British Bridges*; Applied Science, 1969
Overman, M.; *Man the Bridge-Builder*; Priory Press, 1975
Hartcup, G.; *Code name Mulberry: Harbour Planning, Building and Operation*; David & Charles, 1977
Albion, R. G. & J. B. Pope; *Rise of New York Port 1815–60*; David & Charles, 1970
Harris, R.; *Canals and their Architecture*; Evelyn, 1969
Smith, N.; *History of Dams*; P. Davies, 1971
Overman, M.; *Water*; Aldus, 1968
Tebbutt, T. H. Y.; *Water Science and Technology*; J. Murray, 1973
Bolton, R. L. & L. Klein; *Sewage Treatment: Basic Principles and Trends*; Newnes-Butterworth, 1971

Communications
Steinberg, S. H.; *500 Years of Printing*; Penguin, 1974
Hutchings, E. A. D.; *Survey of Printing Processes*; Heinemann, 1970
Spellman, J. A.; *Printing Works Like This*; Dent, 1964
McMurtrie, D. C.; *Book*; Oxford U.P., 1943
Moran, J. (Ed.); *Printing in the 20th Century*; Northwood, 1974
Moran, J.; *Printing Presses: History and Development from 15th century to 20th century*; Faber, 1973
Durrant, W. R. et al.; *Machine Printing*; Focal Press, 1973
Cimming, R. F. & W. E. Killick; *Single Colour Lithographic Machine Operating*; Pergamon, 1969
Biegeleisen, J. I.; *Complete Book of Silk Screen Printing Production*; Dover, 1963
New, P. G.; *Reprography for Librarians*; Bingley, 1975
Chambers, H. T.; *Copying, Duplicating and Microfilm*; Business Books, 1972
Leafe, M.; *Workbook on Duplicating and Photocopying*; Cassell, 1974
Grundy, B.; *Press Inside Out*; W. H. Allen, 1976
Looseley, A. E.; *Business of Photojournalism*; Focal Press, 1970
Cudlipp, Lord; *Walking on the Water: Autobiography*; Bodley Head, 1976
Jones, M. W.; *History of the World Newspaper*; David & Charles, 1974
Mumby, F. A.; *Publishing and Bookselling*; Cape, 1974
Unwin, Sir S.; *Truth About Publishing*; Allen & Unwin, 1976
Williamson, H.; *Methods of Book Design*; Oxford U. P., 1966
Walford, A. J.; *Guide to Reference Material*; Library Association, 1973–77
Kister, K. F.; *Encyclopaedia Buying Guide*; Bowker, 1976
Hulbert, J. R.; *Dictionaries British and American*; Deutsch, 1968
Lock, R. N.; *Manual of Library Economy*; Bingley, 1977
Sayers, W. C. B.; *Manual of Classification*; Deutsch, 1975 (Maltby ed.)
Needham, C. D.; *Organizing Knowledge in Libraries*; Deutsch, 1972
Hedgecoe, J.; *Book of Photography*; Nat. Mag. Co., 1976
Bowskill, D.; *Photography Made Simple*; W. H. Allen, 1975
Techniques of Photography; Time-Life, 1976
Feininger, A.; *Successful Photography*; Prentice-Hall, 1975
Lacour, M. & I. T. Lathrop; *Photo Technology*; American Technical Soc., 1972
Fellows, M. S.; *Home Movies*; Pelham, 1973
Gilmour, E.; *Photographer's Guide to Movie-Making*; Focal Press, 1969
Metcalfe, L.; *Post Office and its Services*; Blandford, 1972
Overman, M.; *Understanding Telecommunications*; Lutterworth Press, 1974
King, G. J.; *Beginner's Guide to Radio*; Newnes Tech., 1970
Gibson, D.; *Teach Yourself Radio*; Hodder Children's, 1970
King, G. J.; *Beginner's Guide to Colour Television*; Newnes Tech., 1973
Cole, H. A.; *Basic Television*; Technical Press, 1972
King, G. J.; *Beginner's Guide to Television*; Newnes Tech., 1970
Wasley, J. & R. Hill; *Guide to Hi-fi*; Pelham, 1977
Borwick, J. (Ed.); *Sound Recording Practice*; Oxford U.P., 1976
Overman, M.; *Understanding Sound and Video Recording*; Lutterworth, 1977
White, G.; *Video Recording: Record and Replay Systems*; Newnes-Butterworth, 1972
Robinson, J. F.; *Videotape Recording*; Focal Press, 1975
Oliver, W. G.; *Introduction to Video-Recording*; Foulsham, 1971
Sonnenberg, G. J.; *Radar and Electronics Navigation*; Newnes-Butterworth, 1970
French, J.; *Small Craft Radar*; Stanford Maritime, 1977
Tucker, D. G.; *Underwater Observation Using Sonar*; Fishing News, 1966
Larsen, E.; *Radar Works Like This*; Dent, 1966

Major contributors and advisers to The Joy of Knowledge

Fabian Acker CEng, MIEE, MIMarE; Professor Leslie Alcock; Professor H. C. Allen MC; Leonard Amey OBE; Neil Ardley BSc; Professor H. R. V. Arnstein DSc, PhD, FIBiol; Russell Ash BA (Dunelm), FRAI; Norman Ashford PhD, CEng, MICE, MASCE, MCIT; Professor Robert Ashton; B. W. Atkinson BSc, PhD; Anthony Atmore BA; Professor Philip S. Bagwell BSc(Econ), PhD; Peter Ball MA; Edwin Banks MIOP; Professor Michael Banton; Dulan Barber; Harry Barrett; Professor J. P. Barron MA, DPhil, FSA; Professor W. G. Beasley FBA; Alan Bender PhD, MSc, DIC, ARCS; Lionel Bender BSc; Israel Berkovitch PhD, FRIC, MIChemE; David Berry MA; M. L. Bierbrier PhD; A. T. E. Binsted FBBI (Dipl); David Black; Maurice E. F. Block BA, PhD(Cantab); Richard H. Bomback BSc (London), FRPS; Basil Booth BSc (Hons), PhD, FGS, FRGS; J. Harry Bowen MA(Cantab), PhD(London); Mary Briggs MPS, FLS; John Brodrick BSc(Econ); J. M. Bruce ISO, MA, FRHistS, MRAeS; Professer D. A. Bullough MA, FSA, FRHistS; Tony Buzan BA(Hons) UBC; Dr Alan R. Cane; Dr J. G. de Casparis; Dr Jeremy Catto MA; Denis Chamberlain; E. W. Chanter MA; Professor Colin Cherry DSc(Eng), MIEE; A. H. Christie MA, FRAI, FRAS; Dr Anthony W. Clare MPhil(London), MB, BCh, MRCPI, MRCPsych; Professor Aidan Clarke MA, PhD, FTCD; Sonia Cole; John R. Collis MA, PhD; Professor Gordon Connell-Smith BA, PhD, FRHistS; Dr A. H. Cook FRS; Professor A. H. Cook FRS; J. A. L. Cooke MA, DPhil; R. W. Cooke BSc, CEng, MICE; B. K. Cooper; Penelope J. Corfield MA; Robin Cormack MA, PhD, FSA; Nona Coxhead; Patricia Crone BA, PhD; Geoffrey P. Crow BSc(Eng), MICE, MIMunE, MInstHE, DIPTE; J. G. Crowther; Professor R. B. Cundall FRIC; Noel Currer-Briggs MA, FSG; Christopher Cviic BA(Zagreb), BSc(Econ, London); Gordon Daniels BSc(Econ, London), DPhil(Oxon); George Darby BA; G. J. Darwin; Dr David Delvin; Robin Denselow BA; Professor Bernard L. Diamond; John Dickson; Paul Dinnage MA; M. L. Dockrill BSc(Econ), MA, PhD; Patricia Dodd BA; James Dowdall; Anne Dowson MA(Cantab); Peter M. Driver BSc, PhD, MIBiol; Rev Professor C.

W. Dugmore DD; Herbert L. Edlin BSc, Dip in Forestry; Pamela Egan MA(Oxon); Major S. R. Elliot CD, BComm; Professor H. J. Eysenck PhD, DSc; Dr Peter Fenwick BA, MB, BChir, DPM, MRCPsych; Jim Flegg BSc, PhD, ARCS, MBOU; Andrew M. Fleming MA; Professor Antony Flew MA(Oxon), DLitt (Keele); Wyn K. Ford FRHistS; Paul Freeman DSc(London); G. S. P. Freeman-Grenville DPhil, FSA, FRAS, G. E. Fussell DLitt, FRHistS; Kenneth W. Gatland FRAS, FBIS; Norman Gelb BA; John Gilbert BA(Hons, London); Professor A. C. Gimson; John Glaves-Smith BA; David Glen; Professor S. J. Goldsack BSc, PhD, FInstP, FBCS; Richard Gombrich MA, DPhil; A. F. Gomm; Professor A. Goodwin MA; William Gould BA(Wales); Professor J. R. Gray; Christopher Green PhD; Bill Gunston; Professor A. Rupert Hall DLitt; Richard Halsey BA(Hons, UEA); Lynette K. Hamblin BSc; Norman Hammond; Peter Harbison MA, DPhil; Professor Thomas G. Harding PhD; Professor D. W. Harkness; Richard Harris; Dr Randall P. Harrison; Cyril Hart MA, PhD, FRICS, FIFor; Anthony P. Harvey; Nigel Hawkes MA(Oxon); F. P. Heath; Peter Hebblethwaite MA (Oxon), LicTheol; Frances Mary Heidensohn BA; Dr Alan Hill MC, FRCP; Robert Hillenbrand MA, DPhil; Catherine Hills PhD; Professor F. H. Hinsley; Dr Richard Hitchcock; Dorothy Hollingsworth OBE, BSc, FRIC, FIBiol, FIFST, SRD; H. P. Hope BSc(Hons, Agric); Antony Hopkins CBE, FRCM, LRAM, FRSA; Brian Hook; Peter Howell BPhil, MA(Oxon); Brigadier K. Hunt; Peter Hurst BDS, FDS, LDS, RSCEd, MSc(London); Anthony Hyman MA, PhD; Professor R. S. Illingworth MD, FRCP, DPH, DCH; Oliver Impey MA, DPhil; D. E. G. Irvine PhD; L. M. Irvine BSc; E. W. Ives BA, PhD; Anne Jamieson cand mag(Copenhagen), MSc (London); Michael A. Janson BSc; G. H. Jenkins PhD; Professor P. A. Jewell BSc (Agric), MA, FIBiol; Hugh Johnson; Commander I. E. Johnston RN; I. P. Jolliffe BSc, MSc, PhD, CompICE, FGS; Dr D. E. H. Jones ARCS, FCS; R. H. Jones PhD, BSc, CEng, MICE, FGS, MASCE, Hugh Kay; Dr Janet Kear; Sam Keen; D. R. C. Kempe BSc, DPhil, FGS; Alan

Kendall MA(Cantab); Michael Kenward; John R. King BSc(Eng), DIC, CEng, MIProdE; D. G. King-Hele FRS; Professor J. F. Kirkaldy DSc; Malcolm Kitch; Michael Kitson MA; B. C. Lamb BSc, PhD; Nick Landon; Major J. C. Larminie QDG, Retd; Diana Leat BSc(Econ), PhD; Roger Lewin BSc, PhD; Harold K. Lipset; Norman Longmate MA(Oxon); John Lowry; Kenneth E. Lowther MA; Diana Lucas BA(Hons); Keith Lye BA, FRGS; Dr Peter Lyon; Dr Martin McCauley; Sean McConville BSc; D. F. M. McGregor BSc, PhD(Edin); Jean Macqueen PhD; William Baird MacQuitty MA(Hons), FRGS, FRPS; Professor Rev F. X. Martin OSA; Jonathan Martin MA; Rev Cannon E. L. Mascall DD; Christopher Maynard MSc, DTh; Professor A. J. Meadows; Dr T. B. Millar; John Miller MA, PhD; J. S. G. Miller MA, DPhil, BM, BCh; Alaric Millington BSc, DipEd, FIMA; Rosalind Mitchison MA, FRHistS; Peter L. Moldon; Patrick Moore OBE; Robin Mowat MA, DPhil; J. Michael Mullin BSc; Alistair Munroe BSc, ARCS; Professor Jacob Needleman; John Newman MA, FSA; Professor Donald M. Nicol MA PhD; Gerald Norris; Professor F. S. Northedge PhD; Caroline E. Oakman BA(Hons, Chinese); S. O'Connell MA(Cantab), MInstP; Dr Robert Orr; Michael Overman; Di Owen BSc; A. R. D. Pagden MA, FRHistS; Professor E. J. Pagel PhD; Liam de Paor MA; Carol Parker BA(Econ), MA (Internat. Aff.); Derek Parker; Julia Parker DFAstrolS; Dr Stanley Parker; Dr Colin Murray Parkes MD, FRC(Psych), DPM; Professor Geoffrey Parrinder MA, PhD, DD(London), DLitt(Lancaster); Moira Paterson; Walter C. Patterson MSc; Sir John H. Peel KCVO, MA, DM, FRCP, FRCS, FRCOG; D. J. Penn; Basil Peters MA, MInstP, FBIS; D. L. Phillips FRCR, MRCOG; B. T. Pickering PhD, DSc; John Picton; Susan Pinkus; Dr C. S. Pitcher MA, DM, FRCPath; Alfred Plaut FRCPsych; A. S. Playfair MRCS, LRCP, DObst, RCOG; Dr Antony Polonsky; Joyce Pope BA; B. L. Potter NDA, MRAC, CertEd; Paulette Pratt; Antony Preston; Frank J. Pycroft; Margaret Quass; Dr John Reckless; Trevor Reese BA, PhD, FRHistS; M. M. Reese MA (Oxon); Derek A. Reid BSc, PhD; Clyde Reynolds BSc; John

Rivers; Peter Roberts; Colin A. Ronan MSc, FRAS; Professor Richard Rose BA(Johns Hopkins), DPhil (Oxon); Harold Rosenthal; T. G. Rosenthal MA(Cantab); Anne Ross MA, MA(Hons, Celtic Studies), PhD, (Archaeol and Celtic Studies, Edin); Georgina Russell MA; Dr Charles Rycroft BA (Cantab), MB(London), FRCPsych; Susan Saunders MSc(Econ); Robert Schell PhD; Anil Seal MA, PhD(Cantab); Michael Sedgwick MA(Oxon); Martin Seymour-Smith BA(Oxon), MA(Oxon); Professor John Shearman; Dr Martin Sherwood; A. C. Simpson BSc; Nigel Sitwell; Julie and Kenneth Slavin FRGS, FRAI; Professor T. C. Smout; Alec Xavier Snobel BSc(Econ); Terry Snow BA, ATCL; Rodney Steel; Charles S. Steinger MA, PhD; Geoffrey Stern BSc(Econ); Maryanne Stevens BA(Cantab), MA(London); John Stevenson DPhil, MA; J. Sidworthy MA; D. Michael Stoddart BSc, PhD; Bernard Stonehouse DPhil, MA, BSc, MInst Biol; Anthony Storr FRCP, FRCPsych; Richard Storry; Charles Stuart-Jervis; Professor John Taylor; John W. R. Taylor FRHistS, MRAeS, FSLAET; R. B. Taylor BSc(Hons, Microbiol); J. David Thomas MA, PhD; D. Thompson BSc(Econ); Harvey Tilker PhD; Don Tills PhD, MPhil, MIBiol, FIMLS; Jon Tinker; M. Tregear MA; R. W. Trender; David Trump MA, PhD, FSA; M. F. Tuke PhD; Christopher Tunney MA; Laurence Urdang Associates (authentication and fact check); Sally Walters BSc; Christopher Wardle; Dr D. Washbrook; David Watkins; George Watkins MSc; J. W. N. Watkins; Anthony J. Watts; Dr Geoff Watts; Melvyn Westlake; Anthony White MA(Oxon), MAPhil(Columbia); Dr Ruth D. Whitehouse; P. J. S. Whitmore MBE, PhD; Professor G. R. Wilkinson; Rev H. A. Williams CR; Christopher Wilson BA; Professor David M. Wilson; John B. Wilson BSc, PhD, FGS, FLS; Philip Windsor BA, DPhil(Oxon), Roy Wolfe BSc(Econ), MSc; Donald Wood MA PhD; Dr David Woodings MA, MRCP, MRCPath; Bernard Yallop PhD, BSc, ARCS, FRAS Professor John Yudkin MA, MD, PhD(Cantab), FRIC, FIBiol, FRCP.